L. A. MUNRO is Professor of Chemistry at Queen's University in Kingston, Ontario. He holds a Ph.D. from McGill University and M.A. from Dalhousie University. A Fellow of the Royal Society of Canada and the Chemical Institute of Canada, Professor Munro's contributions to applied chemistry and education have been published in various Canadian and U.S. journals.

CHEMISTRY

in Engineering

PRENTICE-HALL INTERNATIONAL, INC., *London*
PRENTICE-HALL OF AUSTRALIA PTY., LTD., *Sydney*
PRENTICE-HALL OF CANADA, LTD., *Toronto*
PRENTICE-HALL OF INDIA (PRIVATE) LTD., *New Delhi*
PRENTICE-HALL OF JAPAN, INC., *Tokyo*
PRENTICE-HALL DE MEXICO, S.A., *Mexico City*

CHEMISTRY

in Engineering

Lloyd A. Munro
Queen's University
Kingston, Ontario

PRENTICE-HALL, INC., Englewood Cliffs, N.J.

Library of Congress Catalog Card No. 64-10744
12941 C

Preface

This book is written for students or graduate engineers whose major interest is in fields other than chemistry or chemical engineering. The subject matter is based on lectures given to second-year students in engineering physics, and in civil, electrical and mechanical engineering. The topics dealt with are those of most interest to students in these courses.

The reader will find the approach less formal (and less formidable) than that used for a treatise on "pure" chemistry. The text supports the conviction of many engineering faculties that the modern graduate should understand something of the chemical as well as the physical nature and properties of the materials he uses. In all fields of engineering, many "mistakes" in the use of materials can be traced to a lack of knowledge of the simple chemistry involved.

The author gratefully acknowledges his indebtedness to the many chemical and industrial firms who provided illustrations, and to the various publishers for their permission to reproduce copyright material. Specific acknowledgments are noted in the text.

Lloyd A. Munro

Contents

17 PLASTICS 253

18 ELASTOMERS 277

19 PROTECTIVE COATINGS 296

20 WATER FOR DOMESTIC USES 334

21 INDUSTRIAL WATER 351

22 SEWAGE DISPOSAL 378

23 EXPLOSIVES 408

CHEMISTRY

in Engineering

1

An Introduction

The student in civil, mechanical, or electrical engineering confronted with another course in chemistry may ask why the engineering faculty insists on a second course in chemistry. Isn't it enough to have passed a first year course in the subject? Why not forget about chemistry and get on with engineering?

Very good answers to these questions were given over twenty years ago.[1] It was pointed out that many of the new products of the chemical industries found application in all the fields of engineering. Their use was often dependent on their *chemical behavior* more than on their physical properties. Physical properties may be altered markedly by slight changes in chemical composition.

With each successive year, the role of chemistry and chemical products in every branch of engineering has been greatly enlarged. Mr. C. L. McCuen, Vice-President of General Motors, head of the engineering division, stated: "Every advance in automotive engineering either produces a new chemical demand, or awaits upon chemical developments for its introduction."[2] In this industry some 256 chemical products are used. Mr. O. H. York of The Curtis-Wright Corporation Research Laboratories believes that "For real

---

1 *Journal of Chemical Education* **12** (1935), 422.
2 Published address, "Chemical Problems of the Automobile."

progress in aircraft, the chemist and engineer are inseparable."[1] The aeronautical engineer must know something of the chemical properties of the new materials provided by the chemist.

Even the highway engineer has to work more and more with chemical materials. He uses his knowledge of colloid chemistry to help create conditions for soil stabilization. He has a choice of materials for de-icing. Different types of paint are used on highways. In 1955 about four million gallons were used on state highways alone.[2] This included not only ordinary outside paints, but also special items such as pavement markers, luminous paints, silicones for the bridges on the New York Thruway and the new Toronto Cross-town Thruway, special paints for masonry, and thousands of tons of fine glass beads. Plastic pipe, tapes and reflectors, rubber, asphalt, pesticides, herbicides, and deionizing resins are some of the materials furnished by the chemical industry for the modern highway.

The selection of the proper metal, alloy, or combination of metals, the best oil for a certain job, the correct plastic or textile for a particular set of conditions, or the best type of synthetic rubber for a given purpose is made by considering the *chemical properties* even more than the physical properties of these related materials.

The engineering graduate who knows the differences in chemical properties of alternative materials and who understands the general chemical principles on which their behavior depends will be a better engineer than one who does not.

Time and again, engineers and contractors could have saved themselves great embarrassment, lawsuits, or their jobs had they known some principles of chemistry in engineering. Here are a few examples observed by the author.

The town engineer of an east coast town, who was a graduate in civil engineering, had the additional task one summer of supervising the construction of a new town hall. He knew that copper was resistant to corrosion, and he accordingly specified copper eaves troughs and down drains supported by iron brackets. In a very few years the rather expensive troughs were hanging loose. He apparently had not heard of the first principles of electrochemical corrosion! At that time, most of the industries and many of the homes of the town burned soft coal with a fairly high sulfur content. The damp salty sea air and a plentiful rainfall were also instrumental in creating the necessary conditions for an ideal electrolytic corrosion cell.

Some years ago, an electrical engineer employed by a company in the communications field was awaiting my return from the lecture room. He wished to know how he could neutralize calcium chloride. As you may remember, pure calcium chloride in aqueous solution becomes acidic because of hydrolysis. He was concerned, however, with an *alkaline* brine, which

---

1 *Chemical and Engineering News* **22,** No. 2 (1944), 86.

2 F. Burggraf, *Industrial and Engineering Chemistry*, **48,** No. 9 (1956), 26A.

indicated that he was using a technical grade containing some slaked lime. Asked what use he made of the material, he replied, "I used it as an antifreeze, but in spite of the fact that I neutralized it to some extent by adding sodium bichromate, when the mechanics removed the engine head, they found terrific corrosion."

I invited him into the laboratory where we connected a square of iron gauze, representing the engine block, to one side of a milliammeter and a square of copper foil, representing the radiator, to the other. When these were placed in a big beaker of calcium chloride brine, a large deflection was obtained, and after a few minutes the brine became distinctly rust-colored. This type of cell was used in the cooling system of the company's trucks. Of course the engineer was wrong in attributing the corrosive action to the alkaline nature of the solution. The success of chromate as a corrosion inhibitor depends on its concentration.

When explanations were over, the visitor departed with the remark, "I sure wish I'd paid more attention to chemistry when I was at college. But being in electrical engineering, we only had the one course."

The electric clock in our kitchen was made by a well-known manufacturer, who employs competent electrical engineers on his staff. However, someone in the firm should be given some instruction in applied chemistry. The white face of this reliable timepiece became darker and darker, until finally the enamel had to be removed and a correct type of enamel applied. The man in charge of the company's finishing department had not heard of the chemical reasons for *never* using a white lead paint or enamel in a kitchen.

Even scientific equipment companies sometimes make such "boners." One company manufactured a constant temperature bath with a chromium plated cylindrical cased stirrer cooled by a coil of tubing made of tin.

Professor M. G. Fontana tells of several examples of how expensive ignorance of chemical principles can be in the realm of building construction.[1] In one case, a new manufacturing plant was built of structural steel with an aluminum roof and sides bolted to the steel. The manufacturing process involved the evaporation of water. In the cold weather, the moisture condensed on the cold aluminum and dripped into the finished product! Another contractor was given the job of insulating the roof and walls. Apparently, he did not know sufficient chemistry either, for he used an alkaline binder to hold the insulation.

The result of the improper use of good materials by the two contractors is described by Professor Fontana: "After a short time the insulation became soaked and gobs of it dropped off the roof [presumably into the manufacturer's product!]. Needless to say the manufacturer was even more unhappy. Corrosion also occurred. Thousands of holes appeared in the roofing, most of them in lines adjacent to the steel perlins .... Defects in

---

1 *Industrial and Engineering Chemistry*, **48** (Nov. 1956), 53A.

the sprayed coating also resulted in small anodes [corrosion sites] . . . . Practically everyone involved hired lawyers and consultants."

You will be expected to explain this "holey mess" and suggest remedies after you have studied the section on corrosion.

There are many other instances where mistakes in engineering design of structures and equipment occurred because of neglect of the chemistry of corrosion. Some of these will be discussed in the later chapters. Your instructor can doubtless supply additional examples from his own experience or knowledge.

This text, written to discuss practical applications of some of the principles and facts of chemistry to civil, mechanical, and electrical engineering, presents the simpler chemical aspects of old and new materials used by the engineer. Its scope may be estimated from the Table of Contents or the review questions.

Here are a few questions taken from different chapters. If you can answer 25 per cent of them correctly, you have more chemical knowledge than the average student who has passed first year chemistry, and you should do well in the course. If you cannot answer 25 per cent of these, then the text will broaden your knowledge of engineering by increasing your understanding of the materials you will use in your future work.

1. A city changed its fuel service from coal gas to natural gas. What burner adjustments were made necessary by the change? Why?

2. Indicate the type of chemical additive used in lubricating oil (a) as a pour-point depressant, (b) a detergent, (c) viscosity-index improver, (d) for heavy loads.

3. What is the difference between "reformed" gasoline and "alkylate"?

4. How would you determine the pH and total acidity of a dark-colored, turbid mine water?

5. How can the formation of silica scale be prevented in high pressure steam boilers?

6. Name five tests required for sewage effluents or trade wastes.

7. What are the differences in chemical components in paints for (a) stucco, (b) ships' bottoms, (c) diesel-exhaust pipes?

8. Indicate the role of interfacial tensions in the spreading of liquid over a surface.

9. Name five different types of synthetic rubber and indicate which you would use for (a) resistance to chlorinated solvents, (b) gas retention, (c) resistance to high temperatures.

10. Give the chemical formula for (a) an organic inhibitor, (b) synthetic lubricant, (c) phenol, (d) a ketone.

11. Name the following compounds, indicating an engineering use for each:

(a) $CH_3 \cdot C(CH_3)_2 \cdot CH_2 \cdot CH(CH_3) \cdot CH_3$

(b) $CH_2 \cdot CH_2$
    | |
   OH OH

(c) CH_2ONO_2
   |
   $CHONO_2$
   |
   CH_2ONO_2

12. What synthetic resin or plastic would you choose for (a) high-frequency insulation, (b) a weatherproof adhesive, (c) an *ab*hesive?

2

Some Elementary
Organic Chemistry

In order to understand the properties and appropriate uses of lubricants, transformer oils, liquid fuels, protective coatings, synthetic resins, synthetic rubber, explosives, adhesives, and many other engineering materials, some knowledge of elementary organic chemistry is necessary.

Organic chemistry deals with the composition and behavior of compounds of carbon. The simplest of these contain only hydrogen and carbon and are called *hydrocarbons*. Petroleum, soft coal, and natural gas are the major sources of hydrocarbons. Natural gas consists of small hydrocarbon molecules, while crude oil contains a great variety of larger and more complex components.

Since carbon has a covalence of 4, the smallest hydrocarbon molecule, methane, may be represented by the formula CH_4 or

$$H-\underset{\underset{\displaystyle H}{|}}{\overset{\overset{\displaystyle H}{|}}{C}}-H$$

The latter formula is called a structural formula. While it does indicate that the hydrogen atoms are arranged symmetrically around the carbon, it does not show that they are actually at the corners of a tetrahedron, with valence angles between hydrogens very different from 90°. However, in spite of dimensional limitations, such formulas are very useful in depicting molecular structure.

In molecules containing two or more carbon atoms, the carbons form the skeleton. When joined by a single bond, that is, one pair of shared electrons, the carbon "joints" in the molecular skeleton are a little more than 1.5 angstrom units apart, and at an angle of approximately 110°. Such a molecule is said to be *saturated*.

Saturated hydrocarbons are commonly called *alkanes* or *paraffins*. The

Table 2-1. NORMAL ALKANES OR PARAFFINS, GENERAL FORMULA C_nH_{2n+2}

Formula	Name	bp (°C)	sg	Radical	Name
CH_4	Methane	−160	0.416	CH_3—	Methyl
CH_3CH_3	Ethane	−93	0.446	C_2H_5—	Ethyl
$CH_3CH_2CH_3$	Propane	−45	0.536	C_3H_7—	Propyl
$CH_3(CH_2)_2CH_3$	Butane	1.0	0.600	C_4H_9—	Butyl
$CH_3(CH_2)_3CH_3$	Pentane	36.4	0.627	C_5H_{11}—	Amyl or pentyl
$CH_3(CH_2)_4CH_3$	Hexane	68.9	0.658	C_6H_{13}	Hexyl
$CH_3(CH_2)_5CH_3$	Heptane	98.4	0.683	C_7H_{15}—	Heptyl
$CH_3(CH_2)_6CH_3$	Octane	125.6	0.702	C_8H_{17}—	Octyl
...	...	...	...	...	...
$CH_3(CH_2)_{14}CH_3$	Hexadecane	287.5	0.775	$C_{16}H_{33}$—	Hexadecyl
...	...	...	...	...	...

three-dimensional structure of two alkanes, propane and butane, are illustrated in Fig. 2-1. The names and formulas of some are also given in Table 2-1. It will be noted that each successive molecule has one more carbon atom and two more hydrogen atoms than the preceding one. The molecular formula for any alkane is C_nH_{2n+2}, where n is the number of carbon atoms per hydrocarbon molecule.

The names of all but the first four compounds are obtained by adding -*ane* to the Greek prefix indicating the number of carbon atoms.

Hexadecane, the 16-carbon atom member, is the first of the family which is solid at room temperatures. Paraffin wax is a mixture or solid solution of hydrocarbons containing from 18–35 carbon atoms per molecule.

2-1 Alkyl Radicals

The alkanes, or saturated hydrocarbons, are more chemically inert than the other hydrocarbons, but they do form derivatives in which hydrogen may

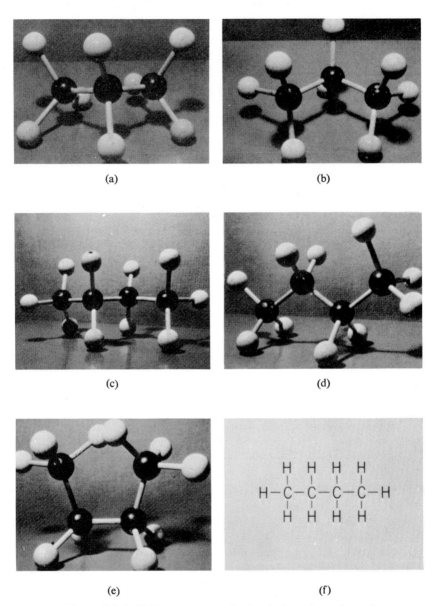

Figure 2-1 (a-b) The propane molecule; (c-e) conformations of
the butane molecule; (f) the structural formula of normal butane.
[From Brewster, R., and McEwan, W. E., *Organic Chemistry* (2 ed.;
Englewood Cliffs, N.J.: Prentice-Hall, 1960), by permission.]

be replaced by other atoms or groups. If only one hydrogen has been replaced, the resulting radical is named by changing the -*ane* of the hydrocarbon to the suffix -*yl*. For example, CH_3—, methyl; C_2H_5—, ethyl; C_4H_9—, butyl; as in methyl alcohol, CH_3OH, ethyl chloride, C_2H_5Cl, monobutylamine, $C_4H_9NH_2$.

Some people are more widely known by a nickname than by their formally given name. The same thing has happened to the pentyl group, C_5H_{11}—, which is more commonly called "amyl." Amyl acetate, C_5H_{11}-$(C_2H_3O_2)$, is an important industrial solvent.

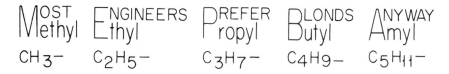

Figure 2-2

An engineer may think it difficult to remember the names and formulas of these radicals. This is not so if he can remember the epochal headline "*Monstrous Explosion Produced By Atom Hits Hiroshima!*" The sequence of the initial letters is identified with the radicals Methyl, Ethyl, Propyl, Butyl, Amyl, Hexyl, Heptyl and the ordinal number of the word is the same as the number of carbon atoms in the group. For some twenty years, the author's students have had no difficulty in remembering radicals because of the questionable statement "Most Engineers Prefer Blonds Anyway . . ." (Fig. 2-2)

The importance of alkyl radicals in naming and indicating the structure of branched-chain compounds will be seen in the following paragraphs.

2-2 Isomers

There can be only one structure for methane, ethane, or propane. There are, however, two different butanes, each having the composition expressed by C_4H_{10}. One of these is the *normal* or "straight-chain" compound. The other has a pitchfork, or branched structure, with the second carbon atom holding three others. The common name for this compound is isobutane. The structural formulas for the two butanes are given below. Molecules having the same composition but differing in structure are called *isomers*.

$$
\begin{array}{c}
\text{H H H H} \\
| \ | \ | \ | \\
\text{H—C—C—C—C—H} \\
| \ | \ | \ | \\
\text{H H H H}
\end{array}
\qquad \text{or} \qquad
$$

Straight-chain compound
Normal butane

Branched-chain compound
Isobutane

The architecture of the molecule determines many of the properties of the substance: for example, boiling point, chemical stability, octane number (see Table 7-1). Normal pentane boils at 36.4 degrees C, isopentane at 30.0° C and a third isomer called neo-neopentane,

$$
\begin{array}{c}
\text{CH}_3 \\
| \\
\text{CH}_3\text{—C—CH}_3 \\
| \\
\text{CH}_3
\end{array}
$$

at only 9.0° C. There are no less than 35 isomers of nonane C_9H_{20}, all of which have been prepared and studied. For bigger molecules, the number of possible isomers is very large; for $C_{20}H_{42}$, found in paraffin wax, the number is 366,319!

Naming Isomers: Obviously it would be impractical to invent a name for every isomer and certainly impossible to remember them. Fortunately, by using a system adopted by the International Union of Chemistry, substances represented by the most formidable-looking formulas can be named correctly. The IUC or IUPAC[1] system treats any branched molecule as being a derivative of the hydrocarbon represented by the longest of the chains in that compound. Looking back at the formulas for the three pentanes, it will be seen that the first, normal pentane, has no branches. Its name is the same by the IUC system. The second isomer, isopentane, has four carbons in its longest segment. Its surname will therefore be butane, and since this four-carbon chain has a methyl group attached to it, the molecule will be called a methyl butane. This methyl group is attached to the second carbon atom. Hence the official name is 2-methyl butane.

Neo-pentane is more properly named 2,2-dimethyl propane since the longest chain consists of three carbon atoms with two methyl groups both attached to the number two carbon.

---

1 Now known as the International Union of Pure and Applied Chemistry.

The hydrocarbon incorrectly called "isooctane" by the laity has a carbon skeleton represented by the formula

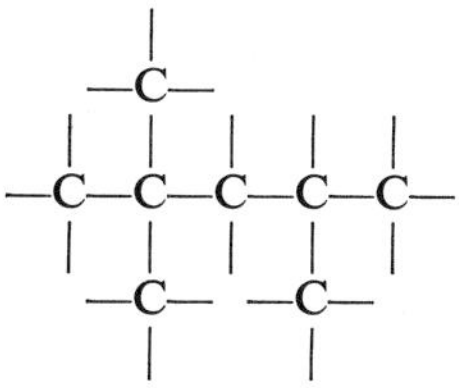

$$
\begin{array}{ccccc}
 & & | & & \\
 & & -C- & & \\
 & | & | & | & | \\
-C- & -C- & -C- & -C- & -C- \\
 & | & | & | & | \\
 & -C- & & -C- & \\
 & | & & | & \\
\end{array}
$$

The carbons are joined by single covalent bonds. This hydrocarbon is used as a standard in grading gasolines. Since it has eight carbons, it is one of the isomers of octane. The longest chain in the molecule contains five carbon atoms, so, according to the IUPAC system, it will be considered a derivative of pentane. It carries three methyl groups and therefore will be a trimethyl pentane. The carbon atoms are next numbered so as to give the lowest numbers to the most methyl groups. The proper name of this important compound is then 2,2,4-trimethyl pentane.

The hydrocarbon represented by the carbon skeleton shown below would be called 2,2,7-trimethyl-5-ethyl octane.

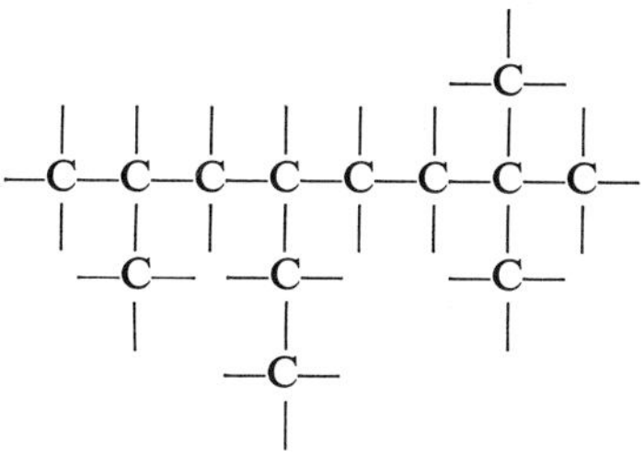

$$
\begin{array}{cccccccc}
 & & & & & & | & \\
 & & & & & & -C- & \\
 | & | & | & | & | & | & | & | \\
-C- & -C- & -C- & -C- & -C- & -C- & -C- & -C- \\
 | & | & | & | & | & | & | & | \\
 & -C- & & -C- & & & -C- & \\
 & | & & | & & & | & \\
 & & & -C- & & & & \\
 & & & | & & & & \\
\end{array}
$$

In this case the carbons are numbered from the right. The radicals are named in the order of their size.

The IUC method for naming compounds will apply to other types of derivatives. Propyl chloride, $CH_3CH_2CH_2Cl$, may also be called 1-chloropropane. Isopropyl chloride,

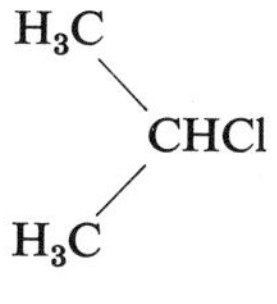

$$
\begin{array}{c}
H_3C \\
\quad \diagdown \\
\qquad CHCl \\
\quad \diagup \\
H_3C
\end{array}
$$

would be 2-chloropropane. The weed killers or herbicides 2,4,D and 2,4,5,T get their trade names from their IUC names, namely, 2,4-dichloro- and 2,4,5-trichlorophenoxyacetic acid respectively.

2-3 Cycloparaffins

If normal pentane or hexane is passed over a suitable catalyst at a moderate temperature, the flexible paraffin molecule may lose a hydrogen atom from each of the terminal methyl groups. A ring structure is produced by the end carbons sharing their unpaired electrons to form the closure.

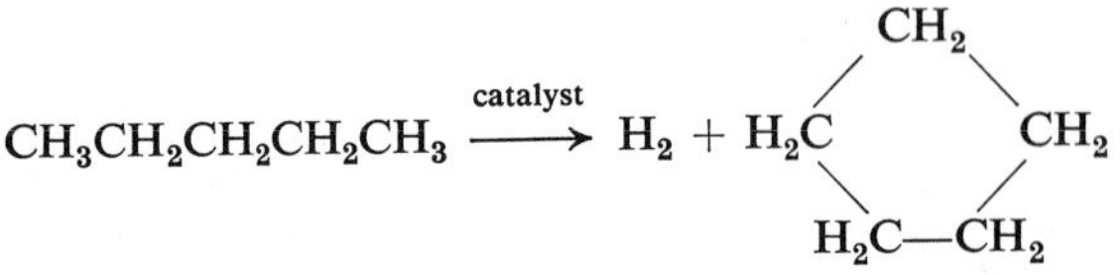

$$CH_3CH_2CH_2CH_2CH_3 \xrightarrow{\text{catalyst}} H_2 + H_2C \underset{H_2C-CH_2}{\overset{CH_2}{\diagup \diagdown}} CH_2$$

pentane → hydrogen + cyclopentane

The resulting hydrocarbon has the general formula C_nH_{2n}. The ring of carbon atoms is held together by single bonds, and each carbon has two hydrogens or monovalent radicals attached. The compound therefore belongs to the alkanes or paraffins. Cyclic paraffins or *alicyclics* and their derivatives are found in certain crude oils, particularly Midcontinent, Californian, and Caucasian. In the oil industry these are also called *naphthenes*; three such naturally occurring naphthenes are depicted below.

The densities and boiling points of the cycloparaffins are higher than those of the corresponding open-chain paraffins.

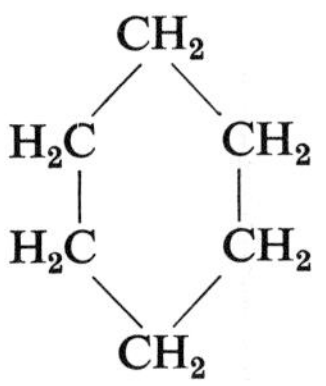

Cyclohexane 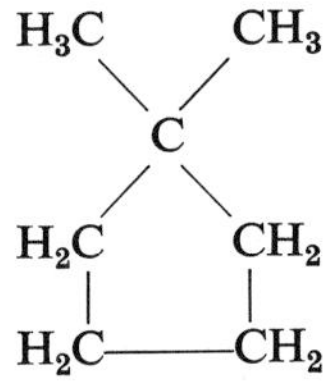   1,1-Dimethylcyclopentane 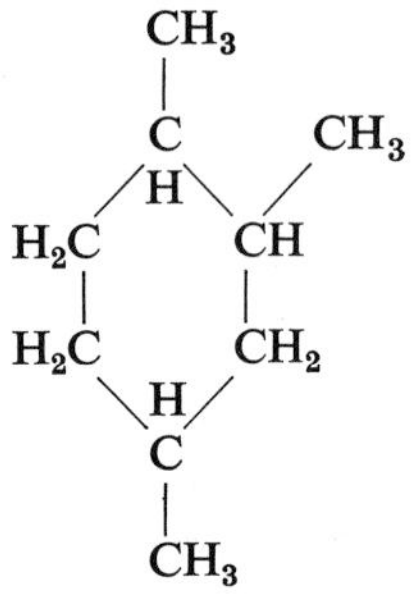   1,2,4-Trimethyl-
cyclohexane

Further Readings

There are many good elementary texts on organic chemistry for further reading and reference on the material in this and following chapters:

Amundsen, L., *Organic Chemistry* (New York: Holt, 1960).

Behr, L., Fuson, R., and Snyder, H., *Brief Course in Organic Chemistry* (New York: Wiley, 1960)

Brewster, R., and McEwen, W., *Organic Chemistry, A Brief Course* (2 ed.; Englewood Cliffs, N.J.: Prentice-Hall, 1960).

Condon, F., and Meislich, H., *Organic Chemistry* (New York: Holt, 1960).

Ernest, C., and Campaigne, E., *Elementary Organic Chemistry* (Englewood Cliffs, N.J.: Prentice-Hall, 1962).

Nomenclature of Organic Chemistry (IUPAC 1957 Rules), London: Butterworths Scientific Publications, 1958; or *Journal of the American Chemical Society*, **82** (1960), 5545.

3

Unsaturated Hydrocarbons

3-1 The Alkenes or Olefins

When an alkane molecule is "cracked" or broken to give two fragments, one of the products is a smaller member of the paraffin family, and the other is a hydrocarbon having the general formula C_nH_{2n}. The latter is not a cycloparaffin, as might be thought from the formula, but rather a straight-chain compound containing less than the amount of hydrogen necessary to saturate all the valences of the carbon atoms. Such a compound is said to be *unsaturated*. It belongs to the *alkenes* or *olefin* family of hydrocarbons.

Suppose normal hexane is split in the middle of the chain. One fragment will be propane, C_3H_8, and the other will be an unsaturated compound C_3H_6. According to the IUC nomenclature, this is called propene, the name being derived from the corresponding alkane by changing the terminal -ane to -ene. It may also be called by its older name propylene. In the older but still common practice, these unsaturated compounds are named by adding -ene to the name of the alkyl radical having the same number of carbon atoms, for example, ethylene, C_2H_4.

The mechanism of the reaction may be represented by the equation shown at the top of the next page. The asterisk indicates one of the two valence electrons which formed the covalent bond between number three and four carbon atoms before rupture. One of the hydrogens of the second radical is lost to the first; this converts the propyl to propane. A shift in

14

$$\underset{\text{n-Hexane}}{\overset{\overset{\displaystyle H\ \ H\ \ H\ \ H\ \ H\ \ H}{|\ \ \ |\ \ \ |\ \ \ |\ \ \ |\ \ \ |}}{\underset{|\ \ \ |\ \ \ |\ \ \ |\ \ \ |\ \ \ |}{\underset{\displaystyle H\ \ H\ \ H\ \ H\ \ H\ \ H}{HC-C-C-C-C-CH}}}} \longrightarrow \underset{\text{Free propyl}}{\overset{\overset{\displaystyle H\ \ H\ \ H}{|\ \ \ |\ \ \ |}}{\underset{|\ \ \ |\ \ \ |}{\underset{\displaystyle H\ \ H\ \ H}{HC-C-C*}}}} + \underset{\text{radicals}}{\overset{\overset{\displaystyle H\ \ H\ \ H}{|\ \ \ |\ \ \ |}}{\underset{|\ \ \ |\ \ \ |}{\underset{\displaystyle H\ \ H\ \ H}{*C-C-CH}}}} \longrightarrow$$

$$\underset{\text{Propane}}{\overset{\overset{\displaystyle H\ \ H\ \ H}{|\ \ \ |\ \ \ |}}{\underset{|\ \ \ |\ \ \ |}{\underset{\displaystyle H\ \ H\ \ H}{HC-C-CH}}}} + \underset{\text{Propene}}{\overset{\overset{\displaystyle H\ \ H\ \ H}{|\ \ \ |\ \ \ |}}{\underset{|\ \ \ \ \ \ \ \ |}{\underset{\displaystyle H\ \ \ \ \ \ \ \ H}{HC=C-CH}}}}$$

hydrogen takes place on the second fragment, so that two adjacent carbon atoms have unpaired electrons. The atoms make the best of things by using these to form another covalent bond between themselves. This tends to put the molecule under a strain. The valence angles are disturbed, and the two carbons are pulled closer together—to 1.37 Å instead of 1.54 Å, which is the separation in the more stable alkanes.

The tension in the molecule at the double or unsaturated bond produces in the alkenes a tendency to revert to the more stable single covalent bond whenever possible. One of the characteristic properties of compounds containing the double bond is their ability to *add* molecules or atoms at the point of unsaturation. Typical addition reactions are illustrated by the following equations.

1. $\underset{\text{Ethylene}}{CH_2{=}CH_2} + H_2 \longrightarrow \underset{\text{Ethane}}{CH_3{-}CH_3}$

2. $\qquad\qquad + Cl_2 \longrightarrow CH_2Cl{-}CH_2Cl$
   1,2-Dichloroethane or
   ethylene dichloride

3. $\qquad\qquad + HOH \longrightarrow CH_3CH_2OH$
   Ethanol or ethyl alcohol

4. $\qquad\qquad + HCl \longrightarrow CH_3CH_2Cl$
   Monochloroethane or ethyl chloride

5. $\qquad\qquad + O \longrightarrow H_2C\underset{\diagdown\ \ \diagup}{\underset{O}{}}CH_2$
   Ethylene oxide

6. $n(CH_2{=}CH_2) \longrightarrow -(CH_2{-}CH_2)_n{-} \overset{H}{\longrightarrow} H(CH_2{-}CH_2)_nH$
   Polythene or polyethylene

The radical derived from ethylene, $CH_2{=}CH-$, is called the *vinyl group*.

As will be seen in the chapters on synthetic resins, plastics, and synthetic rubber, unsaturated hydrocarbons may be persuaded to unite with each other to produce giant molecules. Such a large molecule made from many small ones is called a *polymer*, and the process is called *polymerization* (Equation 6).

You will find examples of the above-stated typical reactions of alkenes in the stabilization and synthesis of "super" gasolines, in the drying of paint, in the manufacture of antifreeze, solvents, additives in gasoline, as well as in the production of high polymers.

Since the double bond is so active chemically, the alkenes are not found to any large extent in crude oil. The large amounts used in industry at

Table 3-1. SOME ALKENES

Common name	Molecular formula	Structural formula	bp °C	IUC (or IUPAC) name
Ethylene	C_2H_4	$CH_2{=}CH_2$	−103.	Ethene
Propylene	C_3H_6	$CH_3CH{=}CH_2$	−48.5	Propene
α-Butylene	C_4H_8	$CH_3CH_2CH{=}CH_2$	−6.3	1-Butene
2- or β-Butylene	C_4H_8	$CH_3CH{=}CHCH_3$	3.6[a]	2-Butene
Isobutylene	C_4H_8	$(CH_3)_2C{=}CH_2$	−6.9	2-Methyl-1-propene

[a] Trans. +1.   Cis +3.6.

present are obtained by the dehydrogenation and cracking of saturated compounds. They can also be obtained by reversing the reactions given in Equations 1 through 4. During World War II, Russia, Germany, and to some extent the United States made ethylene by pulling an H and an OH group out of ethyl alcohol, using alumina or sulfuric acid as the catalyst.

$$
\begin{array}{c}
\quad\ \overset{\displaystyle H}{|}\ \ \overset{\displaystyle H}{|} \\
H{-}C{-}C{-}H \longrightarrow HOH + \\
\overset{|}{\underset{H\ \ OH}{\big\lfloor \quad \big\rfloor}}
\end{array}
\qquad
\begin{array}{c}
\overset{\displaystyle H}{|}\ \ \overset{\displaystyle H}{|} \\
C{=}C \\
\underset{H}{|}\ \ \underset{H}{|}
\end{array}
$$

3-2 Alkene Isomers

While there are only two butanes, the normal and "iso" structures, there can be three different butenes (Fig. 3-1). The location of the double bond is another structural factor.

In naming the compound, the location of the unsaturated bond is indicated by citing the number of the carbon atom preceding it. The carbons are numbered from the end nearest to the double bond. The "surname" of the compound is the longest carbon chain which includes the unsaturated linkage.

Thus the hydrocarbon

$$\underset{4321}{CH_3\overset{\displaystyle \overset{CH_3}{|}}{C}HCH=CH_2}$$

is numbered from right to left. Number three carbon holds a substituent methyl group. The compound is then a methyl butene, and its correct name is 3-methyl-1-butene. The compound

$$\underset{76543}{CH_3CH_2CH_2CH_2\overset{\displaystyle |}{C}HCH_2\overset{\displaystyle |}{C}HCH_3}$$

$$_2\,\overset{\displaystyle ||}{C}H \qquad CH_3$$

$$_1\,CH_2$$

2 – Butene

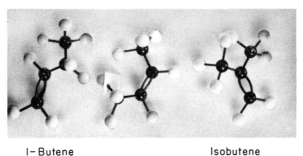

I – Butene   Isobutene

Figure 3-1 Isomers of butene or butylene.

is called 3-isobutyl-1-heptene. 2-methyl-1-butene, has the formula

$$CH_2=\overset{\displaystyle \overset{|}{C}}{C}CH_2CH_3$$
$$CH_3$$

Students should practice naming such isomers by doing the exercises at the end of the chapter.

3-3 Dienes: Hydrocarbons with Two Double Bonds

Hydrocarbons having two double bonds are called dienes. 1,3-butadiene, $CH_2=CHCH=CH_2$, is one of the materials used in the manufacture of Buna S or GRS rubber and other polymers. It is obtained by further dehydrogenation of butene produced in the cracking of petroleum. The

1,2-isomer CH_2=C=$CHCH_2$ is not as important. The monomer or unit segment of the natural rubber molecule is 2-methyl-1,3-butadiene or "isoprene" as it is commonly called.

In naming derivatives or isomers of dienes, the surname is obtained by taking the longest chain containing both double bonds. The carbon atoms are numbered from the end nearest an unsaturated bond. For example,

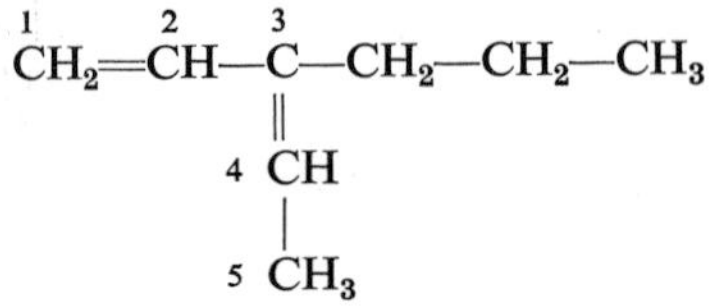

$$\overset{1}{CH_2}=\overset{2}{CH}-\overset{3}{C}-CH_2-CH_2-CH_3$$
$$\|$$
$$\underset{4}{CH}$$
$$|$$
$$\underset{5}{CH_3}$$

is 3-propyl-1,3-pentadiene.

3-4 Acetylene

Acetylene CH≡CH is produced from the raw materials coal, limestone, and water. It shows the maximum degree of unsaturation between carbon atoms. It is therefore a very reactive gas. With air it forms an explosive mixture over a wider range of concentrations than any other fuel gas. The engineer is most familiar with its use in cutting and welding, but this gas is the grandparent of a large number of chemical materials used in engineering. Vinyl plastics and resins, chlorinated solvents, ester solvents for lacquers, adhesives, and many other substances—even blood plasma substitute—are derived from acetylene.

$$HC≡CH + H_2O \longrightarrow CH_3CHO$$
$$\text{Acetaldehyde}$$

$$HC≡CH + 2 Cl_2 \longrightarrow CHCl_2{\cdot}CHCl_2$$
$$sym\text{-Tetrachloroethane}$$

$$HC≡CH + HCl \longrightarrow CH_2{=}CHCl$$
$$\text{Vinyl chloride}$$

$$HC≡CH + 2 HCl \longrightarrow CH_3CHCl_2$$
$$\text{1,1-Dichloroethane}$$

Acetylene forms derivatives in which the hydrogens are replaced by metal atoms. Silver acetylide, AgC≡CAg, is very explosive. It is so sensitive that a fly walking on a crumb of the material will detonate it. The formation of cuprous acetylide CuC≡CCu is used as a test for the triple carbon-to-carbon bond. In acetylene the carbon atoms are only 1.28 Å apart.

Acetylene is soluble in acetone. This property is made use of in marketing the compressed gas. Cylinders containing a porous material saturated with acetone are filled with the gas. At 180 psi acetone dissolves 300 times its own volume of the gas.

When passed through a hot tube, three molecules of acetylene polymerize to give benzene: $3 \ CH{\equiv}CH \rightarrow C_6H_6$. In the presence of traces of copper, polymerization proceeds much further giving a soft-felted solid, "cuprene." Figure 3-2 is an electron micrograph of this substance.

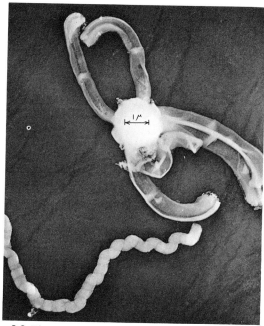

Figure 3-2 Electron photomicrograph of the acetylene polymer, "Cuprene." (Courtesy Imperial Oil Ltd.)

3-5 The Aromatic or Benzene Series of Hydrocarbons

Benzene, a light oily liquid derived chiefly from coal tar, was shown by Faraday to have the composition represented by the formula C_6H_6. Its structure is represented by a six-carbon ring or hexagon in which the carbons are joined by alternate single and double bonds. The remaining single valence of each carbon holds one hydrogen atom at each corner of the hexagon.

The benzene ring is a very symmetrical structure. It is much less reactive than would be expected from the presence of three unsaturated linkages. The modern concept of the structure is that the extra electron associated with the double bond moves from one carbon to the next, so that each of the carbons is held by something intermediate between a single and a double bond.

The chemist, either from laziness or for convenience, uses a hexagon to denote the benzene molecule

If one or more of the hydrogens of the benzene are replaced by other atoms or groups, the structure is indicated by a hexagon with the formula for the substituent group shown in its particular position. Monochlorobenzene is written

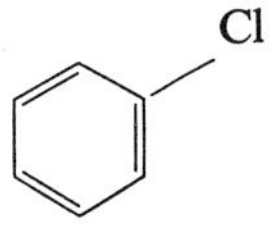

Cl

Symmetrical (1,3,5)-trimethyl benzene is represented by the formula

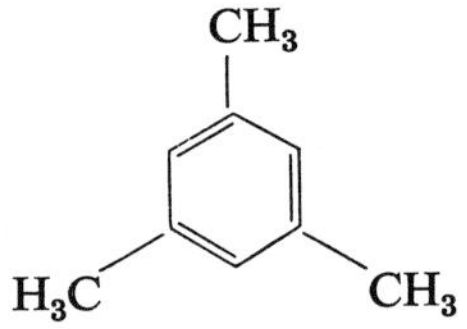

CH₃

H₃C   CH₃

It is apparent that there can be only *one* monochlorobenzene since the benzene ring is perfectly symmetrical, and each corner is the same. An examination of the di-substitution products such as dichlorobenzene, $C_6H_4Cl_2$, reveals that there can be only three possible isomers: (1) The chlorines may be attached to adjacent carbon atoms; (2) they may be separated by a carbon atom and its hydrogen; or (3) they may be at opposite ends of the molecule. These three positions are known as *ortho*, *meta*, and *para* respectively and are indicated by their initials. According to IUC they may be referred to as the 1,2; 1,3, and 1,4 isomers.

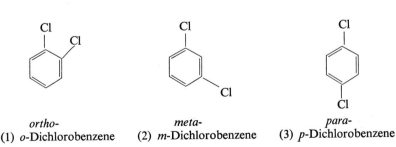

ortho-   meta-   para-
(1) *o*-Dichlorobenzene   (2) *m*-Dichlorobenzene   (3) *p*-Dichlorobenzene

Toluene or methyl benzene resembles benzene in physical and chemical properties. It can have only one structure. Xylene, however, since it is dimethyl benzene, exists in three different isomeric forms;

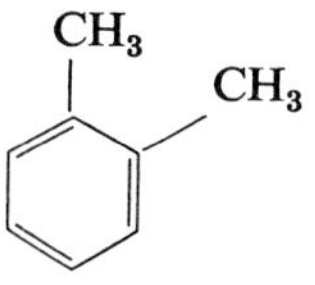

	o-Xylene (1,2)	m-Xylene (1,3)	p-Xylene (1,4)
mp	−25° C	−47.8° C	13.2° C
bp	144.5	139.2	138.4
sp gr	0.880	0.864	0.860

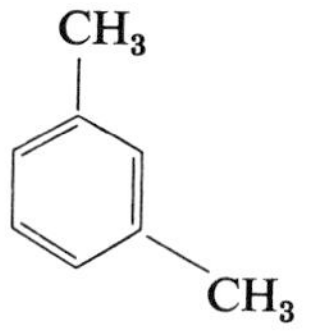

Other common and important members of the aryl or aromatic hydrocarbons are ethyl benzene used in the preparation of styrene, and *cumene* or isopropyl benzene used in blended high-octane gasoline.

Styrene is the hydrocarbon on which is based the manufacture of styron plastics and GR-S or Buna S rubber. In the latter the S refers to styrene, which has the formula

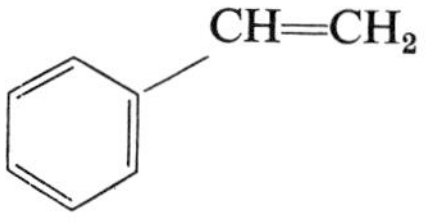

Styrene may be called vinyl benzene. It is related to the other vinyl compounds forming a variety of synthetic resins and polymers (*cf.* Chap. 17).

Long before the International Union of Chemistry systematized the naming of chemical compounds, the radical C_6H_5— derived from benzene was called *phenyl*. Thus monochlorobenzene may still be referred to under the name of phenylchloride. Styrene could then be phenylethylene, that is, ethylene in which one hydrogen has been replaced by the phenyl radical. Biphenyl,[1] C_6H_5—C_6H_5 (or diphenyl), is a very stable hydrocarbon used as a heat-transfer agent under the trade name "Dowtherm." In the manufacture of nylon the polymer is kept molten during ejection of the filament by hot biphenyl pumped to each unit from a central boiler. Halogen derivatives of biphenyl are important insulating fluids for transformers and circuit breakers.

Naphthalene may be thought of as consisting of two fused benzene rings.

---

1 IUPAC name.

It is a white solid hydrocarbon familiar to everyone as "moth balls." It is a very important raw material for making phthalic acid, used in the manufacture of glyptal resins for the paint and varnish industry. Naphthalene is also used in making detergents and wetting agents, and plasticizers for plastics. Figure 3-3 shows the structure of benzene and naphthalene.

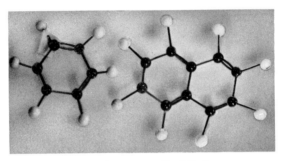

Benzene   Naphthalene

Figure 3-3 Benzene and naphthalene.

In naming derivatives of naphthalene the carbons are numbered as shown below. For mono derivatives, positions 1, 4, 5, or 8 are also called α, and positions 2, 3, 6, 7 are called β.

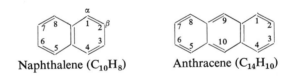

Naphthalene ($C_{10}H_8$)   Anthracene ($C_{14}H_{10}$)

α-Methyl naphthalene is used with cetane to prepare standard diesel test fuels to determine the "cetane number."

Anthracene is another condensed hydrocarbon obtained from coal tar. It is used for making dyes and smoke screens.

Review Questions

1. What is the chief chemical property of alkenes?

2. Write the equation representing the manufacture of glycol from ethylene.

3. What would you expect to obtain from the reaction of propylene and hydrogen bromide?

4. Name the following:

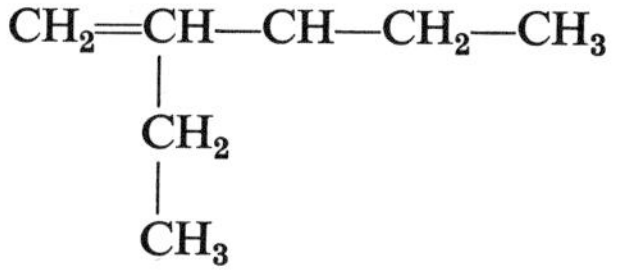

$$CH_2=CH-CH-CH_2-CH_3$$
$$|$$
$$CH_2$$
$$|$$
$$CH_3$$
(a)

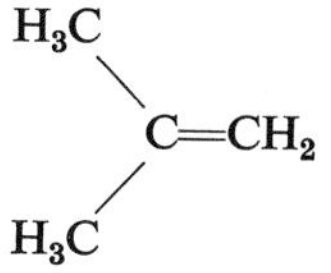

$$H_3C$$
$$\diagdown$$
$$C=CH_2$$
$$\diagup$$
$$H_3C$$
(b)

CH=CH₂

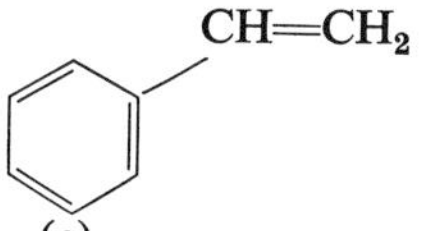

(c)

$$CH_2=CH-CH_2-CH=CH_2$$
(d)

5. Write the formulas and name all the isomers of pentene.

6. Write the formula for: (a) 1,2,4-trimethyl benzene, (b) *p*-dichloro-benzene, (c) phenyl bromide, (d) vinyl chloride, (e) tetrafluoro-ethylene, (f) *s*-trinitrotoluene.

4

Organic Types

In referring to the behavior of an individual, someone may remark, "Oh that's the type he is!" or, "That's the way he's built!" Fortunately, the very large number of organic derivatives used in engineering can be divided into a few classes or "types," each having its own characteristic behavior. The behavior of an organic molecule depends on its make-up, on the presence of particular structural groups. Substances having the same functional groups for example, OH groups, will have many similar chemical properties.

This chapter is meant to be an introduction to several types of organic compounds with one or two examples of each. The general behavior of each will be described. By learning to recognize these types and their functional groups, the behavior of a material can be predicted and its possible use indicated.

4-I Alcohols

Alcohols may be thought of as being derived from hydrocarbons with the replacement of one or more hydrogens by hydroxyl (OH) groups. The simplest alcohols are represented by the general formula ROH, where R is an alkyl radical.

They may be named by replacing the terminal -e of the hydrocarbon by

Table 4-1. COMMON TYPES OF ORGANIC COMPOUNDS

General formula	Type	Example	Formula	Functional group	
ROH	Alcohol	Methanol	CH_3OH	—OH	Hydroxyl group
RCHO	Aldehyde	Acetaldehyde	CH_3CHO	—CH $\\\parallel$ O	Aldehyde group
RCOR	Ketone	Acetone	CH_3COCH_3	—C— $\\\parallel$ O	Keto or carbonyl group
RCOOH	Acid	Acetic acid	CH_3COOH	—C—OH $\\\parallel$ O	Carboxyl group
RCOOR	Ester	Amyl acetate	$CH_3COOC_5H_{11}$	—C—OR $\\\parallel$ O	Ester group
RNH_2	Amine	Monobutyl amine	$C_4H_9NH_2$	$—NH_2$	Amino group

the suffix -*ol*, or identified by the name of the particular radical R; for example,

$$CH_3OH$$
Methanol or methyl alcohol
$$C_2H_5OH$$
Ethanol or ethyl alcohol
$$(CH_3)_2CHOH$$
Isopropanol or isopropyl alcohol
$$C_5H_{11}OH$$
Pentanol or amyl alcohol

Methanol is now synthesized from carbon monoxide and hydrogen. Much of the ethyl alcohol used in industry is still produced by fermentation. Molasses, starch, and grain are the substrates. Large tonnages are also made by the catalytic hydration of ethylene. Isopropyl alcohol is also manufactured from refinery gases.

The hydroxyl group increases the solubility of a molecule in water. Ethane (C_2H_6) is only very slightly soluble, whereas ethanol (C_2H_5OH) is miscible with water in all proportions. If, however, the alkyl hydrocarbon radical is very large, its oily nature overcomes the effect of the hydroxyl group. Amyl alcohol is only slightly soluble in water.

Alcohols having the structure RCH_2OH are normal or primary alcohols. If a second radical is attached to the carbon bearing the OH group,

$$\begin{array}{c} R \\ \diagdown \\ CHOH \\ \diagup \\ R \end{array}$$

as in isopropyl alcohol, the compound is called a *secondary alcohol*. A tertiary alcohol has the structure represented by the formula

$$
\begin{array}{c}
R \\
\diagdown \\
R\!-\!COH \\
\diagup \\
R
\end{array}
$$

An example of this is tertiary butyl alcohol,

$$
\begin{array}{c}
CH_3 \\
| \\
H_3C\!-\!C\!-\!OH \\
| \\
CH_3
\end{array}
$$

The three types of alcohols behave differently on oxidation. Primary alcohols yield aldehydes, and secondary alcohols give ketones having the original

Table 4-2. COMMON ALCOHOLS

Common Name	Formula	bp	Density	IUC Name
Methyl alcohol	CH_3OH	64.5° C	0.792	Methanol
Ethyl alcohol	C_2H_5OH	78.5	0.789	Ethanol
n-Propyl alcohol	$CH_3CH_2CH_2OH$	97.8	0.804	1-Propanol
Isopropyl alcohol	$(CH_3)_2CHOH$	82.3	0.786	2-Propanol
n-Butyl alcohol	$CH_3(CH_2)_2CH_2OH$	117.7	0.810	1-Butanol
Isobutyl alcohol	$(CH_3)_2CHCH_2OH$	107.3	0.802	2-Methyl-1-propanol
sec-Butyl alcohol	$C_2H_5\!-\!CHOH\!-\!CH_3$	99.5	0.808	2-Butanol
ter-Butyl alcohol[a]	$(CH_3)_3COH$	82.8	0.789	2-Methyl-2-propanol
n-Amyl alcohol	$CH_3(CH_2)_3CH_2OH$	138.	0.817	1-Pentanol
Isoamyl alcohol	$(CH_3)_2CHCH_2CH_2OH$	131.	0.812	3-Methyl-1-butanol
Lauryl alcohol[a]	$CH_3(CH_2)_{10}CH_2OH$	259.	0.831	1-Dodecanol

[a] Solids at room temperature.

number of carbon atoms. Tertiary alcohols are not oxidized as readily but finally break down yielding smaller oxidation products.

The alcohols are important as solvents and as raw materials for the synthesis of other products. Their application in industry and for the manufacture of engineering materials will be noted in succeeding chapters.

4-2 Alcohols with More than One Hydroxyl Group

Alcohols containing two hydroxyl groups are called *glycols*. The simplest and most common glycol is ethylene glycol

$$CH_2-CH_2$$
$$\;\; | \qquad |$$
$$OH \quad OH$$

so widely used in antifreeze. Propylene glycol,

$$CH_3-CH-CH_2$$
$$\qquad | \qquad |$$
$$OH \quad OH$$

is also used as an antifreeze fluid in refrigeration machines. These and other glycols are good solvents. They are used to make special water-soluble waxes and synthetic lubricants.

Glycerol, frequently called *glycerine*, has three hydroxyl groups. Its formula is

$$CH_2-CH-CH_2$$
$$\;\; | \qquad | \qquad |$$
$$OH \quad OH \quad OH$$

This is a viscous liquid boiling at 290° C. It is very hygroscopic. Since OH groups impart sweetness as well as water solubility, this "polyhydric" alcohol is used in cough syrups and for sweetening and humectifying tobacco. Large quantities are consumed in the manufacture of resins for paint and varnish. It is also a raw material for nitroglycerine and dynamite. Glycerol has many other uses, but the above three account for most of the two and a quarter million pounds produced annually in the United States.

Other compounds containing hydroxyl groups will be discussed in subsequent chapters.

4-3 Aldehydes

When methanol is treated with air in the presence of a catalyst, oxidation takes place, which produces water and formaldehyde.

$$\underset{\text{Methanol}}{H-\overset{\displaystyle H}{\underset{\displaystyle H}{C}}-OH} + O \longrightarrow \underset{\substack{\text{Unstable} \\ \text{product}}}{H-\overset{\displaystyle OH}{C}-OH} \longrightarrow H_2O + \underset{\text{Formaldehyde}}{\overset{\displaystyle H}{\underset{\displaystyle H}{\diagdown}}C=O} \overset{O}{\longrightarrow} \underset{\text{Formic acid}}{H-\overset{\displaystyle OH}{C}=O}$$

The oxidation of ethanol may be controlled to give acetaldehyde

$$\underset{\text{Ethanol}}{CH_3CH_2OH} \overset{+O}{\longrightarrow} \underset{\text{Acetaldehyde}}{CH_3-\overset{\displaystyle H}{C}=O} + H_2O \overset{O}{\longrightarrow} \underset{\text{Acetic acid}}{CH_3-\overset{\displaystyle OH}{C}=O}$$

Further oxidation converts the aldehydes into acids. The name of the aldehyde indicates the acid formed by its oxidation; thus formaldehyde gives formic acid, while acetaldehyde yields acetic acid.

Since aldehydes are easily oxidized and make good reducing substances, they will reduce certain metal ions to the metallic state. They also act as corrosion inhibitors. Formaldehyde is one of the components for the production of phenol-formaldehyde (Bakelite) and other resins and adhesives.

4-4 Ketones: $\overset{\overset{\displaystyle O}{\|}}{RCR}$

If isopropyl alcohol

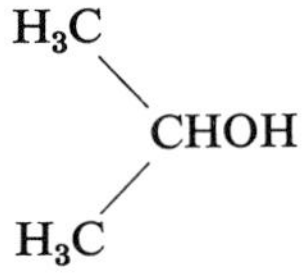

$$\begin{array}{c} H_3C \\ \diagdown \\ CHOH \\ \diagup \\ H_3C \end{array}$$

a secondary alcohol, is oxidized, both hydrogens are removed from the second carbon atom to give the product

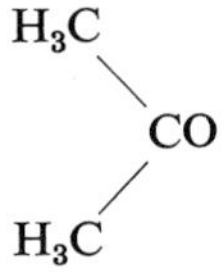

$$\begin{array}{c} H_3C \\ \diagdown \\ CO \\ \diagup \\ H_3C \end{array}$$

This is *acetone.* It corresponds to the general formula

$$\overset{\displaystyle R}{\underset{\displaystyle R-CO}{\vert}}$$

and is therefore a *ketone.* Acetone can be manufactured from cracked petroleum as indicated below:

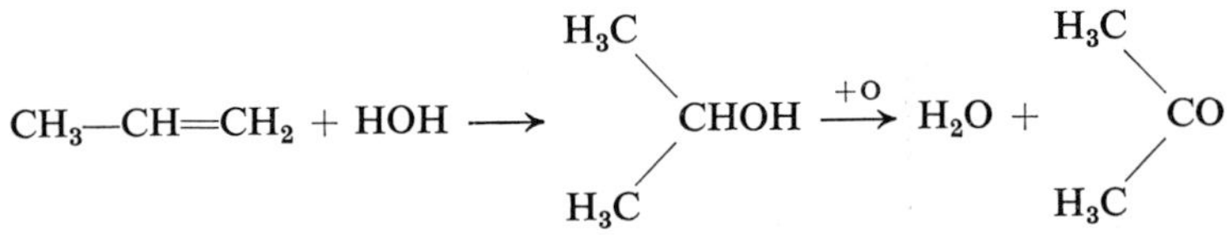

$$CH_3-CH{=}CH_2 + HOH \longrightarrow \begin{array}{c} H_3C \\ \diagdown \\ CHOH \\ \diagup \\ H_3C \end{array} \xrightarrow{+O} H_2O + \begin{array}{c} H_3C \\ \diagdown \\ CO \\ \diagup \\ H_3C \end{array}$$

| Propylene | Isopropyl alcohol | Acetone or dimethyl ketone |

Another commercial process makes use of acetylene generated from calcium carbide and water. The acetylene in the presence of a suitable catalyst first combines with water, and the product so formed undergoes a rearrangement giving acetaldehyde which is oxidized to acetic acid. Vaporized acid is converted to acetone, CO_2, and water.

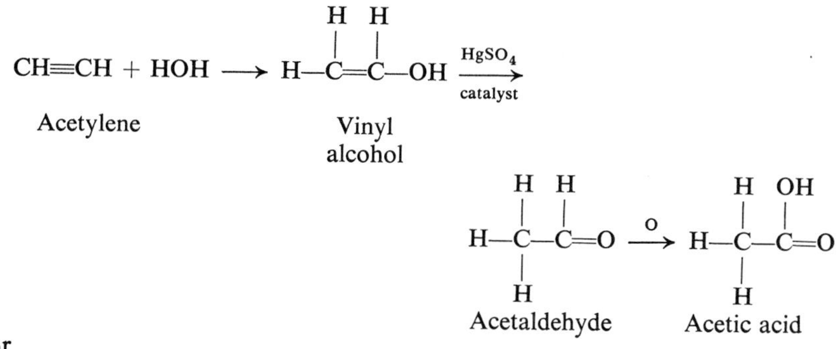

$$CH{\equiv}CH + HOH \longrightarrow H-\underset{\underset{}{}}{\overset{\overset{H\quad H}{|\quad|}}{C}}{=}C-OH \xrightarrow[\text{catalyst}]{HgSO_4}$$

Acetylene   Vinyl
                            alcohol

$$H-\overset{\overset{H\quad H}{|\quad|}}{\underset{\underset{H}{|}}{C}}-C{=}O \xrightarrow{\;\;O\;\;} H-\overset{\overset{H\quad OH}{|\quad|}}{\underset{\underset{H}{|}}{C}}-C{=}O$$

Acetaldehyde   Acetic acid

or

$$CH{\equiv}CH + H_2O \longrightarrow CH_2{=}CHOH \longrightarrow CH_3CHO \xrightarrow{\;O\;} CH_3COOH$$

Then

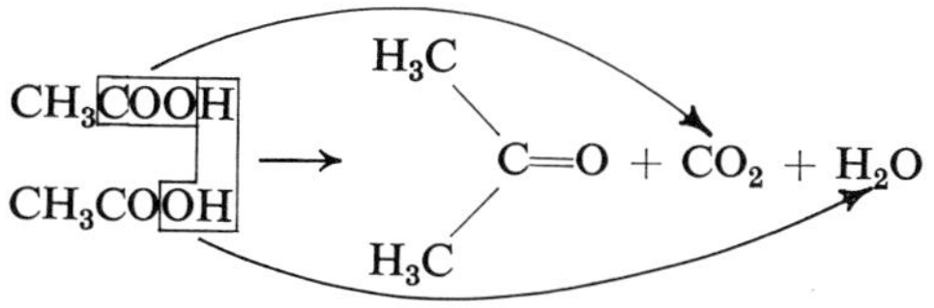

$$\begin{matrix} CH_3\boxed{COOH} \\ CH_3CO\boxed{OH} \end{matrix} \longrightarrow \overset{H_3C}{\underset{H_3C}{}}C{=}O + CO_2 + H_2O$$

or

$$2\,CH_3COOH \longrightarrow CH_3COCH_3 + CO_2 + H_2O$$

Acetone is also manufactured on an industrial scale by a fermentation process devised by Dr. C. Weizmann, who later won renown as the first president of Israel.

Acetone and methylethyl ketone are of importance as organic solvents. They are used as solvents for lacquers, paint and varnish removers, in the manufacture of cordite, celanese, and certain plastics, and in the de-waxing of lubricating oil.

4-5 Organic Acids

The second stage in the oxidation of a primary alcohol gives an acid. Aliphatic acids are characterized by the presence of the carboxyl group

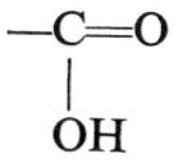

$$-\underset{\underset{OH}{|}}{C}{=}O \qquad \text{also written } -COOH$$

The hydrogen of the —OH attached to the carbonyl group is acidic. This should not be surprising if we look at the structural formulas for nitric and sulfuric acids

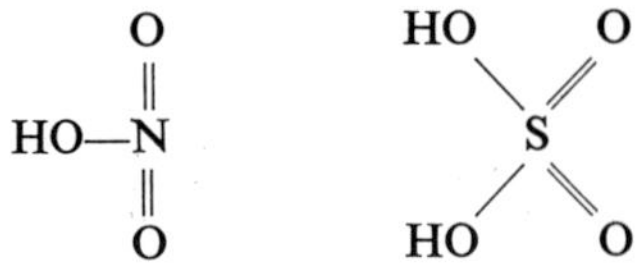

$$
\begin{array}{ccc}
 & O & \\
 & \parallel & \\
HO-N & & \\
 & \parallel & \\
 & O &
\end{array}
\qquad
\begin{array}{cc}
HO & O \\
 \diagdown \; \diagup & \\
 S & \\
 \diagup \; \diagdown & \\
HO & O
\end{array}
$$

When an inorganic acid reacts with an inorganic base, the products are water and a salt.

$$NaOH + HCl \longrightarrow HOH + NaCl$$

or

$$Ca(OH)_2 + 2\,HNO_3 \longrightarrow 2\,HOH + Ca(NO_3)_2$$

Organic acids also react with inorganic bases to give salts, the metal ion

Table 4-3. Common Organic Acids

Aliphatic acids		Aromatic acids	
HCOOH	Formic acid	C_6H_5COOH	Benzoic
CH_3COOH	Acetic acid	$C_6H_5SO_3H$	Benzene sulfonic acid
C_2H_5COOH	Propionic acid	C_6H_5OH	Phenol[a] (Carbolic acid)
C_3H_7COOH	Butyric acid	$CH_3C_6H_4OH$	Cresols
. . .			
$C_{17}H_{33}COOH$	Oleic acid		
$C_{17}H_{35}COOH$	Stearic acid		

Dibasic acids		
COOH | COOH	Oxalic acid	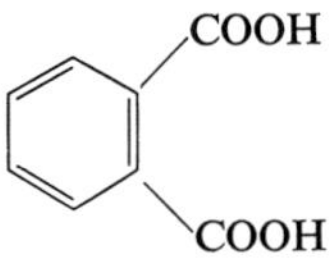 Phthalic acid[b]
CH_2COOH | CH_2COOH	Succinic acid	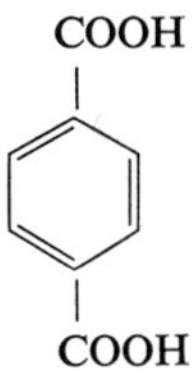
CH_2CH_2COOH | CH_2CH_2COOH	Adipic acid	Terephthalic acid[b]

[a] An —OH group attached to the benzene ring ionizes to a slight extent, and its hydrogen can be replaced by a metal ion. Trinitrophenol is a relatively strong acid.
[b] Phthalic and terephthalic acids are aromatic dibasic acids.

replacing the hydrogen of the carboxyl group. For example,

$$(a) \quad Ca(OH)_2 + 2\ HOC\!-\!CH_3 \longrightarrow Ca \begin{array}{c} OC\!-\!CH_3 \\ \diagup \\ O \\ \diagdown \\ OC\!-\!CH_3 \end{array} + 2\ HOH$$

Acetic acid   Calcium acetate

or

$$(b) \quad NaOH + HOOC\!-\!C_{17}H_{33} \longrightarrow NaOOC\!-\!C_{17}H_{33} + HOH$$

Oleic acid   Sodium oleate

Salts of the long fatty acids are called *soaps*. They are important components of lubricating greases, detergent oils, and emulsions (see Chapter 13).

Some important organic acids are listed in the Table 4-3.

4-6 Esters

When organic acids react with alcohols, the product that is formed in addition to the water is called an *ester*, and the process is called *esterification*.

$$CH_3CO\!-\!OH + C_2H_5OH \longrightarrow HOH + CH_3CO\!-\!OC_2H_5$$

Acetic   Ethanol   Water   Ethyl
acid   acetate
(an ester)

The esters are important solvents for lacquers and certain plastics and resins. "Banana oil," used extensively in dopes and other protective coatings, is amyl acetate. Many modern detergents are esters. Similar types of esters are formed with polyalcohols to produce a great variety of engineering materials such as explosives, plastics, insulating materials, and synthetic fibers. Fats and drying oils are esters of glycerol and long fatty acids (see Chapter 19).

4-7 Amines

Amines are derivatives of ammonia, NH_3. The simplest of these may be represented by the general formula RNH_2, where R is an organic radical. Such a compound is called a *primary amine* because only one of the hydrogens of the ammonia has been replaced. A secondary amine would obviously be one in which two of the ammonia hydrogens were replaced by organic radicals: RNHR. All three hydrogen atoms may be replaced by radicals,

giving a tertiary amine,

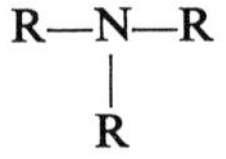

$$R—N—R$$
$$|$$
$$R$$

This replacement of hydrogens by organic radicals can be extended to include the ammonium ion

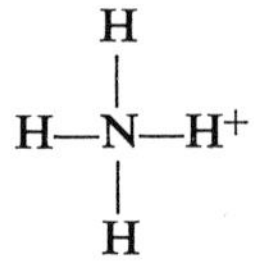

$$H$$
$$|$$
$$H—N—H^+$$
$$|$$
$$H$$

These compounds are called quaternary ammonium salts. They form a very important class of modern detergents. Some examples of this family of ammonia derivatives are

$$C_2H_5NH_2 \qquad (C_4H_9)_3N \qquad CH_3—\overset{\displaystyle CH_3}{\underset{\displaystyle C_3H_7}{N}}—C_2H_5^+Cl^-$$

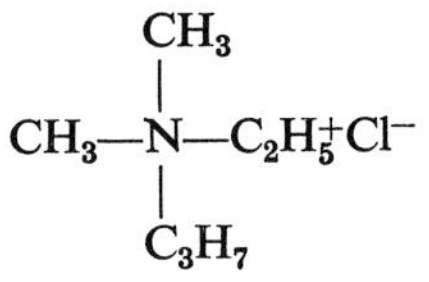

named primary ethyl amine, tributyl- or tertiary butyl amine and dimethyl-ethyl propyl ammonium chloride, respectively.

The primary amine $C_6H_5NH_2$, phenyl amine, has been known for many years. It is commonly called *aniline*.

Amines find extensive use in engineering as corrosion inhibitors. (see Chapters 15, 16, and 21.)

Review Questions

1. Classify each of the following compounds:

(a) $(CH_3)_2CH—CH_2OH$

(b) 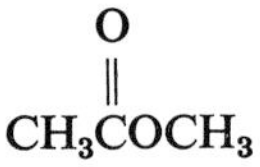
$$\overset{\displaystyle O}{\overset{\displaystyle \|}{CH_3COCH_3}}$$

(c) 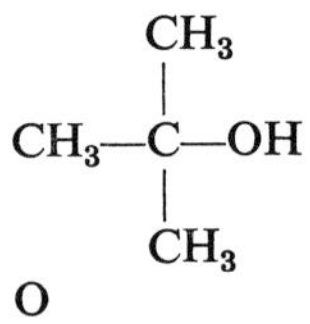 $CH_3—\overset{\displaystyle CH_3}{\underset{\displaystyle CH_3}{C}}—OH$

(d) 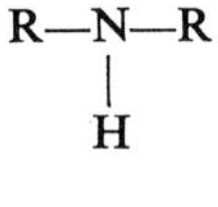 $R—\overset{}{\underset{\displaystyle H}{N}}—R$

(e) 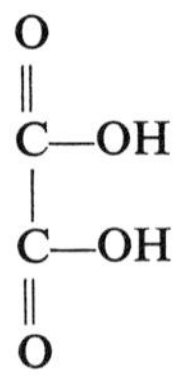
$$\overset{\displaystyle O}{\overset{\displaystyle \|}{C}}—OH$$
$$|$$
$$\overset{\displaystyle C}{\underset{\displaystyle \|}{\underset{\displaystyle O}{}}}—OH$$

2. According to the rhyme:[1]

A mosquito was heard to complain
That a chemist had poisoned his brain.
The cause of his sorrow
Was *para*-dichloro-
diphenyltrichloroethane!

Write the formula. (First, 1,1,1-trichloroethane; then 2,2-diphenyl-trichloroethane.) If a chlorine is put in the *para* position on each phenyl group, the new substance is DDT.

3. Name one characteristic chemical property or reaction of (a) an amine, (b) alkyl halides, (c) the carboxyl group.

4. Write the formula for possible products formed during the oxidation of glycol in an antifreeze.

5. What is produced when isopropyl alcohol is oxidized?

6. If the structural formula for nitric acid is

$$HO-N=O$$
$$\overset{\|}{O}$$

show by an equation using structural formulas the formation of nitroglycerine.

7. To what class of organic compounds does this product belong?

8. The formula for lauryl alcohol is $CH_3(CH_2)_{10}CH_2OH$. Sulfuric acid may be written

$$\begin{array}{cc} HO & O \\ \diagdown & \diagup \\ & S \\ \diagup & \diagdown \\ HO & O \end{array}$$

What would be the formula for monolaurylsulfate?

9. If the acid ester above is treated with NaOH what would be the formula of the product? This was one of the first synthetic detergents marketed for domestic use.

---

1 From May & Baker Ltd. "Laboratory Bulletin," III, No. 5, 1959, by permission.

10. Sodium benzoate can be used in antifreeze. What is its formula?

11. Pentachlorophenol prevents termite damage of timbers and poles. What is its formula?

12. Magnesium adds on such compounds as ethyl iodide forming what is known as a *Grignard reagent*. Write the formula and name of the product.

5

Solid Fuels

5-1 Sources of Power

A century ago power was obtained from steam or the kinetic energy of wind or water. The fuels chiefly used were wood and coal. Sources of power have changed with the years, so that now approximately 11 per cent of the world's power is supplied by hydroelectric plants and the remaining 89 per cent from fuels. Gas provides 14 per cent of the total power; petroleum, 30 per cent; and coal, 45 per cent; of which 5 per cent is derived from hard coal and 40 per cent from the soft coals. Nuclear fuels provide less than 1 per cent. It is expected that oil will shortly displace coal as the major fuel.

All of these sources of power are derived indirectly from the energy of the sun. Doubtless more direct use of solar radiation will be made in the near future. Since the time Archimedes set fire to the Roman fleet by concentrating reflected rays from the sun, there have been many attempts to make use of the energy of direct sunlight. An acre of ground at the equator receives energy from the sun at a rate equivalent to about 4400 hp. A reflector 20 feet in diameter placed in this sunlight would receive approximately 1300 Btu or the equivalent of the heat produced by burning two cubic feet of a good fuel gas per minute. Recently, small solar boilers have been developed for use in fuel-deficient, underdeveloped areas, and small solar stills, for preparing potable water from sea water. Sunlight energy has been stored by using

35

Glauber's salt, $Na_2SO_4 \cdot 10 H_2O$, which melts at 90° F and gives out heat upon solidifying. This method has been proposed for the solar heating of houses. A skylight bed of the material would melt under the sun's rays. At sunset, or when the temperature falls, heat would be given out and the house temperature regulated until complete crystallization of the material occurred.

Solar energy can now be converted to electrical energy through such photochemical devices as the silicon strip battery developed by Bell Telephone Laboratories or the cadmium sulfide battery of the Wright Air Development Center. In 1960, a battery of solar cells was used to power an old electric auto. In satellites, similar cells make use of solar radiation to charge the batteries employed for the transmission of data by radio signals.

However, for many years to come, the greatest portion of the world's power will come from the combustion of fuels.

5-2 Classification of Fuels

Since the physical state of the fuel determines the method of utilization and the type of equipment required, fuels are classified as solid, liquid, or gaseous. Each class may subdivided into *primary* and *derived* fuels. A primary fuel is one found in nature; a derived fuel is manufactured from a primary fuel or some other source.

Table 5-1. GENERAL CLASSIFICATION OF FUELS

Solid fuels	Primary fuels	Coals (lignite, bituminous and anthracite), wood, peat.
	Derived fuels	Coke, charcoal, petroleum-coke, solid rocket fuels, such as thiokol, hydrazine, nitrocellulose
Liquid fuels	Primary fuels	Crude oil, natural gasoline
	Derived fuels	Liquid hydrocarbons from carbonization of coal, oil shale, tar sands; refined oils, gasoline; oils synthesized from water gas; alcohols
Gaseous fuels	Primary fuels	Natural gas
	Derived fuels	Coal gas, producer gas, water gas, Lurgi gas, sewage digester gas, blast furnace gas, light petroleum gas (LPG) from oil refining.

5-3 Wood and Charcoal

Wood is no longer used as an industrial fuel, but it is still used in some rural areas along with bottled gas. Green wood contains from 26 to 50 per cent water; dry wood from 12 to 15 per cent. The resinous woods, like cedar or pine, yield 7900 to 8100 Btu/lb of air-dried wood or, allowing for the moisture content, 9000 to 9200 Btu on the dry weight. On the latter basis most hardwoods have a heating value of 8300 to 8400 Btu/lb.

Charcoal, a derived fuel, gives about 13,000 Btu/lb and burns with no smoke and little or no flame. The Romans used it in open, portable braziers to heat their houses. During wartime it was used in Britain and Europe as a source of producer gas, a substitute for gasoline in trucks, automobiles, motorcycles, and even motorboats.

5-4 Peat

Peat represents the first stage in the conversion of cellulosic materials into coal. As cut from the peat bog, it is a spongy mass saturated with water. Eight tons of peat yield about one ton of fuel after drying; a commercial grade containing about 25 per cent water. Air-dried peat has a heating value of about 7000 Btu.

Peat is not used in North America as a fuel, but in Europe it is employed for domestic heating and to produce fuel gas and coke. In the U.S.S.R., it is used to generate power for electricity, and one of the many installations making use of peat in that country is reported to generate 200,000 kw.

5-5 Coals

Coal is a generic term applied to solid fuels, which range from *lignite*, which is little more than a matured and modified peat, to meta-anthracite, which is almost 100 per cent carbon. Some method of representing the rank and quality of different coals is therefore needed. Several schemes for classifying coal have been suggested. All of them are based on the chemical composition or the percentage of some particular component and/or the heating value of the fuel (Btu/lb).

5-6 Analysis of Coal

There are two ways of expressing the composition of coal. One is called the *proximate analysis*, and the other, the *ultimate analysis*.

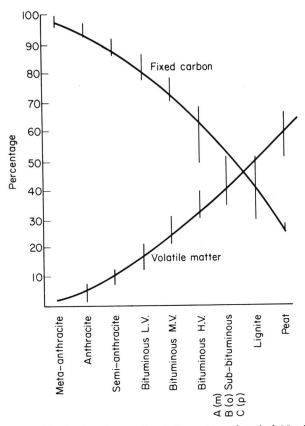

Figure 5-1 Fixed carbon and volatile matter of typical North American coals.

The quantities determined in the proximate analysis are the percentage of moisture, volatile matter, fixed carbon, and ash. In the ultimate analysis of coal, the percentages of carbon, hydrogen, nitrogen, sulfur, and oxygen are determined. The composition of the ash may also be obtained.

The *moisture content* of coal is obtained by drying a weighed sample (20 mesh screen size) at 110° C in a stream of dry air for one hour.[1] Total moisture may include extraneous or "free" water, that is, water on the surface of the coal or in cracks, picked up after mining from rain or snow. Moisture content labeled by the United States Bureau of Mines as *intrinsic moisture*[1] represents the water distributed more or less uniformly throughout

───────

1 "Notes on Sampling and Analysis of Coal," U.S. Bureau of Mines, 1938, Technical Paper 589.

the coal as mined. In the evaluation of these quantities, the sample is first dried in a current of air at 30° C, which causes the evaporation of the free water. The process is continued until the loss in weight is less than 0.1 per cent per hour. The total weight lost represents *free water*. The intrinsic moisture is determined from the further loss in weight when the sample is dried at 110° C.

The dry sample is next heated in the absence of air at 900° C. This process eliminates hydrocarbons, other gases, and liquids. The loss in weight gives the percentage of *volatile matter*. The residue contains the fixed carbon and ash. The carbon is burned, and the ignited residue, *the ash*, is weighed. The percentage of *fixed carbon* is calculated from the difference. The caloric or *heat value* of the fuel is measured in a bomb calorimeter.

5-7 Coal Rank or Class

Figure 5-1 depicts the data given by different authorities for the volatile matter and fixed carbon for coals of different rank. The curves represent the mean values. They show that, as the fuel increases in rank, the percentage of fixed carbon increases while the volatile matter decreases. Inherent moisture also decreases from lignite to anthracite.

Figure 5-2 shows the variation and limits in total carbon and oxygen content of North American coals. Ultimate analysis indicates that the coals in the eastern region are older and of higher rank than those of the western fields. It is obvious that the total carbon increases and the percentage oxygen decreases as the metamorphic process goes from peat to anthracite.

5-8 A.S.T.M. Classification

Each of the classes described above can be divided into subgroups according to composition, appearance, specific properties, or uses. Thus in the bituminous class there may be *gas coals*, *coking coals*, and *steam coals*. To avoid confusion in classifying types of coal, definite criteria must be established. Two A.S.T.M. classifications are given in Table 5-1. The volatile matter and the fixed carbon obtained from the proximate analysis are expressed as a percentage of mineral-free and moisture-free fuel. Either of these may be used to classify coals of higher rank than the most volatile bituminous coals. The classification of lower rank coals is based on their caloric or heating value and is expressed as Btu per pound of coal calculated on a mineral-free but *not* a moisture-free basis. (The mineral content is considered to be equal to 1.1 times the ash.)

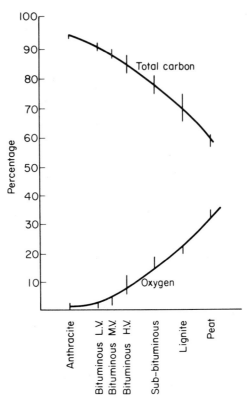

Figure 5-2 Total carbon and oxygen content of typical North American coals.

The proximate analysis of typical North American coals are given in Table 5-3. The data are for the coals as mined, or in a few instances as received. The values for the volatile matter, fixed carbon will be higher when calculated on the basis of dry, ash-free (or mineral-free) fuels as required for A.S.T.M. classification. The heating value calculated for the theoretical ash-free fuel will also be greater.

As an example, for Wyoming coal (Table 5-3), the percentage of volatile matter on a dry ash-free basis will be $33.6 \times \frac{100}{73} = 46.0$ per cent and the fixed carbon $39.4 \times \frac{100}{73} = 54$ per cent of the fuel substance. The heating value per pound of moist but mineral-free fuel equals $9382 \times \frac{100}{96}$, or 9757 Btu. By A.S.T.M. standards, this coal would be classified in the sub-bituminous B group. Similarly, calculations from the proximate analysis of the Pennsylvanian coal give the volatile matter and fixed carbon as 39.3 and 60.7 per cent of the dry ash-free fuel substance. The coal is classed as bituminous group A.

Table 5-2. A.S.T.M. Classification by Rank

Rank and Group	Method I % Volatile Matter	Method II (D388-36T) % Fixed Carbon (moisture and mineral free basis)
I. *Anthracite*		
Meta-anthracite	2 or less	98 or more
Anthracite	2–8	98–92
Semi-anthracite	8–14	92–86
II. *Bituminous.*		
Low-volatile group	14–22	86–78
Medium-volatile group	22–31	78–69
High-volatile A group	More than 31	Less than 69
	Heating value: Moist, Btu more than 14,000	
High-volatile B group	13,000–14,000	
High-volatile C group	11,000–13,000 either agglomerating or nonweathering	
III. *Sub-bituminous*		
Sub-bituminous A group	11,000–13,000 weathering and non-agglomerating	
Sub-bituminous B group	9,500–11,000	
Sub-bituminous C group	8,300–9,000	
IV. *Lignite*		
Lignite (consolidated)	Less than 8,300	
Brown coal group (unconsolidated)	Less than 8,300	

5-9 Specific Volatile Index

Another method of classifying coal is based on a quantity called the *specific volatile index*.[1] This makes use both of the per cent of volatile matter and fixed carbon as well as the heating value of the fuel to obtain a numerical value which serves to classify fuels from wood to meta-anthracite. The specific volatile index (SVI) is calculated from the formula

$$\text{SVI} = \frac{\text{determined Btu/lb} - (\% \text{ fixed carbon} \times 145)}{\% \text{ volatile matter}}$$

on a dry, ash-free basis.

---

1 B. F. Haanel and R. E. Gilmore, *Investigation of Canadian Coal* (Mine and Geological Branch, Department of Mines and Resources, Ottawa, 1937).

Table 5-3. PROXIMATE ANALYSIS OF SOME NORTH AMERICAN COALS, AS MINED
OR AS RECEIVED[a]

Rank and Source	Moisture	Ash	Volatile Matter	Fixed Carbon	Heat Value (Btu/lb)
Lignite:					
Montana	37.5%	6.1	26.8	29.6	6,580
N. Dakota	36.8	5.1	28.2	29.3	7,204
S. Dakota	39.2	8.4	24.7	27.7	6,307
Texas	33.7	7.3	29.3	29.7	7,348
Ontario	46.7	7.4	30.2	16.0	5,280
Saskatchewan	33.5	6.7	24.0	35.8	7,576
Sub-bituminous:					
Wyoming	23.4	3.6	33.6	39.4	9,382
Alberta	15.0	6.3	33.3	45.4	10,890
Bituminous:					
Utah	7.5	5.6	39.7	47.2	12,520
Illinois	7.9	9.1	40.7	42.3	11,527
British Columbia	6.7	11.3	34.8	47.2	11,690
Alberta	7.4	7.1	32.1	53.4	11,630
Pennsylvania	3.4	5.3	35.9	55.4	13,734
Alabama	3.9	7.5	35.1	53.5	13,343
Nova Scotia	4.0	8.4	32.2	55.4	13,340
Anthracite:					
Pennsylvania	3.2	11.5	9.3	76.0	13,043

[a] Data derived from Fiedler and Selvig, "Notes on Sampling and Analysis of Coal," *Technical Paper* 586 (U.S. Bureau of Mines, 1938); Warren and Bowles, "Tests on Liquefaction of Canadian Coals," *Paper No.* 798 (Canadian Department of Mines and Resources); B. R. MacKay, "Coal Reserves of Canada," *Report of the Royal Commission on Coal*, 1946).

Table 5-4. SVI CLASSIFICATION

SVI	Rank or Class
Under 50	Woods
50–82	Peat
82–99	Brown coal (lignite)
99–125	Black lignite
125–160	Sub-bituminous
160–175	Bituminous C
175–190	Bituminous B
190–210	Bituminous A
210–230	Super-bituminous (low volatile)
230–255	Semi-anthracite
255–300	Anhtracites

EXAMPLE

A bituminous coal gave the following analysis:

Moisture	7.5%
Ash	6.8
V.M.	32.3
F.C.	53.4
Heat Value (Q)	13,580

on a dry, ash-free basis,

$$\text{V.M.} = 37.7\%$$
$$\text{F.C.} = 62.3$$
$$Q = 15,846$$

$$\text{SVI} = \frac{15,846 - (62.3 \times 145)}{37.7} = 181$$

The SVI gives the coal a slightly lower rank than the A.S.T.M. For typical coals in appropriate groups, the approximate yields and the quality of the gas, coke, and tar obtained on coking can be predicted from the SVI. Other classifications widely used are the Parr[1] (United States) and Seyler[2] (Great Britain).

The proximate analysis is usually sufficient for grading coals of the same rank when the analysis is supplemented with data on the caloric value, the percentage of sulfur, and the fusion point of the ash. Ultimate analysis, giving the percentage of carbon, hydrogen, nitrogen, and oxygen, as well as sulfur, is only necessary when very specific characterization of the coal is desired. The ultimate analysis does, however, provide a means of calculating the heating value of a coal or other fuel. As will be shown in a following chapter, the calculated value agrees very well with the determined value. Physical or structural properties of the coal, such as its coking ability, its friability, its resistance to weathering, are often important to the purchaser; they are considered in grading the coal.

Free moisture, ash, and sulfur are unwanted constituents of a fuel. The consumer does not want to pay for water at coal prices. The high water content of lignite makes its transportation over long distances uneconomical. Any moisture in the coal not only means that there is so much nonfuel constituent, but also that 13 Btu/lb must be expended for each per cent of moisture. In coals of the sub-bituminous class, which have 15 to 25 per cent moisture, the loss in heating value amounts to 195 to 325 Btu/lb of coal. However with coals containing from 5 to 10 per cent moisture, the water, if uniformly distributed in the coal, is reported to give a more-uniform fuel bed and reduced fly ash in mechanically fired boilers. The moist coal is also desirable for the production of improved metallurgical coke.

1 S. A. Parr, *The Classification of Coal* (Bulletin 180, Engineering Experimental Station, University of Illinois, 1928).

2 C. H. Seyler, "Coal Classification," *Colliery Guardian* (1931). *See Chemical Abstracts* **25**, (1931), 5271.

5-10 Ash

High ash content means less fuel per pound of coal and bigger ash-disposal costs. Ash may be intrinsic or adventitious. The intrinsic or inherent ash consists of mineral matter derived from the vegetation which was converted to coal. Adventitious mineral material is usually clay or other inorganic matter deposited in layers or lenses, in cracks, or mixed less uniformly through the coal. Ash is composed of the inorganic residue after the combustion of the fuel. The ash is not the same material as the original mineral matter. Some of the minerals, for example, the clays, may lose water; others may lose sulfur as sulfur dioxide; any calcium carbonate may lose carbon dioxide. The percentage of ash is usually multiplied by 1.1 to obtain the mineral content of the coal.

Except when coal is to be used in a finely powdered state, some ash is desirable. It serves to protect the fuel grates unless its fusion temperature is too low. An ash with a low-fusion point will form clinkers or in extreme cases may melt and combine with the grates. High-melting ash is one which has a softening point above 2600° F. The ash has a medium softening point if the temperature at which the ash fuses to a spherical lump ranges from 2200° F to 2600° F. Low fusion points are those below 2200° F. In general, the softening temperatures of coal ash of North American coals range from 1900° to 3100° F.

5-11 Composition of Ash

The composition of the ash largely determines its fusion point, which in turn is closely related to the probability of clinker formation. Ash from coal consists chiefly of silicates, derived from clay, shales, and feldspar. The composition of coal ash is usually expressed in the amounts of the oxides of the metals present. Typical limits of coal-ash analyses for United States coals are given in the following table. Variation in the fusion point with composition is shown in Fig. 5-3.

It is obvious from the table that the *proportions* of the different mineral components may vary greatly in coals having the same percentage of ash.

Table 5-5. COAL ASH COMPOSITION

Silica, SiO_2	30–60%	Magnesia, MgO	0.5–4%
Alumina, Al_2O_3	10–40	Titania, TiO_2	0.5–3
Ferric oxide, Fe_2O_3	5–30	Sulfur trioxide, SO_3	1–18
Calcium oxide, CaO	2–20		

One coal may burn to a fine powdery ash, while a second coal having the same percentage of ash, yields a hard, glassy clinker. Ash with a high silica and alumina content has a high softening point. It has been suggested that the closer the composition of the ash approximates the formula Al_2O_3, $2\ SiO_2$ (alumina, 45.8 per cent, and silica, 54.2 per cent), the higher will be the fusion temperature. In contrast, the higher the iron oxide, the lower the temperature of fusion, and hence the greater the tendency to clinker. High percentages of lime or magnesia also tend to decrease the fusion temperature. If the ferric oxide undergoes reduction to the ferrous state, the clinker forms

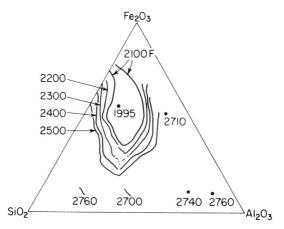

Figure 5-3 Diagram showing the variation in fusion point with the proportions of silica, alumina, and ferric oxide.

still more easily. Ashes that have high fusion temperatures are called *refractory ashes.*

If the mineral matter in the coal is not distributed uniformly, or if the fire bed is uneven so that hot spots develop, fusion of the ash will start at scattered points. The molten ash may be so fluid that it spreads and bonds unmelted ash and unburned fuel in a matrix of dark glass. These aggregations reduce the combustion area, so that other high-temperature regions develop, giving further agglomerates. If uneven firing produces mildly reducing conditions at some points and strongly oxidizing conditions at others, clinkers may occur at the former zones, although the temperature there may be lower.

5-12 Coal Improvement

The grade of a coal may be improved by washing the screened material. Lump coal has a lower ash content than "slack" and "fines" from the same coal. Slack coal consists of small lumps (no larger than $\frac{3}{4}$ in. to no smaller than $\frac{1}{32}$ in., in diameter). The "washing process" consists of passing the coal into a tank or trough containing calcium chloride brine, sp gr 1.35. The coal floats across the bath while the extraneous mineral matter is wetted by the water; being heavier than the brine, the mineral matter sinks and is removed. Screening and washing not only reduce the ash content of the fuel, but may raise the softening point of the ash, since the heavy pyrite, a native compound of sulfur and iron, is readily removed by this treatment.

Unfortunately this process of cleaning the coal does not work well with fines having particle sizes less than 2 mm. The fine particles tend to form a slurry containing about 81 per cent water and 19 per cent solids, of which approximately one-third is mineral matter. Modern mining methods using mechanical cutters and loaders and high explosives tend to give a greater proportion of slack and fines than the older hand methods. The recovery of the fines is becoming of increasing importance. Recovery and purification of a large fraction of this type of fuel are now being effected by flotation, particularly in Great Britain.

In the flotation of the coal dust and fines, the slurry is diluted with additional water to which is added a cresote-cresylic acid mixture from coal tar to act as a frothing agent. Air is blown into the "pulp" to form a metastable froth. The coal collects in the froth which is skimmed off, and allowed to collapse. The air-dried fines are finally mixed with a small amount of tar to act as a binder and are compressed into briquettes.

Improvement in the fuel for a particular use may be achieved by altering the fusion point of the ash. A coal having a low fusion point ash is mixed with one having an ash of high softening point in proportions calculated to give the desired composition and softening point to the resultant ash.

For some mechanical stokers the formation of a porous, friable clinker, but one strong enough to be removed from the fire bed, is desirable. By adding iron oxide to a coal in which the calcium oxide of the ash is between 1.5 and 6 per cent, anthracite can be converted to a fuel which gives clinkers having all the required characteristics. The proper iron compound is added in amounts ranging from 15 to 75 lb/ton depending on the anthracite used. While the addition reduces the Btu/lb and increases the ash somewhat, the practice is justified by the improvement in the facility of handling the ash as clinker and the increase in the efficiency of the furnace.

5-13 Sulfur

Sulfur is an undesirable element in coal, indeed in any fuel. It is usually present in coal in amounts varying from 0.5 to 3.0 per cent, although some coals as mined may show much higher amounts. Sulfur is chiefly found in pyrite (FeS$_2$), a mineral mined with coal, but one that is doubly unwelcome because of its effect on the fusion point of the ash and on the weathering of the coal. Smaller amounts of sulfur are present in organic compounds. Gypsum, CaSO$_4$ · 2 H$_2$O, and iron sulfate may occur in small quantities, the latter being found principally in weathered coals.

When the coal is burned, sulfur is oxidized to sulfur dioxide. At high temperatures the calcium sulfate and any other sulfate present will decompose to give sulfur trioxide and the oxide of the metal:

$$CaSO_4 \cdot 2\,H_2O \longrightarrow CaO + SO_3 + 2\,H_2O$$

The calcium sulfate may also react with silica to yield sulfur trioxide:

$$CaSO_4 + SiO_2 \longrightarrow SO_3 + CaSiO_3$$

Sulfur dioxide and sulfur trioxide react with moisture to give sulfurous and sulfuric acids and are therefore active corrosion agents.

Organic sulfur compounds, if not completely oxidized, may appear in the smoke as hydrogen sulfide, carbon bisulfide and other compounds, all of which are malodorous.

Because sulfur furnishes a small amount of heat when burned to sulfur dioxide, namely, 4,050 Btu/lb, it must be included with carbon and hydrogen as a component fuel.

5-14 Calculation of Fuel or Heating Value of Coals

Calculation from ultimate analysis. The heating or caloric value of a coal can be estimated with a good degree of accuracy from the ultimate analysis. Carbon furnishes 14,544 Btu/lb; hydrogen, 62,028 Btu/lb; and sulfur 4050 Btu/lb. Knowing the percentage of these fuel elements and the amount of oxygen in the coal, and using a formula proposed by Dulong, we can obtain the approximate heating value of the coal.

$$Q = \frac{1}{100}\left[14{,}544 \times \%C + 62{,}028 \left(\%H - \frac{\%O}{8}\right) + 4050 \times \%S\right]$$

It is assumed in the formula that all the oxygen in the coal has already combined with hydrogen, so that it is only the uncombined or available hydrogen which can furnish heat during combustion. The available hydrogen is the total hydrogen minus the hydrogen equivalent to the oxygen present.

Despite certain theoretical objections to the formula, the good agreement between calculated and measured heating values makes it acceptable. For the sake of convenience, the formula may be written:

$$Q = \frac{(14{,}600 \times \%C) + 62{,}000 \left(\%H - \dfrac{\%O}{8}\right) + (4050 \times \%S)}{100}$$

For anthracites and bituminous coals, the Dulong formula gives values which agree within 1.5 per cent with the bomb calorimeter data. With lignites and sub-bituminous coals, the agreement is not quite as good. Tests on nineteen United States coals gave a mean algebraic error of 3.1 per cent. In Great Britain, of some 350 coals tested, 216 showed a difference between calculated and determined heating values of less than 50 Btu/lb and 101 of these high-rank coals differed by less than 100 Btu/lb.

EXAMPLE Calculation from ultimate analysis (dry basis).

A Pennsylvanian anthracite gave the following analysis:

C	81.9%
H	2.9
S	0.9
N	0.9
O	3.8
Ash	9.6
	100.0

Heat value Q, 13,580 Btu/lb

$$Q = \frac{1}{100}\left[(81.9 \times 14{,}600) + 62{,}000 \times \left(2.9 - \frac{3.8}{8}\right) + (4050 \times 0.9)\right]$$
$$= 0.01(1{,}195{,}740 + 62{,}000 \times 2.43 + 3645)$$
$$= 13{,}500 \text{ Btu/lb}$$

The difference between the calculated and the measured values equals 80 Btu/lb, which is within the precision limits of the analysis.

5-15 Calculation from the Proximate Analysis

The calculation of caloric values by formulas based on the proximate analysis is not as reliable as those derived from the ultimate analysis. However, a formula proposed by Goutel gives moderately accurate estimates of Q values for coals of high rank. The formula is

$$Q = 1.8(82 \times \text{F.C.} + \alpha \times \text{V.M.})$$

where α is a factor which varies with the percentage of volatile matter as expressed on a dry, ash-free fuel; F.C., the percentage of fixed carbon, and

V.M., the per cent of volatile matter as given by the original analysis. The values assigned to the α factor are given in the table below.

Table 5-6.

"Corrected" V.M. (dry, ash-free basis)	5	10	15	20	25	30	35	40%
α	145	130	117	109	103	98	94	80

The following example will illustrate the method. The sample fuel is again a Pennsylvania coal having a proximate analysis as follows: moisture, 3.2 per cent; V.M., 9.3 per cent; ash, 11.5 per cent; F.C., 76 per cent; Q, 12,971 Btu/lb. To obtain the desired α factor, the V.M. must be corrected for the moisture and ash in the coal. On this basis, the V.M. becomes 10.9. The factor corresponding to a corrected V.M. of 10.9 is 128. Substituting the values in the formula,

$$Q = 1.8(82 \times 76 + 128 \times 9.3) = 13,360 \text{ Btu/lb}$$

which is approximately 3 per cent too high.

The caloric value as calculated from the ultimate analysis was 13,043 Btu, only 72 Btu above the calorimeter value, that is, approximately 0.6 per cent in error.

For the bituminous Pennsylvania and Alabama coals given in Table 5.3, the heating values calculated from the proximate analysis are 13,540 and 13,140 respectively, the first being 1.4 per cent too low and the second 1.5 per cent too low. Calculations using the ultimate analysis gave estimated values of 13,777 and 13,370, both slightly higher than the calorimeter values.

The Goutel formula is useless for the estimation of the heating value of sub-bituminous, lignites, and even some highly volatile bituminous coals.

5-16 Present and Future Utilization of Coal

Extensive deposits of lignite are found in Europe, India, Australia, New Zealand, Canada, and the United States. This low-grade fuel is very high in moisture, 33 to 43 per cent. It must first be dried before it can be used. Lignite is widely used in Germany (175 million tons annually) for power and for domestic and industrial fuel. The dried lignite is sold in the form of briquettes. It is also used as a raw material for the synthesis of gasoline and oils. In the United States and Canada, lignite finds a limited use as fuel, principally in areas adjacent to its occurrence. Work by the United States Bureau of Mines and the Canadian Department of Mines and Resources shows that North American lignites can be readily hydrogenated to yield 54 to 56 pounds of hydrocarbon oils per hundred pounds of dried lignite, as well as fuel gases and coke.

The displacement of coal by oil as a fuel for domestic heating and the substitution of diesel power for steam by the railroads have convinced some that coal is no longer of importance. Such is not the case.

The amount of coal mined in the United States has stabilized around 400 million tons per year. Recent production figures are given in Table 5-7 for the United States, Canada, and Great Britain. Past production and predicted trends in the use of coal in the United States are shown graphically in *Industrial and Engineering Chemistry*, March 1956.

The maintenance of a high production of coal in the United States can be attributed to two factors: the expansion of the steel and chemical industries, which use coal or coke as raw material; and the widening use of coal-fired

Table 5-7. COAL PRODUCTION (MILLIONS OF TONS)

	Bituminous	Anthracite
1959		
United States	412	20.7
Canada	10.6	
Great Britain	216.	
1960		
United States	416.	18.8
Canada	11.2	
Great Britain	193.7	
1961		
United States	415[a]	18.1
Canada	10.4	
Great Britain	192.	

[a] Of which 179×10^6 ton were used for generating electricity.

units for the generation of electrical power. In 1961, 80.7 per cent of the electricity used in the United States came from thermal generating plants. A 65.7 per cent increase in such plants is expected by 1970.

In Canada, coal production dropped 50 per cent between 1950 and 1960. The province of Ontario consumes more coal than all the rest of Canada. Most of the coal used comes from the United States. An increasing proportion of this coal is going into steam-generating plants. That this trend will continue is indicated by the prediction of the chairman of the Provincial Hydro-Electric Commission. Of the 23,600,000 kw capacity projected for 1980, he states, 10,600,000 kw will be provided by coal-fired plants. The Gordon Commission (1957) estimates that this will require 20,000,000 tons of United States coal per year. Predicted total Canadian consumption of coal in 1980 will be between 55 and 80 million tons, depending on the cost of power from nuclear plants. It is expected that Canadian coal production will gradually increase from its present low value to around 20 million tons, or enough to meet one-quarter to one-third of requirements.

Figure 5-4 The R. L. Hearn Generating Station, Toronto. A coal pile of 1,500,000 tons feeds this thermal electric power plant. At capacity, pulverized coal is consumed at a rate of approximately 460 tons per hour, giving 7.5 million pounds of steam at pressures up to 1800 psi. [Courtesy Ont. H-E. Power Commission.]

A modern thermoelectric generating plant is pictured in Fig. 5-4. This $156 million plant has a capacity of 1,200,000 kw. A diagram of one unit is given in Fig. 5-5.

In areas such as Ohio, where over 90 per cent of the state's electricity is generated from coal, other fuels, including nuclear energy, will be more expensive. The cost of a nuclear generator is considerably higher than that of a conventional steam plant. Nuclear power at 1.5 mills/kw appears to be a reasonable expectation by 1972, and 1.25 mills/kw in 1982. Present costs and estimated trends are indicated in Fig. 5.6.

Coal gasification (see Chapter 10) at the pithead or underground may be developed to give fuel gas which can be transported cheaply by pipeline. A slurry containing up to 60 per cent pulverized coal in oil can be pumped and distributed in the same manner. This type of slurry is being used in place of heavy oil as fuel and as the reducing agent in blast furnaces with a reported saving of 75¢ to $1.75/ton of metal. The first pipeline for long distance transportation of coal slurry was completed in 1957. It carries a coal and water slurry 108 miles from Cadiz, Ohio, to the Eastlake power station. The water is removed by vacuum filtration and flash-drying. Approximately one million tons of coal are moved annually by pipeline with a saving in transportation costs.

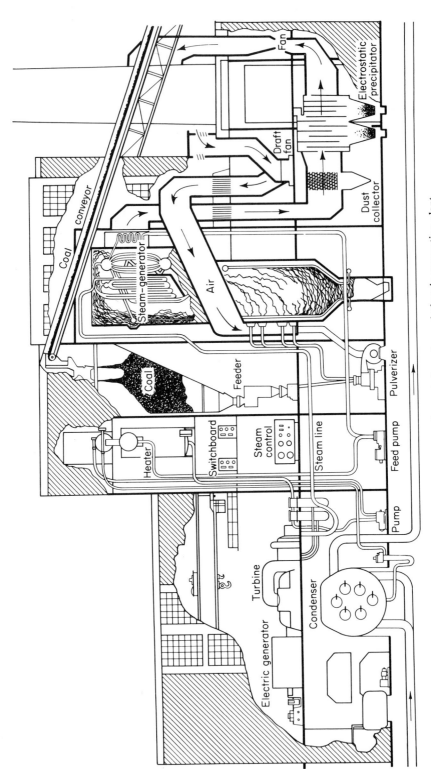

Figure 5-5 Diagram of a coal burning unit in a thermal electric generating plant.

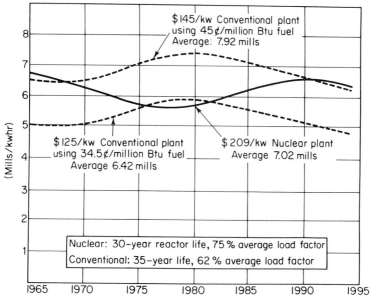

Plants completed in 1965

Figure 5-6 A conventional power plant burning gas or oil is cheaper to operate than a nuclear plant if fuel costs are held to 34.5 cents per million B.t.u.'s and initial plant costs are under $125 per kilowatt.

However, a nuclear plant has the advantage if fuel costs jump to 45 cents per million B.t.u. and capital costs to $145 per kilowatt. [Reproduced by permission from The *Oil and Gas Journal*, **60**, (April 16, 1962), 72.]

5-17 Coal Reserves

It has been estimated that 50 per cent of the world's coal reserves consists of lignite. A large deposit lies in the northern United States, Montana and the Dakotas, and extending into Saskatchewan and Manitoba. There are also reserves in the Gulf of Mexico region, in the Yukon, British Columbia, and smaller deposits in northern Ontario and the Northwest Territories. Lignite reserves in the United States are estimated at 463,000 million tons.

Reserves of anthracite are very small in comparison with the proven deposits of bituminous coals. Practically all of the anthracite coal of North America is found in eastern Pennsylvania. Bituminous coals form the largest fuel reserve on the continent, enough for several thousand years.[1] The coals

1 Canadian coal reserves are estimated at 99,000 million tons, of which 28 per cent is lignite and 63 per cent is bituminous coals of the various grades. If only the bituminous were mined in the future at the present rate of production, they would last 4000 years.

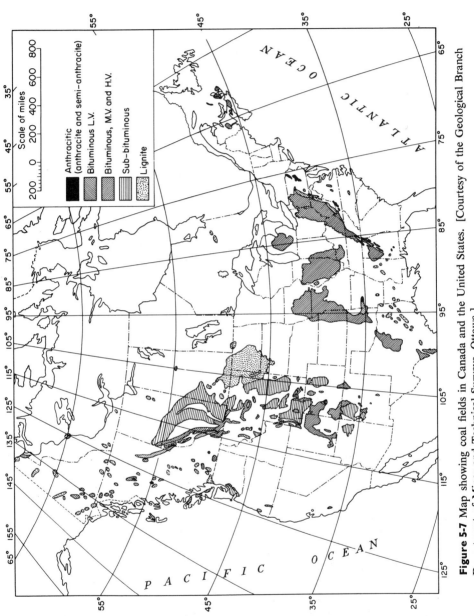

Figure 5-7 Map showing coal fields in Canada and the United States. [Courtesy of the Geological Branch Department of Mines and Technical Surveys, Ottawa.]

of the Eastern Seaboard are older and of higher rank than those of the western fields, Alberta, Utah, and Colorado. A large band of sub-bituminous coal stretches from the center of Alberta to the center of New Mexico. The distribution of these and minor reserves is shown on the map, Fig. 5-7.

5-18 Coke

Coke is a secondary or derived fuel, a chemical raw material, a reducing agent, and a source of graphite for electrodes and lubricants. Coke is prepared from bituminous coals by pyrolysis or dry distillation. It may also be obtained from lignites or even petroleum residues (petroleum-coke). The production of coke in the United States was 63.1×10^6 tons in 1959, 70.0×10^6 tons in 1960.

During the pyrolysis of a coal suitable for the manufacture of coke, gas and moisture are removed first. At about 260° C (500° F), hydrocarbon gases and some hydrogen sulfide may be evolved, followed by hydrocarbons of higher molecular weight and boiling point, as the temperature is raised to 310° C (600° F). The framework of the coal begins to break down around 750° F, and the hot mass becomes soft and plastic. Escaping gases and vapors produce a porous, sponge-like structure. The final texture and bulk density of the coke depend on the extent to which the walls of the retort have confined the swelling plastic mass. Above 1100° F, the primary coke shrinks.

The final temperature to which the coal is heated in the coking process determines the amount of volatile material left in the coke; this has a great influence on the structure and ignition temperature of the product. *Low-temperature coke* is produced at about 1000° F and *high-temperature coke* at approximately 1000° C (1850° F). The low-temperature coke is formed in the manufacture of city gas. Metallurgical coke is a high-temperature coke. The temperature applied during its preparation is so high that many of the hydrocarbons are cracked, and the distillation products are therefore poorer in oils and liquid hydrocarbons such as benzene, toluene, and xylene. As would be expected, the high temperature favors the production of gas (small molecules) and the deposition of free carbon. The high temperature also favors the rearrangement of the carbon atoms to form graphite, thereby making the coke more difficult to ignite. The effect of the coking temperature of two bituminous coals on the ignition temperature, volatile matter, and hydrogen content of the resulting coke, is shown in Fig. 5-8.

Since high-temperature cokes are practically all carbon, except for the ash content, the approximate heating value of the coke may be calculated from the formula

$$Q = 14,600 \frac{(100 - \% \text{ ash})}{100}$$

14,600 being the heating value of 1 lb of carbon in Btu.

For low-temperature coke which may contain over 1 per cent hydrogen, a correction should be applied for the heating value of the hydrogen.

Coke and coal in the plastic state are poor heat conductors. For this reason coking is carried out in narrow retorts or ovens, which are heated on both sides. These ovens may be 40 feet long and 18 to 20 feet high, but can only be 14 to 20 inches wide. With a wall temperature of 1850° F, penetration of the heat is so slow through the mass that the plastic zone proceeds inward at less than one inch per hour. This means that the outer layers of coke will

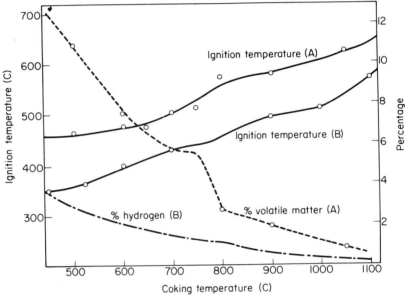

Figure 5-8 The effect of coking temperature on the ignition temperature of coke from two coking coals (A and B), and on the percentage of volatile matter and hydrogen.

be graphitized by the time the coal in the central region has started to coke. Figure 5-9 shows a battery of coke ovens. These two units use 1800 tons of coal per day and produce 1,320,000 tons of coke per year.

Not all coals, indeed not all bituminous coals, are suitable for coking. The coal may not have good plastic properties; the ash may have too low a melting point; or the product may be too friable. A high sulfur content is objectionable in metallurgical coke because of its effect on the metal. In the United States, coking coals are obtained from some Pennsylvania and West Virginia fields. In Canada, the chief coking coals are found on the east coast. Different coals are blended or mixed to obtain a more desirable product, or to make possible the use of a local coal whose properties make its use unsuitable alone.

Figure 5-9 A modern coking plant, which produces 47 million cu ft of gas per day. [Courtesy Steel Co. of Canada, Hamilton, Ont.]

Coke may be burned for its fuel value alone, or it may be used for the manufacture of fuel gases such as producer gas and water gas. These will be dealt with under the topic Gaseous Fuels. The controlled combustion of coke in the blast furnace also provides carbon monoxide which acts as a reducing agent to remove oxygen from the iron ore. Coke is also a raw material in the manufacture of calcium carbide, from which many organic products such as solvents, plastics, and explosives are prepared.

In the light of the abundant reserves of coal and its favorable position in terms of Btu per dollar in relation to other fuels, it seems probable that coal will continue to supply a large portion of the world's power for many years.

Review Questions

1. Discuss the statement "Fuel is packaged sunshine."

2. Distinguish between a primary and secondary fuel.

3. Why does charcoal have a higher heat content than wood?

4. What physical changes have taken place in the conversion of wood into fuels of increasing rank?

5. Cite some chemical changes that occur during the metamorphosis of coal.

6. What data are given in the proximate analysis of coal?

7. What quantity is reported in *both* proximate and ultimate analyses?

8. What is the difference between total and intrinsic moisture?

9. How is each determined?

10. Explain the difference between ash and mineral matter in coal analysis.

11. Calculate the V.M. and F.C. of an eastern and a western Canadian or American bituminous coal on the dry, ash-free basis and the heating value as Btu/lb of mineral-free fuel.

12. Use the data from Equation 11 to classify each according to the A.S.T.M. classification.

13. Calculate the SVI for each.

14. Calculate the caloric value of the following coals:

Coal	% Carbon	% Hydrogen	% Sulfur	% Nitrogen	% Oxygen	% Ash
Pocahontas	82.2	4.2	0.58	1.1	5.3	5.5
Dakota lignite	39.34	6.9	0.48	0.68	47.2	5.4
Nova Scotian	74.3	4.9	4.9	1.3	3.6	11.0

15. The average V.M. for twenty coals of the Appalachian field is 20.0 per cent and for twenty from the Rocky Mountain region, 36.0 per cent. Are these two groups of the same rank? How would you classify each group?

16. Plot the data in Table 5-5 on 8 × 11 graph paper.

17. Use the graph plotted for Question 16 and the data in Question 11 to test the Goutel formula for the estimation of the heating value of coals.

18. Suggest a method for producing a granular ash from a coal which, as mined, has a tendency to clinker.

19. What is the difference between fixed carbon and total carbon?

20. What are some of the deleterious properties of iron sulfide in coal?

6

Crude Oil

6-1 Petroleum

Although several types of organic liquids may be burned, liquid fuels are predominately hydrocarbons derived from crude oil. Crude petroleum is a solution of solid, liquid, and gaseous hydrocarbons. The liquids and solids may be paraffins (alkanes), cycloparaffins (naphthenes), or aromatics (benzene and its homologues, the asphalts). The Texas Company research laboratories obtained 85 aliphatic paraffins, 27 cyclic paraffins, and 34 aromatic hydrocarbons from a crude oil. Crude oil is therefore a very complex mixture of components. Crudes are classified roughly as (a) paraffin type, (b) asphaltic type, and (c) mixed type. Type (a) contains very little of the naphthenes and asphaltenes. Type (b) consists largely of aromatic and/or naphthenic hydrocarbons. Type (c) has a higher paraffin content than type (b) but a lower content than type (a).

Oils are also described by reference to the localities from which they come, for example, Pennsylvanian, Gulf Coast, Midcontinent, Mexican, and so on. An oil having the same or similar composition to that of an established class, for example, Pennsylvanian, may be so designated, although the oil may not have come from that locality. Oils from Pennsylvania, the Gulf Coast, and Iran are paraffinic crudes. Californian oil is asphaltic. Mexican is a mixed type containing paraffins and asphalts and is high in sulfur. Venezuelan oil is a heavy sulfur-bearing crude. Oil from Baku or Iran is high in volatile paraffins.

6-2 The Beginning of the Oil Industry

Natural petroleum seepages in Asia Minor were used in early times. The waxy and bituminous residues were used as waterproofing materials and mortar. Young, in 1847, marketed a lubricating oil from such seepage. In America, oil from a similar seepage was bottled and sold as "Seneca Oil, for man and beast." It was later applied to engineering uses.

The first oil well on this continent was dug and drilled at Black Creek (later named Oil Springs) near Sarnia, Ontario, by J. M. Williams in 1857. This well averaged sixty barrels per day. In 1859, Colonel Drake drilled the first oil well in the United States, in Pennsylvania. At the same time, Dr. H. C. Tweedel, consultant to the Pennsylvania Rock Oil Co. was drilling at some likely spots near Moncton, New Brunswick. He was busy at his fifth hole, the others having produced some oil and gas but more brine, when word was received of Drake's strike in Pennsylvania. It is related that he called his men, "Boys," said he, "line up and get paid off. Drake has struck oil and his well is giving 25 barrels a day. There's only room in North America for one real oil well!"[1] In 1963, North America was producing 11.4 million barrels per day![2]

6-3 World Production of Crude Oil

Between 1950 and 1963, world production of oil increased at an average rate of approximately 7.5 per cent each year, until it is now considerably over 12 billion metric tons per year. The percentage contributed by different geographical areas in 1962 is shown in Fig. 6-1.

For many years the United States has been the world's leading producer of petroleum (10,181,000 bbl/day in 1962, and approximately 10,480,000 bbl/day in 1963). Although this represents an increase over previous years, several other areas showed even higher rates of growth in production. Indeed, the percentage contributed by the United States to the world supply, decreased from 45 per cent in 1956 to 31.6 per cent in 1961. For the same period, Canada increased its production from 2.3 per cent to 2.8 per cent of the total world production. In the same five years, new producing areas were developed, notably in the Sahara. The Middle East also showed a marked increase. Russian production rose sharply from 9.3 per cent of the world's

---

1 *Imperial Oil Review*, **44** (Feb. 1955) 21.
2 One barrel equals 42 United States gallons or 35 Imperial gallons.

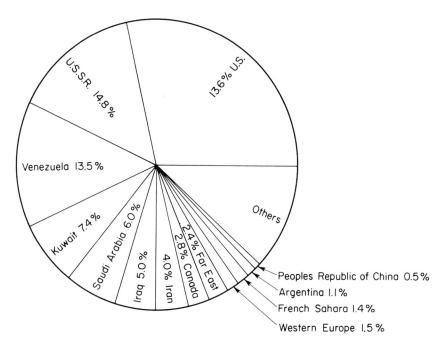

Figure 6-1 Percentage of world oil production for various countries in 1962. (In 1962, production totalled 1,214,000,000 metric tons: in 1963, 1,304,000,000 metric tons.)

oil in 1956 to 14.3 per cent in 1961. In 1963 Russian output was reported to be over four million barrels per day.

The center of the oil industry in Russia has been shifted from the Baku region to the Volga and Urals, where 65 per cent of Soviet oil is now produced. Until recent years, all of the oil was consumed within the U.S.S.R. It is now an important factor in world markets.

The United States is not only the world's greatest producer of oil, but also the largest consumer. Its demand for oil is shown in Table 6-1. On the basis of population, Canada ranks second among the nations in the use of

Table 6-1. UNITED STATES' OIL DEMAND

1956	8,779,000 bbl/day
1960	9,500,000 bbl/day
1961	9,774,000 bbl/day
1962[a]	10,072,000 bbl/day

[a] Canadian demand in 1962 totalled 433,700,000 bbl;
1962 Canadian production 735,189 bbl/day

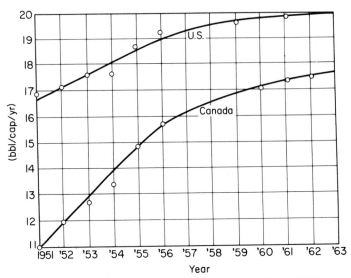

Figure 6-2 The increase in *per capita* use of petroleum (bbl/yr) from 1951—1962.

petroleum and its products. In 1961 the annual per capita use of oil and petroleum products in the United States was 19.8 bbl, in Canada 17.6 bbl. Figure 6-2 indicates the growth in per capita consumption of oil in both countries in the years 1951 through 1962. Domestic crudes supply approximately 80 per cent of United States demands, while Canada's production furnishes about 73 per cent of its requirements. Europe provides only 12 per cent of the oil it uses.

6-4 Reserves

Estimates of oil reserves change from year to year, but the relative position of the major producing fields does not vary greatly. Approximately 70 per cent of the world's oil reserves outside the U.S.S.R. are in the Middle East. The United States is thought to possess 16 per cent of the "Free World's" oil. Reserves in the Caribbean area are estimated to amount to 7 per cent; Canadian reserves are 2 per cent; with all others accounting for 5 per cent. Data on oil reserves in the Soviet Union are not available. Oil reserves in oil shale or bituminous sands are not included in the estimates above.

6-5 The Preparation of Petroleum Fractions

Crude oil is the source of many products. The most valuable fraction obtained in 1857 from William's retort-still was kerosene. The naphtha, "petroleum spirits," and the asphalt were discarded. Small quantities of other products were marketed during the next thirty years, but not until the invention of the internal combustion engine was there any market for almost 40 per cent of the fuel components in the crude oil.

The early oil refineries consisted of a series of "bench stills" or horizontal boilers. Crude oil was made to flow through the series, each still being maintained at a temperature higher than the preceding one. In the first bench still the gases and naphtha containing C_4 to C_8 hydrocarbons were removed. The second heater boiled gasoline components from the preheated oil. The next still removed the kerosene or light-oil fraction, and so on. The percentage yield of each fraction depended on the choice of temperature of each still, the rate of flow, and the composition of the crude.

In the modern refinery the first distillation is carried out in a tall vertical still or fractionating column. The preheated oil enters the bottom of the column at a temperature around 700° F. As the vapors from the hot oil

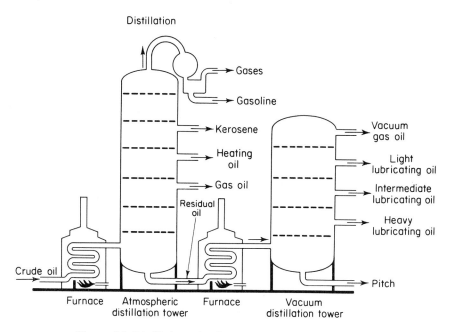

Figure 6-3 Distillation, the first step in oil refining, separates crude oil into a number of products. First, the crude oil is heated by being pumped through pipes in a furnace. The resulting mixture of vapors and liquid goes to a tower where the vapors rise, condense on trays, and are drawn off through pipes as products. The part of the crude that does not boil in the first distillation step is reheated and distilled in a vacuum. Again, vapors rise, condense, and are drawn off as products. Some of the very heavy oil, which doesn't boil even under the reduced pressure, is used in factories and ships, or made into asphalt. [Courtesy Imperial Oil **Ltd.**]

make their way up the tower, they must pass under bubble caps on a series of trays. These trays contain condensed liquid hydrocarbons having boiling points which correspond to the temperature of the column at their particular position. Temperatures are highest at the bottom and lowest at the top.

When a hydrocarbon vapor pushes its way into the scrubbing liquid around the rim of the bubble cap, it may be dissolved. If, however, its boiling point is lower than that of the liquid in the tray, its vapor pressure will be higher and its stay will be short. It will continue on its way up the tower until it is absorbed by liquid which has a similar vapor pressure. The fractions collected in the trays will therefore show a continuous gradation from high to low boiling points.

The condensates from several adjacent trays may be combined to form a "cut" having any desired range of boiling points. In the first distillation unit, shown in Fig. 6-3, the fractions recovered may be "straight-run" gasoline, solvents, kerosene, stove oil, or diesel fuel, at temperatures of 250°, 338°, 400°, 425°, and 518° F respectively. In the second, a "vacuum" distillation, cuts are taken at somewhat different temperatures to give different products. The residual, a heavy fraction, called "reduced" or "topped" crude, is in each case separated for further treatment.

6-6 The Proportion of Major Products

The proportion of the different fractions derived from petroleum oil is largely determined by consumer demand. The chemist and chemical engineer have made it possible to convert heavy residues or lighter oils into light fuels or gasoline and to convert gases or molecular fragments into high-grade fuels. The change in the proportion of four major fractions derived from crude petroleum from 1950 to 1961 is illustrated in Table 6-2, which contains data combined from the reports of two large Canadian oil companies.

It will be noted that, although the actual tonnage of gasoline has increased tremendously since 1950, the percentage of the oil processed to gasoline is decreasing. Furthermore, the proportion processed to other products is increasing. The very rapid expansion of domestic oil heating and the lesser

Table 6-2. PROPORTION OF FRACTIONS DERIVED FROM EACH BARREL OF OIL IN PER CENT

	1950	1951	1952	1956	1957	1958	1959	1960	1961
Gasoline	43.2	41.4	40.9	38.1	38.6	38.0	35.8	35.9	34.5
Light oil	27.6	29.2	30.9	34.4	34.7	35.6	37.8	32.6	31.6
Heavy oil	21.7	22.8	19.8	19.3	16.8	14.9	16.7	16.1	16.0
Other products	7.5	6.6	7.8	8.2	9.9	10.9	9.7	15.4	17.9

advance in the use of light diesels and jet fuels have given a boost to the statistics on light oil.

The proportion of various fractions used in the United States during 1961 is given in Table 6-3.

Changing trends can be seen in data for the consumption and production of Canadian oil during 1961: while production of crude rose 18 per cent between 1960 and 1961, consumption of jet fuel increased 22 per cent, furnace

Table 6-3. UNITED STATES CONSUMPTION OF PETROLEUM PRODUCTS IN 1961
(bbl/day $\times$ 10^6)

L.P. gases	632	Jet fuel	(military)	290	Lube oils	115
Gasoline	4187		(civilian)	131	Residual	1486
Kerosene	262	Distillate		1909	Asphalt	309

oil 12.5 per cent, with minor increases of 4.3 and 5.6 reported for stove oil and middle distillates. Diesel fuel decreased 2.5 per cent.

All fuel oils, especially stove and furnace oils, are being subjected to increasing competition from natural gas. This trend will be reflected in changes in the relative volumes of petroleum products.

The data for gasoline (Table 6-3) include not only straight-run gasoline from the initial distillation of crude oil, but also gasoline produced by other processes in the refinery.

To understand the developments in the production of modern gasolines, it is necessary to examine fuel requirements for maximum power and the relation of fuel quality to chemical structure. These topics are dealt with in the next chapter.

7

Fuel to Match the Engine

7-1 Power Output and Fuel Quality

It can be shown from thermodynamics that the power output and mechanical efficiency increase with the increase in the engine's compression ratio. The latter is defined as the ratio of the volume of gas at the bottom of the down stroke to the volume between the same surfaces at the end of the up stroke. The compression ratio, C/R, obviously indicates the degree of compression of the air-fuel mixture exerted by the piston. Figure 7-1 shows a plot of the power versus C/R for an engine in which the stroke can be varied. The power is expressed as the *Indicated Mean Effective Pressure* (IMEP) in pounds per square inch measured during the explosion of the fuel-air mixture. Curve A is obtained with a synthetic fuel triptane. With a gasoline similar to that available in 1928, curve B is obtained. It shows that there is a loss of power at a critical compression ratio of 5.6. At this point

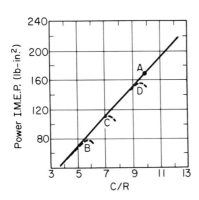

Figure 7-1 The relation between compression ratio and power for different fuels.

66

the engine develops a knock. A regular gasoline of 1948 gives curve C, a 1959 gasoline gives power curve D.

The reason for this improvement in gasoline has been the demand for more and more power and more efficient use of the fuel. The average C/R has doubled in the past few years. An increase in the compression ratio from 5.1 to 10.1 results in an increase in efficiency of 25 per cent. In terms of horsepower, this means from 16.5 to 22 per gallon. The maximum, 25 hp/gal, is obtained at a C/R of 15.1. It is apparent that advances in engine design must be accompanied by advances in the chemistry of fuels. Modern cars would knock on the best gasoline available twenty years ago.

7-2 Knock

Knock represents spontaneous ignition of the air-fuel mixture caused by too-high compression and other factors. The proper combustion of the fuel is initiated by an electric spark timed to fire a fraction of a second before the completion of the compression stroke. The charge should burn with a rapid but smooth rate, during which the expanding hot gases push the piston down. A knock is caused by a much-faster explosive combustion, usually started by the increase in pressure either before or after the spark. A shock wave is produced which hits the cylinder walls and piston, dissipating its energy in sound and heat. If this explosion occurs before the spark (that is, pre-ignition), the force of the blow works against the upward moving piston and acts as a brake.

Knock may be diminished by retarding the spark so that combustion of the fuel takes place at lower pressures as the piston is on its way down. This, of course, means loss of power. When knock occurs, the temperature of the cylinder head rises rapidly. This tends to increase fouling of the engine by a poor fuel, which in turn increases the tendency to knock.

7-3 The Grading of Gasoline

Gasolines may be graded by a number of methods, each of which requires the tests to be made using a standard engine. One way of comparing fuels is to determine the critical compression ratio for each by altering the C/R of the engine until knock occurs. The dependence of fuel quality on chemical structure can be demonstrated by this method, as is shown in Fig. 7-2. The solid curve gives the C/R for isomers of heptane, arranged in order of merit. The broken line indicates the C/R for the same liquids treated with the fuel improver, tetraethyl lead. The points on the curves marked △ show the critical C/R for "isooctane."

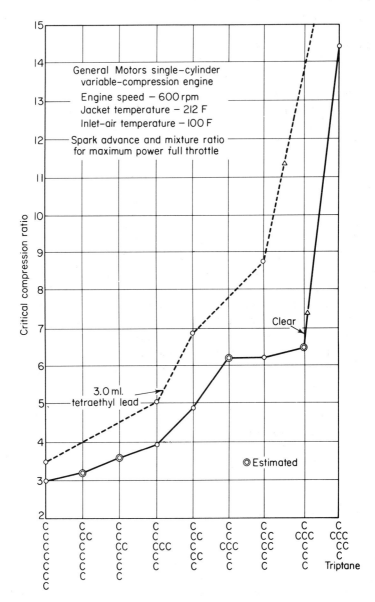

Figure 7-2 The dependence of fuel performance on chemical structure. [From C. Kettering, *Industrial and Engineering Chemistry*, **36**, (1944) 1083, by permission.]

7-4 Octane Ratings

The system of grading gasoline in common use since 1928 is known as the *octane rating*. At that time the best-behaved liquid hydrocarbon tried as a fuel in the standard engine was the branched paraffin molecule 2,2,4-trimethyl pentane:

$$
\begin{array}{c}
CH_3 \\
| \\
CH_3CCH_2CHCH_3 \\
|\quad\quad | \\
CH_3\ \ CH_3
\end{array}
$$

This is commonly called *isooctane*.

Another hydrocarbon named *normal heptane*, having practically the same boiling point as isooctane, was found to be a very poor fuel. Standard fuels were prepared using these two hydrocarbons. Isooctane was rated at 100 and *n*-heptane at 0. Mixtures of the two were given numerical ratings equivalent to the percentage of isooctane *by volume*.

In carrying out the test, the sample is put in the standard test engine and the compression ratio gradually increased until a specified amount of knocking occurs. When this point is established, the C/R is fixed, and a series of runs is made with the standard fuels until the one is found for which the fixed C/R is critical, that is, incipient knock occurs. The percentage of isooctane in the standard fuel having the same knocking characteristics as the gasoline, gives the *octane number* of that fuel.

Octane numbers obtained by the Co-op Fuel Research Committee engine are called *Research Octane Numbers* (RON) to distinguish them from those of another scale called *Motor Octane Numbers* (MON). Since the standard C.F.R. engine is quite different from the ordinary automobile engine, the fuel may behave differently under road conditions. The MON method was devised in an attempt to evaluate the tendency of different gasolines to knock in actual use.

The motor method of testing differs from the research method in three principal factors: engine speed, spark timing, and mixture temperature. In the motor method, the temperature of the mixture is at 300° F, and the spark is varied with the compression ratio. Engine speed is 900 rpm, as compared with 600 rpm in the research method.

These different conditions give octane numbers which are the same only in the case of paraffins and isoparaffins. In general, the RON is higher. Since the RON indicates the tendency of a fuel to knock at low speed and the MON at high speeds and temperature, the difference in values of the RON and MON is a measure of the *sensitivity* of the fuel to temperature. If the same gasoline has an RON of 80 and an MON of 75, the sensitivity is said to be five units.

Sensitivity increases with the amount of unsaturates and aromatic hydrocarbons in the fuel.

Motor octane numbers vary with the richness of the mixture, so that a gasoline may have two MONs, for example, lean/rich of 87/89.

Research octane numbers are more widely used. *Octane rating* refers to the RON unless otherwise stated.

7-5 Molecular Structure and Octane Ratings

When pure hydrocarbons are used as gasoline, each has its octane number which is related to its molecular size and structure. Table 7-1 gives the octane numbers of a number of hydrocarbons belonging to different groups.

For a series of normal alkanes, only four have octane ratings within the scale, unless we count the gas propane with its octane number of 100. The cycloparaffins have higher ratings than their corresponding normal paraffins. Cyclopentane has an octane number of 94 and normal pentane only 62.

Branched hydrocarbons have better ratings than the corresponding unbranched isomers. Isohexane has an octane number of 74 in contrast to 26 for normal hexane. It is apparent, then, that branching in the fuel molecule and ring structures make for easier, smoother burning. It will be noted also from the table that the position of the branch and the number of branches affect the fuel rating.

Table 7-1. RESEARCH OCTANE NUMBERS OF HYDROCARBONS

Compound	Octane number	Compound	Octane number
n-Paraffins		*Isomers of heptane*	
n-Propane	100	2-Methyl hexane	55
n-Butane	96	3-Methyl hexane	56
n-Pentane	62	2,2-Dimethyl pentane	80
n-Hexane	26	2,3-Dimethyl pentane	94
n-Heptane	0	3,3-Dimethyl pentane	98
		2,2,3-Trimethyl butane	101
Alicyclics			
Cyclopentane	94	*Isomers of hexane*	
Cyclohexane	77	3-Methyl pentane	74
		2,2-Dimethyl butane	94
Alkanes		2,3-Dimethyl butane	95
Isopentane	90		
Isohexane	74	2,3,3-Trimethyl pentane, an	
Isoheptane	55	isomer of the standard 2,2,4	
		compound	102
Alkenes			
1-Hexene	85	*Benzene*	108
2-Hexene	100		

The presence of unsaturated bonds also makes for higher octane numbers, the specific effect being determined by the number and position of the double bonds. Combined ring structure and unsaturation, as found in benzene and its derivatives, give the aromatic hydrocarbons very good antiknock qualities.

The generalizations obtained from such data furnish the basis for the development of the super gasolines necessary for tomorrow's cars.

7-6 Gasoline Improvers

One of the greatest advances in the improvement of gasolines was made by a young mechanical engineer, Dr. Thomas Midgley, who was bright enough to realize the importance of chemistry in the automotive industry. He became convinced that knock was caused by the fuel, and that the fuel could be improved by additives. The first "chemical" used to repress knock was tincture of iodine, which gave also some unwanted results. The young man's persistence resulted in his discovering the antiknock properties of tetraethyl lead. Although it has been over thirty years since tetraethyl lead was put on the market as an improver of gasoline, no better catalyst has yet been adopted. In 1941, Dr. Midgley was awarded the Priestley Medal by the American Chemical Society for his discovery.

The raw materials for tetraethyl lead are pig lead, sodium metal, ethylene, and hydrogen chloride. The lead is melted and amalgamated with the metallic sodium under an inert atmosphere. The resulting alloy, in a finely divided state, reacts with ethyl chloride:

$$4\,C_2H_5Cl + 4\,PbNa \longrightarrow Pb(C_2H_5)_4 + 4\,NaCl + 3\,Pb$$

Since it was found that the combustion of tetraethyl lead left a deposit of lead and lead oxide, ethylene dibromide and dichloride are added to the tetraethyl lead, giving a mixture called *ethyl fluid*. During combustion of the mixture, volatile lead bromide and chloride are formed and are carried out with the exhaust gases.[1] To supply bromine in sufficient quantities to meet the demand for ethyl fluid, new sources of the element had to be found. The element is found as bromide salts in sea water. In spite of the low concentration (67 parts per million) in the sea, a method was perfected for tapping this inexhaustable source. The chemistry is simple.

$$2\,Br^- + Cl_2 \longrightarrow Br_2 + 2\,Cl^-$$
$$CH_2{=}CH_2 + Br_2 \longrightarrow CH_2BrCH_2Br$$

ethylene dibromide or 1,2-dibromoethane.

---

1 Since lead compounds are poisonous, these fumes may be a health problem (U.S. Public Health Service Publ. No. 712, 1959). Concentrations of 42 micrograms of Pb/cu. meter of air have been reported by the Los Angeles Pollution Control Board. Because of the volatility of T.E.L., leaded fuels should not be used in gasoline stoves or lanterns, nor as a solvent.

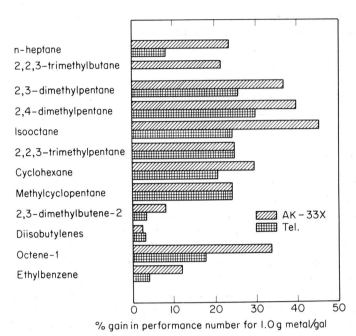

Figure 7-3 Comparison of T.E.L. and a manganese antiknock compound (methyl cyclopentadienyl manganese tricarbonyl). [From J. Brown and W. Lovell, *Industrial and Engineering Chemistry*, **50**, (1958), 1547, by permission.]

The antiknock action of ethyl fluid (61 per cent tetraethyl lead and either 36 per cent 1,2-dibromoethane or 18 per cent dibromo- and 19 per cent dichloroethane) is illustrated by the data in Table 7-2 and by the dotted curve in Figure 7-2.

The response to ethyl fluid differs with the individual fuel. This is also true of the new manganese improver (a methyl derivative of cyclopentadienyl manganese tricarbonyl) as shown in Fig. 7-3.

The mechanism of the action of tetraethyl lead in reducing knock is still

Table 7-2. IMPROVEMENT IN OCTANE NUMBER ON ADDITION OF 4 ML OF ETHYL FLUID/GAL (U.S.)

	From	To
Isopentane	90	102
n-Pentane	62	87
2,2-Dimethylbutane	94	106
2,3-Dimethylbutane	95	104
Isohexane	74	96
n-Hexane	26	69

under investigation. Gaseous explosions are known to proceed by a chain reaction where an excited molecule activates more than one molecule. Such chain reactions are sensitive to traces of inhibitors. For example, the reaction between hydrogen and oxygen is inhibited by traces of iodine; so is the combustion of hydrocarbons. It is thought that tetraethyl lead acts as a "stopper," terminating or decreasing the branching of these energy chains.

7-7 Ratings above 100

The chemist has now synthesized hydrocarbon fuels of higher quality than 100 octane. These cannot be rated by using test mixtures of *n*-heptane and isooctane. It has been suggested that the octane rating be replaced by a

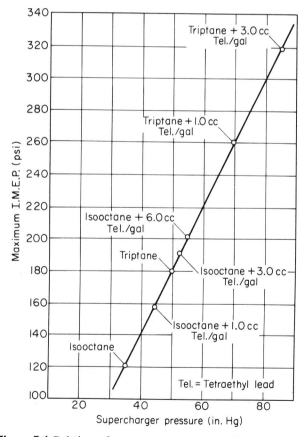

Figure 7-4 Relation of power output to supercharge pressure. [From C. Kettering *Industrial and Engineering Chemistry* **36**, (1944), 1084, by permission.]

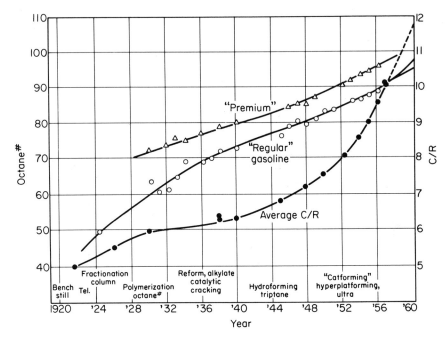

Figure 7-5 The development of fuels and refining methods to meet advancing engine requirements.

"triptane rating" in which the fuel under test would be compared with standard mixtures of heptane and 2,2,3-trimethylbutane or "triptane." Octane ratings above 100 can, however, be obtained by extrapolation of a plot of the critical compression ratio *vs* octane number and by other indirect methods.

In the standard method for obtaining octane rating, the degree of compression of the air-gas mixture is increased by increasing the compression ratio. Another method to evaluate super gasolines is that of using a fixed C/R and increasing the initial pressure by supercharging until a knock is obtained. At the same time, the power developed at that point (IMEP) is measured. A plot of such values, using a C/R of 6.5, is shown in Fig. 7-4. By this method the relative merit of any gasoline can be determined.

Figure 7-5 indicates the changes which have been made in octane numbers of regular and premium gasolines over a period of years. Major developments in the chemistry of automotive fuels are also indicated.

Review Questions

1. Define compression ratio, critical compression ratio, and IMEP.

2. Describe a method for determining the octane rating of a gasoline.

3. Write the formula for *iso*octane; "isooctane"![1]

4. How does the RON differ from the MON?

5. What is meant by the sensitivity of the gasoline?

6. Arrange the isomers of hexane according to their RON.

7. Which of the following isomers of decane will have (a) the highest, (b) the lowest octane number?

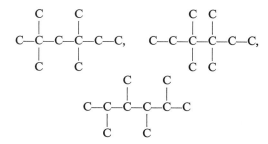

8. Name each of the isomers in Question 7.

9. Is there any advantage in using premium gasoline in a 1949 car? Why?

10. How can gasolines above 100 octane be graded?

11. What is the structural formula of cyclopentadiene?

12. Tetramethyl lead is now being used in gasoline. Suggest a method for its preparation.

---

[1] A chemist will always maintain
This is NOT truly isooctane!
I.U.P.A.C.
Says its real name should be
2,2,4-Trimethyl pentane

8

The Manufacture of
Modern Gasolines

In the previous chapter it was shown how the chemical structure of fuel molecules is related to engine efficiency and maximum power. The present chapter describes how the oil industry has applied such information to produce high-quality gasolines.

Modern gasoline is very different from the low-boiling fraction of crude oil obtained by straight distillation, which powered the early automobile. It is also quite different from the blend of straight-run and cracked gasoline with added tetraethyl lead of the 1920's. Today's gasoline contains several tailor-made hydrocarbons not found in nature's crude oil at all, or present only in traces. The methods of synthesis of these new fuels found by the research chemists are adapted to the refinery by the chemical engineers. A number of different processes may be involved, such as debutanization, stabilization, alkylation, polymerization, isomerization, treating, reforming, and related procedures, platforming, houdriforming, cat forming, power forming, ultraforming, and others. Most of these processes, including some type of "reforming," are in operation in the modern refinery.

8-1 Cracking

Cracking was first aimed at producing more, rather than better, gasoline. As the number of motor vehicles and tractors increased, the demand for gasoline outran the capacity of the refineries. As a result, the refineries were forced to crack the heavy residues and other less-desirable fractions from the distillation column. This treatment doubled the amount of gasoline which could be derived from a barrel of crude oil.

At first cracking was achieved by subjecting the oil to high temperature and pressure, "soaking" it for a considerable time. Under these conditions the molecules have very high kinetic energy. The long straight-chain or coiled molecules writhe and lash about like a string of children playing crack the whip. Some of the chain is broken off. Other long hydrocarbons are cut in two by the impact of high-speed molecules. Sometimes the molecule gets the H knocked out of it, giving free hydrogen gas and leaving a carbon skeleton which produces a coke-like residue. This is, of course, an over-simplification! As was indicated in Chapter 3, about half of the new molecules are olefins or alkenes. Cracking also furnishes some more branched chains, diolefins, and ring compounds. All these changes increase the octane number.

A patented improvement in cracking technique used heavy mercury atoms to break the long oil molecules. Since impact depends on the kinetic energy of the charging particle, increasing its mass would mean that the same blow would be given by the particle moving at a lower velocity and at a lower temperature. The lower temperature results in lower losses by coking.

8-2 Catalytic Cracking

Other improvements followed. Cracking pressure, as well as temperature, was lowered by the use of catalysts. The mechanism of catalytic cracking differs from thermal cracking. Catalytic cracking involves adsorption, activation of the adsorbed oil molecule, reaction, rearrangement, desorption, and other steps which occupy the attention of many oil research laboratories.

The first catalytic cracker employed a fixed bed of alumina-silica gel. A fluid bed is now in common use in the huge "cat-crackers" of the modern refinery. These consist of a reactor and a regenerator, the latter being the larger vessel. In one type of installation, the reactor and regenerator are side-by-side (Fig. 8-1); in others, the regenerator is built above the reactor. (Figure 8-2.)

The modern cat-cracker is more efficient than older methods. One cat-cracker in Louisiana ran continuously for 1058 days and during this run processed 41,800,000 bbl of oil.

The cracking stock, consisting of reduced crude, "gas oil," and other fractions from the straight-run still, is heated; and, as it enters the reactor, hot catalyst from the regenerator is introduced in the form of powder or pellets. Cracking takes place on the surface of the catalyst as it circulates

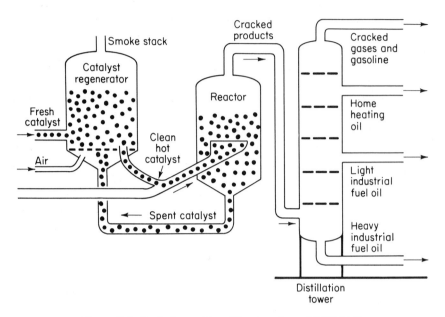

Figure 8-1 Catalytic cracking. [Courtesy Imperial Oil Ltd.]

with the oil vapors in the reactor at pressures of 9 to 12 psi and a temperature of about 1000° F. The lighter molecules move out the top of the reaction vessel into the fractionating column. The product has a higher proportion of aromatics and isoparaffins, and less gum-forming diolefins than thermally cracked gas.

A part of the fluid catalyst is removed continuously from a sump in the reactor and is forced by high-pressure air into the regenerator. There the carbon and tarry residue on the catalyst are burned off, the temperature rising to 1100° F or more. The hot flue gases pass through a waste heat boiler to generate steam, and then through a cyclone and Cottrel precipitators to remove any powdered catalyst. From 17 to 35 tons of catalyst are regenerated per minute. Any catalyst carried over with the vapors into the fractionating column, collects in the heavy bottom fraction, which is subsequently recycled to the cracking stock (Fig. 8-3).

8-3 Recovery of Reaction Products

Light gases produced in cracking are no longer vented to the air or burned. They form the valuable raw materials for the synthesis of new types of fuels and other materials such as antifreeze, plastics, and synthetic rubber. Gases

Figure 8-2 Cat-cracker and regenerator with a heating furnace in foreground. [Courtesy BA Oil Co.]

of three carbons (or less) may be removed in a unit called a *depropanizer*, or compounds of four carbons and less can be taken off in the *debutanizer*.

Light ends, very volatile components of gasoline, go to a *stabilization tower* where dissolved gases are removed. These gases may carry with them small amounts of light-end vapors, so they are "scrubbed" by an oil wash in the *absorption tower*. The light oil absorbs the light ends, which are later recovered by distillation. These volatile light ends are kept in refrigerated storage because the vapor pressure is too *high* at ordinary temperatures. Refrigeration lowers the vp. They are added to other components of regular gasoline to promote quick starting, an important factor in winter driving! The equipment for the debutanization, stabilization, and absorption is collectively known as the "D. S. & A. plant."

8-4 Treating

Cracked gasoline, because of its high olefin content, has a tendency to form undesirable gummy polymers and color bodies. This change in color,

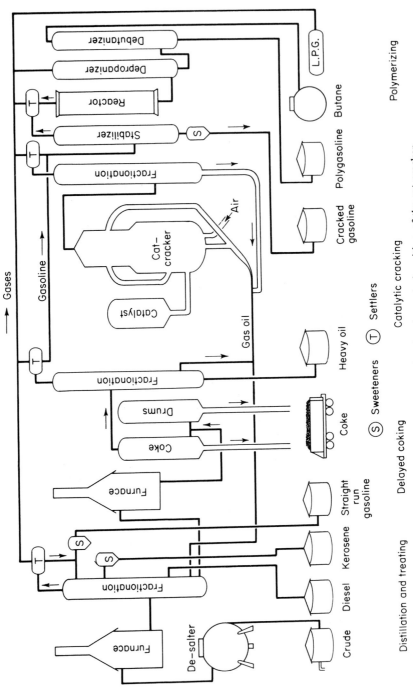

Figure 8-3 Diagram of an oil refinery showing the central position of the cat-cracker.

Distillation and treating   Delayed coking   Catalytic cracking   Polymerizing

(S) Sweeteners   (T) Settlers

which betrayed early cracked gasoline, was masked by the addition of an oil-soluble dye. Modern chemical treatment can, for the most part, remove any objectionable qualities and enhance the superior features of cracked gasolines. Antioxidants, such as amino derivatives of phenol, are added to act as inhibitors of polymerization and gum formation. Traces of metals, usually copper, which catalyze gum formation, are eliminated by small amounts of an additive, a diamino derivative of propane.

Sulfur has always been an unwanted element in fuels. The refiner is concerned more than ever before with the removal of sulfur-containing compounds because of the poisoning effect sulfur has on several of the catalysts used in the synthesis of high-octane gasolines. Any sulfur in the gasoline also tends to react with added tetraethyl lead, reducing the octane number. Elemental sulfur attacks iron, copper, and other metals; hydrogen sulfide attacks zinc, copper, and iron, causing metal embrittlement and hydrogen blistering in the refinery equipment. Organic sulfides, polysulfides, and thiophenols tend to form sludges during storage of the oil or gasoline. The thioalcohols or mercaptans (RSH) are evil-smelling compounds. The odor of the skunk is due chiefly to one of these, butyl mercaptan. The old saying that one can smell a skunk a mile away is not far from the truth, as the compound can be detected in concentrations of one part in several billion. The name given to the early automobile in the Gaelic language, translated into English, was "stink wagon." The refinery of that time did not remove these sulfur compounds.

The combustion of any sulfur compound produces sulfur dioxide and trioxide which, combined with the steam formed by the burning of the hydrogen in the hydrocarbons, give highly corrosive acids.

8-5 Removal of Sulfur

Several processes are used to remove sulfur from fuels. Spencer, in 1885, patented a process for removing sulfur compounds by adding copper oxide to heated crude oil. Treatment with finely divided metals, such as copper and even sodium and potassium, has been used. It has been found that the metallic sulfides adsorb mercaptans. Hydrogen sulfide can be easily removed by a caustic wash.

$$H_2S + 2\,NaOH \longrightarrow Na_2S + 2\,HOH$$

Doctor treatment, using sodium plumbite, is effective in removing mercaptans which are converted to lead mercaptide.

$$Na_2PbO_2 + 2\,RSH \longrightarrow Pb(SR)_2 + 2\,NaOH$$

Sodium plumbite   Lead mercaptide

If the radical R of the mercaptide is large, the compound may be soluble in the oil. Treatment of the mercaptide with sulfur converts it to a disulfide, and the lead is recovered as lead sulfide.

$$Pb(SR)_2 + S \longrightarrow RSSR + PbS\downarrow$$

The disulfides, which are soluble in gasoline, are not odorous but are still undesirable.

"Sweetening" can also be accomplished with an alkaline oxidizing agent such as sodium hypochlorite.

$$2 RSH + NaOCl \longrightarrow NaCl + RSSR + H_2O$$

$$H_2S + NaOCl \longrightarrow NaCl + S\downarrow + H_2O$$

The sulfur in the compounds may be oxidized to the sulfonate, RSO_3Na.

In some of the cracking and reforming processes sulfur compounds are converted to hydrogen sulfide, from which free sulfur may be obtained by partial oxidation and reaction of the resulting sulfur dioxide with more hydrogen sulfide. The reactions may be summarized by the equations:

$$2 H_2S + 3 O_2 \longrightarrow 2 H_2O + 2 SO_2$$
$$2 SO_2 + 4 H_2S \longrightarrow 6 S + 4 H_2O$$
$$\overline{\overset{2}{6} H_2S + \overset{}{3} O_2 \longrightarrow \overset{2}{6} S + \overset{2}{6} H_2O}$$

that is,

$$2 H_2S + O_2 \longrightarrow 2 S + 2 H_2O$$

Other sweetening and treating agents are cupric chloride, activated bauxite, or organic bases like sodium phenolate, ethanolamines, p-phenylene diamine, sodium isobutyrate, and sodium naphthenate.

8-6 Isomerization

Isomerization, or the rearrangement of the atoms within the molecule, results in a different structure but without the loss of any atoms. Straight-chain compounds are converted to branched isomers of higher octane ratings. However, isomerization is not only applied to gasolines, but it is also used to convert normal gases, such as n-butane, to the iso form, necessary for the manufacture of the high-test gasoline component, *alkylate*.

Isomerization is carried out by passing the hydrocarbon through a catalyst consisting of hydrogen chloride, aluminum chloride, and some-times antimony chloride. Sixty-two per cent of n-pentane can be converted to isopentane with one pass through the catalyst. In practice some heavier molecules are also produced. The isomerization of n-pentane yields about 1.7 per cent butane, indicating that there is a little decomposition or cracking.

Hexane with an octane number of 26 can be converted to a fuel with octane number of 80 by one pass through the catalyst, or 91.4 by recycling.

The addition of 4 cc of tetraethyl lead per gallon raises the rating of the first product to 100 and of the recycled gasoline even higher. As indicated in Table 7-2 the hexane with the highest octane number is neohexane, (2,2-dimethyl butane). The formation of this isomer is favored by a relatively low reaction temperature, but the *total* conversion to mixed isomers increases with increasing temperatures; a compromise temperature is therefore used.

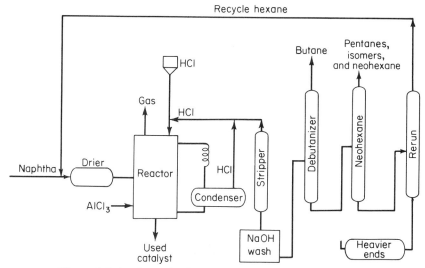

Figure 8-4 An isomerization unit producing neohexanes and pentane isomers from naphtha.

Figure 8-4 is a diagram of an isomerization unit which gives 91 to 94 per cent conversion of a midcontinent naphtha consisting chiefly of *n*-pentane and *n*-hexane into an aviation gasoline of more than 100 octane.

Hydrogen chloride is removed and recovered in a *stripper*, and the "isomate" is freed of any residual HCl by washing with water and dilute caustic soda. The gases removed in the debutanizer are 75 per cent isobutane. Pentanes come off the top of the hexane tower. The rerun tower removes heavier components amounting to about 10 per cent, and the purified hexane is then recycled.

8-7 Cyclization and Aromatization

These processes convert straight-chain hydrocarbons to cyclic paraffins, such as cyclohexane, C_6H_{12}, or benzene, C_6H_6, by use of a suitable catalyst, for example, mixed nickel and tungsten sulfides. The ring compounds have good octane ratings.

8-8 Polymerization

In this process two small olefin molecules, by-products of the cracking unit, are combined and hydrogenated to give a molecule of gasoline size.

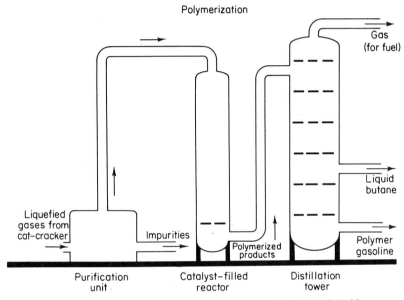

Polymerization

Figure 8-5 Polymerization unit. [Courtesy Imperial Oil Ltd.]

The product is called "polymer gasoline," although it should really be called dimer gasoline since only two, rather than *many*, similar molecules have been linked together. Branched or isoalkenes give dimers which are super fuels. Suppose the monomer is isobutene (isobutylene). Two molecules in the presence of acid catalysts unite to form 2,2,4-trimethylpentene.

Since this dimer is of gasoline size, no further polymerization is wanted. Hydrogenation converts it to 2,2,4-trimethylpentane, the saturated and satisfactory 100 octane standard fuel. A polymerization unit is shown in Fig. 8-5.

8-9 Alkylation

Alkylation is the name given to the union of an isoalkane with an alkene gas to form a molecule in the gasoline size range. In the refinery, isobutane, obtained chiefly by the isomerization of n-butane, is combined with n-butene or some other olefin.

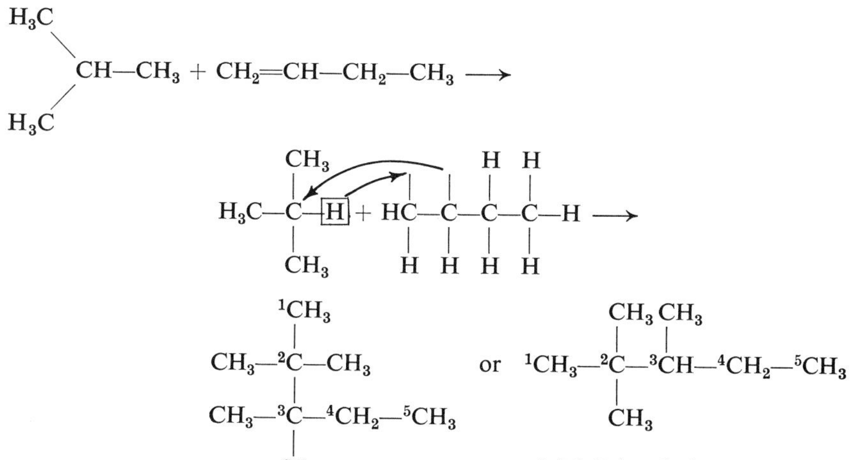

$$H_3C \diagdown$$
$$CH-CH_3 + CH_2=CH-CH_2-CH_3 \longrightarrow$$
$$H_3C \diagup$$

$$H_3C-\underset{\underset{CH_3}{\overset{CH_3}{|}}}{\overset{|}{C}}-\boxed{H} + HC-\underset{\underset{H}{\overset{H}{|}}}{\overset{H}{\underset{|}{C}}}-\underset{\underset{H}{\overset{H}{|}}}{\overset{H}{\underset{|}{C}}}-\underset{\underset{H}{\overset{H}{|}}}{\overset{H}{\underset{|}{C}}}-H \longrightarrow$$

$$\underset{\underset{\underset{\underset{H}{|}}{CH_3-{}^3C-{}^4CH_2-{}^5CH_3}}{|}}{\underset{\underset{|}{CH_3-{}^2C-CH_3}}{{}^1CH_3}}$$
    or
$${}^1CH_3-\underset{\underset{CH_3}{|}}{\overset{\overset{CH_3\ CH_3}{|\ \ \ |}}{{}^2C}}-{}^3CH-{}^4CH_2-{}^5CH_3$$

                                                 2,2,3-Trimethylpentane

Isobutane also unites with ethylene and propylene. The isoparaffin may be isopentane but since like isohexane it is a good gasoline constituent, it is more often added to the synthesized alkylate to raise the vapor pressure.

8-10 Reforming

Straight-run gasolines contain unbranched saturated molecules which contribute to low octane rating. *Thermal reforming* consists of heating the gasoline under pressure, which causes some of the molecules to crack and reform by alkylation. The resulting branched structure gives a higher octane rating to the product.

Catalytic reforming achieves the improvement in fuel character at lower pressures, and with less cracking and coke formation, than thermal reforming does. Several types of reactions are involved: isomerization, hydrogenation and dehydrogenation, and aromatization. Straight paraffins become benzene or other aromatics or highly branched molecules. Several different types of reformers are now being used which differ chiefly in the catalyst employed and in the details of the mechanical arrangements.

Hydroforming uses a molybdenum catalyst at about 950° F and 200 psi in the presence of hydrogen maintained at 60 moles per cent concentration with the hydrocarbon. It gives a product having an octane number several units higher than the same stock which has been subjected to thermal reforming. The product is high in aromatics, low in olefins, and high in susceptibility to tetraethyl lead.

Platforming is a reforming process using platinum with a little fluorine on alumina. Losses due to methane formation are small.

Houdriforming, *catforming*, and *ultraforming* all use platinum on alumina catalysts. They differ chiefly in the pressures employed and in the manipulation of the catalyst. *Hyperforming* uses a cobalt-molybdenum oxide catalyst; *Thermoforming*, Cr_2O_3-Al_2O_3 beads.

8-11 Factors Influencing the Product

Yields and octane rating of the product, reformate, depend not only on the catalyst used, but also on the concentration of naphthenes in the original stock. California crudes are higher and Pennsylvanian lower in naphthenes than Mid-continent oils. The yield of 95 RON reformate from a standard mid-continent stock is highest when a platinum catalyst is used at relatively low pressures (200 psi). Yields with a molybdenum oxide or molybdate catalyst are lower, but more butane is produced. This contributes to the higher volatility of the product.

Approximately 85 per cent of the catalytic reforming plants in the United States use platinum catalysts. These represent 70 per cent of reformer capacity in bbl per day.

A reformer unit is shown in Fig. 8-6 and diagrammatically in Fig. 8-7.

8-12 Natural or Casinghead Gasoline

A highly volatile gasoline called "natural" or "casinghead" gasoline is obtained from natural gas by removing the vapors of the C_4 to C_7 hydrocarbons which it carries. Gas containing such vapors is said to be "wet," in contrast to others which are chiefly methane and are therefore "dry" or "lean." The recovered gasoline is called casinghead gas because it is

Figure 8-6 This night scene shows a towering powerformer unit for making high octane gasoline. [Courtesy Imperial Oil Ltd.]

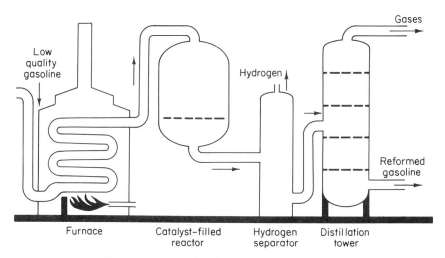

Figure 8-7 Reforming. [Courtesy Imperial Oil Ltd.]

obtained from the gas which accumulates or comes off at the head of the casing of the oil well.

The vapors may be recovered by three methods: (1) by combined pressure and cooling after which the condensed liquid is stabilized (see page 79); (2) by absorption in a light oil, with subsequent "stripping" in a distillation column; (3) by adsorption on charcoal, silica, or alumina gels. This method is particularly good when the concentration of the vapors in the natural gas is low. The gasoline is removed from the adsorbent or "desorbed" by live steam or inert gas at a slightly elevated temperature. After repeated use the adsorbents are reactivated by heating them to 600° to 750° F in a current of steam or in the case of the alumina or silica gel, heated air.

8-13 Gasoline, A Varied and Composite Product

It is apparent that there are a number of liquid fuels that qualify as gasoline: straight-run gasoline, casinghead, benzol gas from coal, reformate, polymer gasoline, cracked gasoline, and alkylate. Various combinations of these with light ends and other additives will give the consumer a gasoline of any desired quality. Several companies now market three octane grades, the composition of which varies with the season and the locality. For example, winter gas in Canada may contain 14 per cent butanes, in Florida 7 per cent.

The terms *premium, high test, high octane* are used indiscriminately to denote a better grade than *regular* gasoline. Primarily these terms denote higher octane rating. The word premium implies something extra. High test also denotes high volatility and quick starting. Actually these higher grades differ in composition from the lower octane regular gas. They may differ in the nature and number of additives or improvers present.

In 1962, the average regular gas had a RON of 92.9. It was estimated that, of all cars in operation at that time, 40 per cent could operate at trace knock on gasoline of RON 90, 52 per cent on gas of RON 92, 70 per cent on 94, and 80 per cent would run satisfactorily on 96 octane gas. In spite of the advertisements for compact cars which "run on regular gas," the *Oil and Gas Journal* (May 14, 1962) reported that only 65 per cent of the 1962 models should use regular gas (RON 92.9). However 80 per cent would operate at trace knock on RON 95, and 85 per cent on gasoline of RON 96.

It should be pointed out that while the octane number is a convenient and universally used index of quality, there are other important properties which are not graded by the octane rating. Two hydrocarbons with exactly the same octane number may vary greatly in their volatility. An extreme example of this is given by propane and "isooctane." Both have an octane number of 100, but "isooctane" boils at 210° F and propane at −44° F.

Thus, two gasolines with the same octane rating may not be equally suitable for quick starting in winter.

Two fuels having the same octane number may not yield the same energy on combustion. Alcohol, which has an octane number of 90, gives around 13,000 Btu/lb while a gasoline of the same rating produces 20,000 Btu/lb. The same is true of hydrocarbons, although to a lesser degree. Thus benzene, a fuel of high octane number, has a greater tendency to "foul-up" an engine than isooctane or alcohol.

The best gasoline as far as the consumer is concerned is the one which gives the best performance in the particular conditions and equipment in which it is used. Thus the motorist's preference for one brand of gasoline may be justified, although the octane rating of other brands is the same.

8-14 Gasoline from Nonpetroleum Sources

In Germany, South Africa, and other countries which have no extensive oil fields, motor fuels are derived from nonpetroleum sources: oil shales, bituminous coals, or lignite. Improvements in methods of mining oil shales and in methods of extracting the oil have reduced the difference in cost between gasoline from this source and from crude oil. Alberta tar sands contain hydrocarbons equivalent to 300×10^9 bbls of oil. It is expected that large-scale production of oil from this source will be achieved by 1965 or earlier.

Oil and gasoline can be produced from coal by two methods: *hydrogenation* and synthesis by the *Fischer-Tropsch process*. In the first process coal in the form of a fine powder is made into a slurry with oil and subjected to hydrogen under high pressure in the presence of a catalyst. The combination of the hydrogen with the carbon framework of the coal yields hydrocarbons from gases to wax. The process is carried out in stages, the number of steps depending on the grade of coal used and the product desired. In the production of gasoline, oils produced in the first stages are subjected to further hydrogenation in the presence of a different catalyst. The resulting gasoline is high in aromatics and branched-chain compounds.

Low-grade coals were extensively hydrogenated in Germany during the war as the major source of gasoline. The Leuna plant alone produced over 3,500,000 bbl/year. In Britain the hydrogenation plant at Billingham treated some 100,000 tons of coal per year. This is equivalent to more than 4,000,000 bbl of motor fuel annually.

The second process for producing gasoline from coal uses the Fischer-Tropsch synthesis of hydrocarbons from carbon monoxide and hydrogen. The coal is first converted to coke and the volatile liquids and tars recovered. The coke is then heated with steam to give water gas.

$$C + H_2O \longrightarrow H_2 + CO$$

This gas mixture, enriched with hydrogen, is passed through a nickel catalyst to give a product consisting principally of gasoline and fuel oil. The product is affected by the catalyst used. A cobalt catalyst gives more olefins. Iron oxide with a little potassium carbonate as a "promoter" gives heavier hydrocarbons than does the iron oxide with the same amount of sodium carbonate added. Mixed catalysts such as cobalt-magnesia-thoria are also used to produce high-grade diesel fuel from the enriched water gas. If a zinc oxide catalyst is employed, alcohols are formed. During the war, edible fats were synthesized from compounds obtained by the Fischer-Tropsch reaction.

Gasoline can be manufactured from natural gas by similar reactions. This is the most promising future source of synthetic gasoline, but on the basis of gallons per ton of raw material and cost of manufacturing plant, crude oil is still the most economical source.

Review Questions

1. Why do you have to pay more for high-octane gas?

2. An oil company markets "gasoline with octane to suit your car" by mixing two different basic fuels in various proportions. What is the difference in the chemical composition of the two fuels?

3. What is the difference between reformed gasoline and alkylate?

4. Define polymer gasoline.

5. Write the reaction between two molecules of isopentene. Name the product.

6. Show how isobutane reacts with n-propene.

7. What is casinghead gasoline?

8. Why are inhibitors added to cracked gasoline?

9. During which stage of the refining may organic sulfur compounds be converted to H_2S?

10. How may thio alcohols (mercaptans) be removed from gasoline?

11. What is the formula for butyl mercaptan?

12. What are some of the undesirable effects of sulfur compounds in gasoline?

13. Define isomerization, platforming, cat-cracker, D.S.&A. plant.

14. In what ways may a gasoline be obtained from coal?

15. Write the equations for the removal of hydrogen sulfide and mercaptan from oil by copper oxide.

9

Diesel and Other Fuels

9-1 Diesel Fuel

It seems paradoxical that the diesel engine which has been the principal factor in the displacement of coal as fuel for prime movers, was designed by its originator to burn coal dust. A suspension of coal dust in air is an explosive mixture which can be ignited by the heat of compression as well as by a spark or flame. It is related that the first diesel engine blew apart, and the inventor subsequently changed the fuel to an oil spray.

In this type of engine, air is drawn into the cylinder and compressed to around 500 psi. This compression is accompanied by a rise in temperature of 1000° F. Near the completion of the compression stroke, oil is sprayed into the heated air whereupon it ignites. This raises the temperature and therefore the pressure, and the energy of the expanding gases speed the piston on its down stroke.

The speed of a compression ignition engine is the most important factor in determining the type of oil that can be used as fuel. Engines may be classified as low-, medium-, and high-speed engines. Low-speed diesels operate at from 100 to 500 rpm. They are usually massive stationary installations or large marine units. Medium-speed diesels give 500 to 1500 rpm. Such engines are used for power generators, pumps, tractors, power shovels, and locomotives. High-speed engines operate from 1500 to 2000 rpm or higher to move buses, trucks, and aircraft. These engines have a weight/hp ratio very much lower than older type diesels. They require very carefully graded fuels. The reason for this will be apparent after the consideration of several factors which determine the suitability of a fuel.

9-2 Combustion Stages

The combustion of the fuel in a diesel engine may be divided into four steps. (1) The oil droplets are shot into the very hot compressed air in the cylinder. Heat is absorbed and the first and smallest of succeeding droplets are completely vaporized. (2) Ignition of the hot vapor occurs with consequent increase in temperature and pressure within the cylinder. (3) The oil spray, still entering, burns like a jet flame, supplying heat and hot gaseous combustion products to keep up the push on the piston. (4) The fuel injection stops. Unvaporized droplets or oil on cylinder surfaces continue to burn. This after-burn is increased by carbon deposits. All of these steps may require only a small fraction of a second for completion.

In a high-speed engine it is obvious that the time lag in getting the oil droplets heated to the ignition point must be brief. The whole injection period must be very short because diesel knock is caused by a retarded ignition. If the delay period (step 1) is too long, oil mist accumulates in the cylinder, and when the charge fires, the combustion is explosive. The ideal operation gives a rapid, but steady, increase in pressure to a maximum at the end of the injection time. This calls for a short delay period and a smooth combustion. The differences between the pressure curves for a short- and long-delay period are shown in Fig. 9-1.

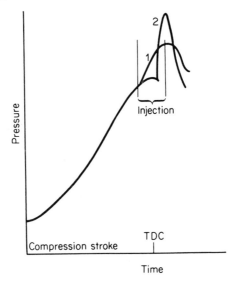

Figure 9-1 Curve 1—Short Delay; Curve 2—Long Delay.

The delay period depends on a number of factors. The engine design, the type of injector, the size of oil droplet, and the way the spray is mixed with the air all affect the delay time, but the most important factor is the chemical nature of the fuel.

9-3 Cetane Number

Diesel fuels are graded in a manner somewhat similar to that used to determine the octane rating of gasolines. The two standard fuels used in the evaluation of diesel oils are normal cetane, $C_{16}H_{34}$, and α-methyl naphthalene,

$$CH_3$$

The alpha indicates that the methyl group is on the peak of one of the joined rings. Cetane is a straight-chain paraffin. This hydrocarbon is better than any commercial diesel fuel and is therefore given a rating of 100. Ring compounds generally, and aromatic compounds especially, are poor diesel fuels. One of these, methyl naphthalene, is rated at zero. The percentage of cetane in the mixture of the high and low standard fuels that matches the diesel fuel under test, gives the cetane number of the fuel. High-speed diesels require fuels of 50 cetane or higher; medium-speed engines operate on 45 cetane fuel; low-speed units can use fuels with a rating of 25.

It will be noted that diesel fuels are chosen for characteristics which are almost the opposite of those required in gasolines. In the latter the highest value is placed on that gasoline which will not detonate under the high compression encountered in the modern car engine. The desirable diesel fuel is one which will ignite readily under such conditions. Thus "isooctane" has a cetane number of only 22, while *n*-heptane, of zero octane number, has a cetane rating of 64.

9-4 Diesel Index

The diesel index is a numerical quantity thought by many to give an indication of the quality of a diesel fuel. This index is calculated from two physico-chemical quantities. The quantities measured are the specific gravity of the oil and the aniline number. The gravity is expressed in A.P.I. degrees, adopted by the American Petroleum Institute. Water at 60° F on this scale has a °API of 10. Liquids denser than water have lower numbers. The relation between °API and specific gravity at 60° is shown in Fig. 9-2.

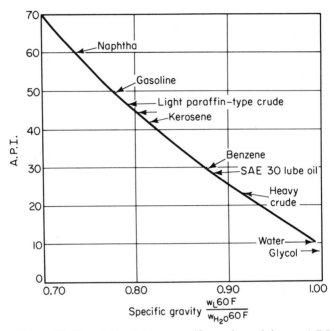

Figure 9-2 The relation between specific gravity and degrees A.P.I.

The position of several oils is indicated on the curve. The aniline number is the temperature at which equal volumes of aniline,

$$NH_2$$

an aromatic amine, and the oil, cease to be completely miscible. The aniline point is related to the amount of aromatics in the oil.

$$\text{diesel index no.} = \frac{°API \ (sp \ gr) \ \times \ \text{aniline point (°F)}}{100}$$

The higher the index the better the fuel. The D.I. is usually about three units higher than the cetane number.

9-5 Ignition Temperature, Flash Point, and Fire Point

Three determinations which indicate important properties of the fuel oil are the *spontaneous ignition temperature*, the *flash point*, and the *fire point*. To insure the rapid firing of the charge, the temperature at which the fuel ignites should be well below the temperature of the compressed air in the cylinder of the engine. The *spontaneous ignition temperature* is closely related to fuel composition. Unfortunately, as determined experimentally, this temperature may differ somewhat from the temperature at which ignition occurs in the engine because it is affected by the presence of any deposits, the material and the physical condition of the walls, the concentration of the

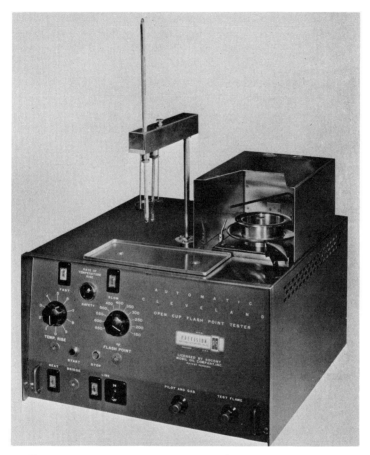

Figure 9-3 An automatic flash point tester. [Courtesy Fisher Scientific Co.]

vapor, and the total pressure. Probably, the experimental method which approximates operating conditions most closely is the adiabatic compression of air and vaporized fuel in a steel cylinder until ignition results. By this method the SIT of hexane is 366° C (690° F); heptane, a good diesel fuel, is 330° C (626° F). The aromatic compound benzene, with a cetane number of −10, has an SIT of 420° C (788° F). Gasoline gives values of 353° to 367° C (667° to 690° F).

The flash point is obtained by gradually increasing the temperature of the oil in a standard flash cup until sufficient vapor is given off to produce a flash when a flame is passed over the mouth of the cup. The temperature of the oil at which this occurs is the flash point. This is an index of the volatility of the oil or liquid. It is used as an indication of the fire hazard in handling combustible liquids.

An automatic flash point tester is shown in Fig. 9-3. The electrical heating unit is controlled by a resistance thermometer immersed in the sample. The heating rate is automatically adjusted so that, for the last 50°, the temperature rise is 10° F/min. A test flame passes over the cup every 6 sec. At the flash point, the flash flame changes the capacitance of a circular condenser, thus triggering a thyratron tube and relay which shuts off the heat. The temperature is marked on a recorder at the same instant.

The fire point is the temperature to which the oil must be heated so that the vapor pressure is sufficient to maintain the flame.

9-6 Additives for Diesel Fuel

The quality of the diesel fuel can be raised by the addition of improvers. Ethyl nitrite and ethyl nitrate are two organic compounds which raise the cetane number of the oil. It has been found that the salt ammonium nitrate has a similar effect.

Other additives are used for different purposes. Inhibitors delay or prevent gum formation. Big polyhydrocarbon molecules prevent alteration of the fluid properties of the oil with temperature changes. Other chemical additives reduce the surface tension and thus promote the formation of a finer spray.

9-7 Smoke Point

The tendency of a fuel to form smoke is important since it is related to the formation of carbon deposits, soot, dirty exhaust fumes, and smog. Research has shown that the smokiness of hydrocarbons increases in the series *n*-alkanes < *iso*-alkanes, < olefins, < the aromatics. The cycloparaffins vary among themselves, so that one cannot put them in the series as a group. Their smoking tendency depends on molecular size and structure. The maximum height of the flame in millimeters, at which the fuel will burn without smoking in a Standard Lamp, is called the *smoke point*. The Standard Oil (Indiana) Smoke Lamp is shown in Fig. 9-4.

In determining the smoke point, the standard wick is first soaked in the test sample and placed in the wick holder. A 20 ml sample is put into the reservoir (*R*) which is then locked in place; the wick is lighted and adjusted so that the flame is 1 cm high. The lamp is allowed to burn for five minutes. The wick is then gradually raised by means of the large levelling screw (S) until the flame starts to smoke and then lowered until the smoky tail just disappears. The height of the flame at this point is read off the scale on the pyrex chimney to the nearest 0.5 mm. Readings are made in triplicate and the average to the nearest millimeter is the recorded smoke point. Some typical values are shown in Table 9-1.

Chemists have found compounds which reduce the smoking propensity of oil. The additive, which like tetraethyl lead is an organometallic compound, has the general formula FeR_2, where R represents the radical from cyclopentadiene. Addition of 0.1 per cent of the compound converts a very sooty flame to a smokeless one.

Workers at the University of California have found that water emulsified in diesel fuel may reduce the amount of smoke in the exhaust and the amount of carbon deposit in the engine. Their research showed that, while 5 per cent or less water increased the amount of petroleum fuel used per horsepower, a greater amount of water increased the thermal efficiency, the maximum increase being 9.7 per cent

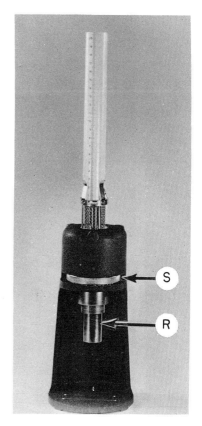

Figure 9-4 Standard Oil (Indiana) smoke lamp. [Courtesy Central Scientific Company.]

with a 22.5 per cent water mixture. Figure 9-5 shows the variation in specific fuel consumption with the percentage of water emulsified in the fuel oil.

Table 9-1. SMOKE POINTS OF SOME COMPOUNDS[a]

n-Hexane	149	Cyclohexane	117
n-Octane	147	Benzene	8
2,2,4-Trimethylpentane	86	Toluene	6
1-Hexene	88	p-Xylene	5
1-Octene	99	Thiophenol	5
Hexyl mercaptan	102	Phenyl sulphide	4
Hexyl sulphide	114	Aniline	15

[a] Selected data from R. A. Hunt, *Relation of Smoke Point to Molecular Structure.* I/EC, **45**, (1953), 602.

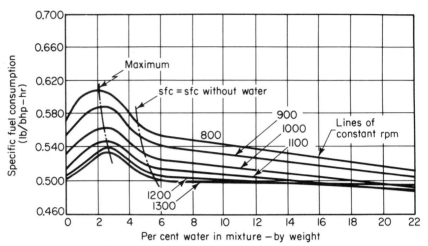

Figure 9-5 Variation of specific fuel consumption with water emulsified in diesel fuel. [From I. Cornet and W. E. Nero, *Industrial and Engineering Chemistry*, **47**, (1955), 2136, by permission.]

When ammonium nitrate solutions were used instead of water in the emulsion, the diesel engine ran more smoothly than with the oil alone; that is, the cetane number was raised. Between 1000 and 1200 rpm the thermal efficiency was also increased. The effect of an ammonium nitrate emulsion on the cetane number of diesel oil is illustrated in Fig. 9-6.

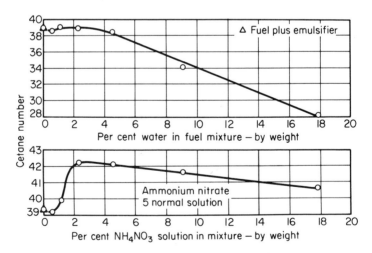

Figure 9-6 Effect of water and ammonium nitrate on cetane number of diesel fuel. [From I. Cornet and W. E. Nero, *Industrial and Engineering Chemistry*, **47** (1955), 2136, by permission.]

9-8 Kerosene and Jet Fuel

The fraction of distillate boiling between 200° and 275° C, called kerosene or "coal oil" (incorrectly), has been of minor importance for many years. With the advent of the jet engine, however, the picture changed. Jet fuels correspond to a kerosene or kerosene-gasoline mixtures, except that the specifications are more rigid. Jet fuel must remain fluid down to −76° F. Ordinary kerosene can be converted to a satisfactory jet fuel by treatment with the compound urea. This chemical has the ability to surround certain types of straight-chain compounds to form rather unusual complexes called *inclusion compounds* or *adducts*. These adducts are crystalline and can be separated from the oil by filtration. They can be decomposed at will.

9-9 Oil for Heating

Oil has displaced coal as a domestic fuel in spite of somewhat higher cost because of its ease of handling, more economical storage space requirements, low ash content and higher BTU per pound.

Domestic fuel oils are light oils of low viscosity having boiling points somewhat higher than the high limit for kerosene. The flash point should be above 175° F.

Various mechanical methods are used to effect rapid and complete combustion. The oil is usually converted to a whirling spray by a stream of air. In certain gravity-feed installations the oil strikes a rotating disc and is distributed in the form of fine droplets around the whole circumference of the fire box.

Industrial fuel oils are usually much heavier than the oils used for domestic furnaces. Atomization of the fuel may be accomplished by injection with steam. In another method the oil is heated and forced through a suitable nozzle where it is divided into several impinging streams and thus broken up into a fine spray.

9-10 Rocket Fuels

Rocket fuels include such prosaic substances as gasoline and kerosene. In rocket propulsion, however, consumption of the fuel takes place at a much faster rate than in the gas turbine or jet engine and temperatures are much higher. Gas temperatures in the rocket motor run from 5000° to 6000° F, whereas a jet aircraft engine operates at about 1800° F. Extremely rapid combustion is achieved by the use of liquid oxygen or other strong oxidizers such as 95 to 100 per cent hydrogen peroxide and fuming nitric acid. Ozone, fluorine, and chlorine trifluoride are being tested as possible oxidizers.

The German V-2 rocket missile of World War II was powered by a fuel system containing three and one-quarter tons of alcohol and six and three-quarter tons of liquid oxygen. The fuel, burning at the rate of 1800 lb per minute, furnished sufficient thrust to drive the 45 foot missile bearing one ton of explosives to a height of 120 miles.

9-11 Classification of Rocket Fuels

Rocket fuels may be classified by a quantity called the *specific impulse*, I Sp, defined as the pounds of thrust per pound of fuel per second. A good rocket fuel has a specific impulse of 250. The I Sp for several combinations of fuels and oxidizers are given in Table 9-2.

9-12 Solid Rocket Fuels

The rockets used for centuries in fireworks displays have been propelled by the hot gases from burning gunpowder. Small rocket missiles such as the 2.75 in. aircraft rockets burn a nitroglycerine-nitrocellulose mixture. The Polaris missile burns solid fuel. Thiokol, hydrazine, certain borides, and various polymers can be used as solid fuels with suitable oxidizers. Powdered metals such as magnesium and aluminum have been suggested as solid fuels.

Table 9-2. THE SPECIFIC IMPULSE OF VARIOUS FUEL SYSTEMS[a]

Combination		I Sp
C_2H_5OH	$: 1.5\ O_2$	242
C_2H_5OH	$: 4.0\ H_2O_2\ (99\%)$	230
JP_4[b]	$: 6.5\ H_2O_2$	233
JP_4	$: 2.2\ O_2$	248
Turpentine	$: 2.2\ O_2$	249
NH_3	$: 1.3\ O_2$	250
JP_4	$: 2.3\ (70\%\ O_2, 30\%\ O_3)$	253
JP_4	$: 1.9\ (100\%\ O_3)$	266
JP_4	$: 2.6\ F_2$	265
$NH_2 \cdot NH_2$	$: 0.63\ O_3$	277
NH_3	$: 2.6\ F_2$	288
B_2H_6	$: 5.0\ F_2$	291
CH_3OH	$: 2.3\ F_2$	296
NH_2NH_2	$: 1.98\ F_2$	298
H_2	$8 : 1\ O_2$	511

[a] From *Chemical and Engineering News* (Vol. 35, No. 21, 1957).
[b] Jet propulsion fuel #4, a hydrocarbon mixture with 0.1 per cent de-icing additive.

The combustion of liquid fuels may be more easily regulated than the combustion of solid fuel; however, the latter can be controlled by the composition, shape, and size of the fuel grain or pellet.

Multi-stage rockets may have solid fuel for one stage and liquid fuel for another.

9-13 Liquid Rocket Fuels

A diagrammatic representation of a rocket burning liquid fuel is given in Fig. 9-7. Compressed nitrogen, or other inert gas, forces the fuel into the

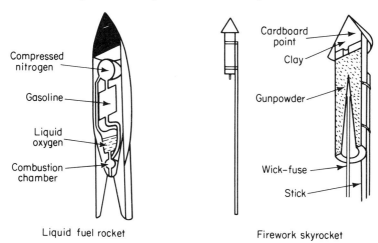

Liquid fuel rocket   Firework skyrocket

Figure 9-7 Comparison of a liquid-fuel rocket with the original solid-fuel "skyrocket."

combustion chamber at a controlled rate. The entering fuel components are preheated and the temperature of the rocket motor is controlled by heat exchangers. The Atlas rocket which propelled Friendship 7 into orbit (Fig. 9-8) burned liquid hydrocarbons and liquid oxygen.

Hydrogen would be an ideal fuel from the standpoint of energy liberated per pound, but it is difficult to liquefy, and the fuel tank has to be built to stand very high pressure. However, liquid hydrogen is now being produced in tonnage quantities. The Pratt-Whitney RL-10 engine for the upper stage of a multiple rocket burns liquid hydrogen.

Owing to the practical problems encountered with elemental hydrogen, chemists have sought other fuels in which hydrogen is built into a combustible molecule. In addition to the hydrocarbon fuels, such as JP#4, other hydrogen-containing compounds such as aniline, $C_6H_5NH_2$, lithium hydride, LiH, and liquid ammonia, NH_3, have been used. The element boron, which itself gives 25,000 Btu/lb on oxidation, has been combined with hydrogen to

Figure 9-8 The launching of Friendship 7. The Mercury capsule carrying Col. John Glenn was propelled by an Atlas rocket burning hydrocarbon liquid fuel and liquid oxygen. [Courtesy N.A.S.A.]

form a series of compounds, (B_2H_6 to $B_{10}H_{14}$), called *boranes*. These give a very high specific impulse and are therefore known as "zip" fuels.

Several of the new rocket fuels and oxidizers are toxic. Some are highly corrosive. Ozone is a rather sensitive substance, although recent methods of production and purification give a more stable product. The chemical properties of these substances must be known by the astro-engineer.

Review Questions

1. Why is a poor gasoline component very often a good diesel fuel?

2. Define cetane number.

3. How can the delay time be shortened?

4. What is the diesel index and what is its significance?

5. There is an old rhyme which relates:

> A woman named Molly McGuire
> Had trouble in lighting the fire.
> The wood was so green
> She used kerosene!
> —She's gone where the fuel is drier.

   Discuss the chemistry involved.

6. In 1846, Dr. A. Gesner distilled an illuminating oil from coal. How would this "coal oil" differ from kerosene derived from a Pennsylvania crude?

7. Which of the following would show the greatest tendency to smoke when burned: C_6H_6, C_6H_{14}, C_6H_{12}?

8. Name three improvers for diesel fuel.

9. Distinguish between flash point, fire point, and ignition temperature.

10. Hydrogen and fluorine have an I Sp of 350. What disadvantages and advantages would this rocket fuel have as compared to a hydrocarbon-fluorine system?

Further Readings

Barker, A., Nonweiler, T., and Smelt, R., *Jets and Rockets* (London: Chapman & Hall, 1959).

Mallan, L., *Space Science* (New York: Arco, 1961).

Newell, H. E., *Guide to Rockets, Missiles, and Satellites* (New York: McGraw-Hill, 1958).

Purdy, C., *Petroleum* (Toronto: Copp Clark Co., 1958).

10

Gaseous Fuels

10-1 Natural Gas

When carbonaceous matter decomposes, combustible gases are produced. "Marsh gas," which can be seen rising from the bottom of a water-covered swamp or marsh as an occasional bubble, is largely methane. "Lean" or dry natural gas is methane with possibly some ethane. "Wet" gas is chiefly methane but with appreciable quantities of the vapors of higher hydrocarbons. The ignition of the natural gas or methane found in some bituminous coal mines has often caused disaster. The miners call the gas "fire damp." This is a corruption of the German *feuer dampf*—fire vapor.

Most of the natural gas used for fuel comes from oil fields. In some instances, the gas, evaporated from the oil and diffused through rocks, is trapped by some impervious dome-shaped structure, which may be a great distance from the original oil deposit; this constitutes a gas field. The gas may be under high pressure. Its sudden escape through a fissure, caused by earth movement or pressure, may result in ignition on its emergence to the atmosphere because of static electricity produced by the rushing gas (the flow potential), or because of elevated temperatures caused by friction.

It is probable that the pillars of fire and cloud or smoke mentioned in the Old Testament account of the escape of the Israelites from Egypt were burning jets of "lean" and "wet" natural gas. People did not understand the cause of the flames and because many of the ancient cultures worshipped fire, they considered the ever-burning flames of gas to be sacred. In Azerbaijan, near Baku, escaping natural gas has been burning for three thousand years. Today, one of the postage stamps of Azerbaijan depicts the "Temple of the Eternal Fires."

The chief gas fields in the United States are in Texas, Louisiana, California, and Oklahoma. In Canada, the major oil fields are found in Alberta, which is responsible for 70 per cent of Canadian production. A network of pipelines is used to carry natural gas from the major fields to distant markets. The longest single pipeline in the world is the Trans-Canada, stretching almost 2300 miles across Canada.

Figure 10-1 Plant for the removal and recovery of sulfur from natural gas. Commencing at the left, the plant processing structures are as follows: (1) amine solution-treating coolers and gas treating area; (2) gas-treating building including amine solution regeneration facilities; (3) acid gas coolers; utilities building including central control room; (4) sulfur plant building; and (5) the incinerator and 250 ft stack. [Courtesy Texas Gulf Sulphur Co., Okotoks Alberta Plant.]

10-2 The Purification of Natural Gas

Natural gas undergoes various treatments before it reaches the consumer. Figure 10-1 shows a natural gas plant. A flow diagram of the different processes is given in Fig. 10-2. Wet natural gas is treated to recover the vapors of liquid hydrocarbons (1) by condensation (pressure and cooling), (2) by

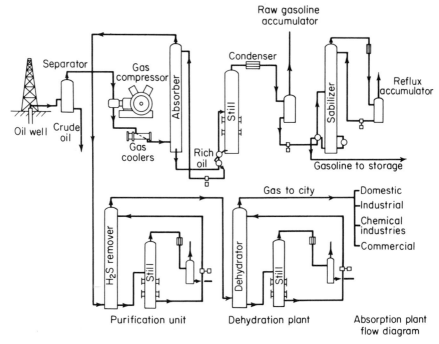

Figure 10-2 Between well and consumer, natural gas passes through a complex purification process.

absorption in oil, (3) by adsorption on charcoal, silica, or alumina gel. The recovered liquid is known as casinghead gasoline.

Natural gas may contain hydrogen sulfide and some carbon dioxide. Both of these can be removed in a number of ways. Removal and recovery may be effected by the use of monoethanolamine ($NH_2C_2H_4OH$) or other ammonia derivatives. The tendency for ammonia to form compounds with acid gases is familiar to all.

$$NH_3 + HCl \longrightarrow NH_4Cl$$

$$2\,NH_3 + H_2S \longrightarrow (NH_4)_2S$$

$$2\,NH_3 + H_2CO_3 \longrightarrow (NH_4)_2CO_3$$

The last two salts decompose readily. In the days when women used to faint, the instability of ammonium carbonate was made use of in "smelling salts," the pungent ammonia acting as a stimulant.

A solution of ethanolamine will also combine with hydrogen sulfide and carbon dioxide, removing them from the natural gas. These gases are readily released by heating the product.

$$2\ HOC_2H_4NH_2 + H_2S \longrightarrow (HOC_2H_4NH_3)_2S$$

or

$$(HOC_2H_4NH_2)_2H_2S \quad \text{and} \quad HOC_2H_4NH_2H$$

$$\diagdown S \diagup$$

$$H$$

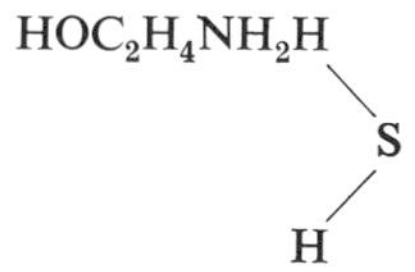

10-3 Industrial Sulfur from Natural Gas

Hydrogen sulfide is a source of elementary sulfur. Some of the hydrogen sulfide is oxidized to sulfur dioxide and steam.

$$2\ H_2S + 3\ O_2 \longrightarrow 2\ SO_2 + 2\ H_2O$$

The sulfur dioxide is then allowed to react with additional hydrogen sulfide to produce free sulfur.

$$2\ H_2S + SO_2 \longrightarrow 3\ S + 2\ H_2O$$

Liquid sulfur becomes more viscous as the temperature is raised, owing to its conversion to other allotropic forms in the melt. The temperature is therefore kept just above the melting point. It is pumped into storage bins where it crystallizes, giving yellow sulfur, or to special tank cars in which it is shipped to market in the molten condition.

Figure 10-3 shows the sulfur stockpile from a gas treatment plant. Molten sulfur flows through an insulated pipe (1) from the treatment plant and is being discharged at (3). The red liquid sulfur makes a tree-like pattern on the underlying yellow solid. The portion marked (4) is a cake of sulfur 400 × 100 × 25 ft. The boxcars are being loaded from an older dump.

Royalite Oil treats 100 million cubic feet of Turner Valley gas per day, recovering 88 to 92 per cent of the sulfur content; Shell Oil Co., 85 per cent of the sulfur from a high-sulfur gas. It is expected that by 1965, Canada will be second only to the United States in the production of sulfur.

Figure 10-3 A sulfur stockpile from a gas treatment plant. [Courtesy Texas Gulf Sulphur Co.]

10-4 Fuel and Chemical Raw Material

Natural gas is finding increasing use as an industrial and domestic fuel and as a raw material. In 1962 the marketed production of natural gas in the United States amounted to $13,750 \times 10^9$ cu ft. It is estimated that by 1980, twenty-five per cent of Canadian energy requirements will be supplied by this gaseous fuel. Natural gas is a source of industrial hydrogen. Ammonia, used in one of the processes for extracting nickel from its ores, is made by reacting nitrogen, from liquid air, with natural gas. Natural gas is a raw material for the synthesis of methanol, formaldehyde, and other compounds.

10-5 Liquid Petroleum Gases (LPG)

Propane and butane are fuel gases obtained from oil refining and natural gas. "Liquid propane" fuel (chiefly C_3H_8), widely used as city gas and industrial fuel, has a heating value of 2750 Btu/cu ft, as compared with 1010 for natural gas. One pound of liquid propane gives about $8\frac{1}{2}$ cu ft of gas at 60° F. A typical propane installation for a city is shown in Fig. 10-4.

10-6 Butane

Butane is also an important fuel gas obtained from the debutanizer of the refinery and from natural gas. It has a boiling point of 31° F, so it

Figure 10-4 Pressure storage tanks for propane. Normally the gas is liquefied and stored under pressure. [Courtesy Imperial Oil Ltd.]

Figure 10-5 Sarnia refinery—butane tanks. [Courtesy Imperial Oil Ltd.]

would not be suitable for outside installations in winter. Its heat of combustion is 3267 Btu/cu ft at 60° F. Figure 10-5 shows Horton spheres for storing butane. Bottled gas, or LPG (liquified petroleum gas), is a mixture of propane and butane. LPG is not only used for domestic and industrial heating, but also as a high-octane fuel for buses, tractors, and trucks. The buses in Chicago, Seattle, and Washington use LPG. Tractors with a high-compression engine, CR 10:1, powered with LPG, are used extensively in the United States. The advantages of using bottled gas as an automotive fuel are high octane number, uniformity, perfect vaporization, clean burning, no sulfur, no tetraethyl lead, and no gum formation. A fuel ratio of 14 air to 1 of fuel is used. The engine idles at 375 rpm, whereas with gasoline the best or leanest mixture usable is 13 air to 1 fuel, with idling rpm of 475 to 500. Disadvantages of the LPG fuel are lower Btu per gallon than gasoline and some inconvenience in exchanging cylinders.

10-7 Manufactured Fuel Gases

Other fuel gases are coal gas, coke-oven gas, producer gas, water gas, carburetted and other modifications of water gas, blast-furnace gas, and

Table 10-1. TYPICAL ANALYSES OF VARIOUS FUEL GASES†

Component	Natural gas	Coal gas	Coke oven	Producer gas	Water gas	Carburetted water gas	Lurgi gas	Blast furnace	Sewage gas
CO	...	7.4	5.1	33.5	43.6	35.4	15.0	26.2	...
CO$_2$	1.0	1.2	1.4	1.0	4.0	5.3	31.0	13.0	24.6
H$_2$	...	52.1	57.4	10.5	47.8	40.0	38.0	3.2	...
CH$_4$	85.0	29.2	28.5	2.5	0.3	10.7	13.0	...	73.3
C$_n$H$_m$	14.0^a	7.9^b	2.9^b	...	...	5.4	...	2.9	0.6^c
N$_2$ and O$_2$	...	2.2	4.7	52.5	4.3	3.2	...	57.6	1.5

^{a} C$_2$H$_6$.　　　　　　　　† Percentage by volume.
^{b} C$_2$H$_4$.
^{c} H$_2$S.

sewage gas. The composition of typical examples of these gases is given in Table 10-1.

Coal Gas

A Scot, William Murdoch, while working for a mining company in Cornwall, England, patented in 1791 a process for the production of illuminating gas by distilling coal. He used the gas to light his office and the cottages of the miners. Westminster Bridge and Pall Mall were the first public places lighted by coal gas, in 1807. In America the first city to use the gas for lighting the streets was Baltimore (1817). It was not until the development of the Bunsen burner in 1855 that coal gas was used for heating purposes.

The yield of gas and its composition depend on the temperature of distillation. Thus a coal which gave 3700 cu ft of fuel gas per ton at 600° C produced 13,000 cu ft at 1000° C, while the percentage of hydrogen in the gas increased from 15.7 to 52 per cent. The manufacture of metallurgical coke yields large volumes of excellent fuel gas. The coke ovens pictured in Fig. 5-7 furnish 47 million cubic feet of gas per day with a fuel value of 560

Figure 10-6 Hot coke is discharged from single retorts in succession. The size of the single retort is indicated by comparison with the operator in the cab window. Gaseous products are drawn off the top of the coking retorts. The coke is a raw material for producer gas, water gas, acetylene, and other products. [Courtesy Steel Co. of Canada.]

Btu/cu ft. Figure 10-6 shows the ejection of coke from one unit into a steel car. Retorts are discharged in succession.

Producer Gas

Producer gas, an important fuel, is made by passing wet air through a thick bed of hot coal or coke. The air flow is regulated so that the combustion is restricted to the reaction

$$C + \tfrac{1}{2} O_2 \longrightarrow CO + 4350 \text{ Btu/lb}$$

of coke. Producer gas is therefore chiefly carbon monoxide and nitrogen.

If the fuel bed is thick, carbon dioxide formed at the bottom of the bed will react with hot carbon as it moves upward, and gives carbon monoxide. This reaction absorbs heat, approximately 5900 Btu/lb of reacting coke.

$$C + CO_2 \longrightarrow 2\,CO - 39\,kcal$$

The percentage of carbon dioxide reacting in the equilibrium mixture decreases as the temperature drops. Table 10-2 gives the percentages of the two gases at equilibrium for three different temperatures.

It is obvious that in the producer-gas generator the temperature should be kept around 1050° C or 1920° F.

Producer gas made by the partial oxidation of pure carbon using dry air has a composition 34.7 per cent CO and 65.3 per cent N_2. Analysis of the gas

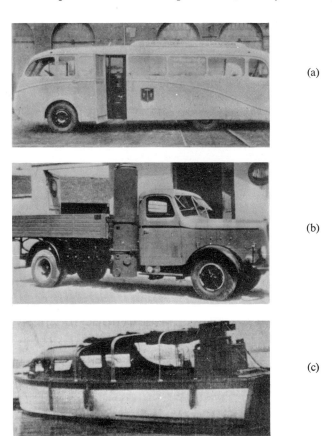

(a)

(b)

(c)

Figure 10-7 (a) French passenger bus; (b) Italian truck [(a) and (b) courtesy of *Industrial and Engineering Chemistry*, **30**, (1938), 1901] (c) Forestry boat. [Courtesy Dept. of Lands and Forests, Ontario.] All these vehicles are powered by producer gas generated from wood or sawdust.

obtained using charcoal gives 33.3 per cent CO, 63.4 per cent N_2, 2.8 per cent H_2, and 0.5 per cent CO_2. From coke, the figures are 33.5 per cent CO, 64.1 per cent N_2, 1.5 per cent H_2, and 0.8 per cent CO_2.

In practice, moist air is used. The water in the saturated air serves to control the temperature by the endothermic reaction,

$$H_2O + C \longrightarrow CO + H_2$$

at the same time providing additional fuel components.

In Britain, the underground gasification of coal is in the pilot plant stage. In this process, boreholes are first sunk to reach the coal seam; then super-heated air is forced down an axial or central tube. The producer gas formed

Table 10-2

Temperature °C	CO %	CO_2 %
450	2.0	98.0
750	76.0	24.0
1050	99.6	0.4

at the coal face flows up the bore hole to the surface. A plant generating 60,000 kw went into operation in 1962. It was designed to convert to gas 400,000 tons of coal from a 3 ft seam, $2\frac{1}{2}$ sq miles in area, annually for thirty years.

Producer gas can be made from waste wood, sawdust, brown coal or peat, natural gas, or oil. During the last war, many buses, cars, trucks, motorcycles, and motorboats were equipped with gas generators to provide producer gas (or water gas) from charcoal or other carbonaceous material, as a substitute for gasoline. Figure 10-7 illustrates typical installations. A diagram of the parts of the gas generator is given in Fig. 10-8.

Water Gas

The reaction involved in the production of water gas is primarily between hot carbon and *steam*.

$$C + H_2O \xrightarrow{900°\,C} CO + H_2 - 28{,}000 \text{ cal/g mole (4200 Btu/lb of C)}$$

This equation indicates that equal volumes of the fuel gases are produced. If, however, the temperature is allowed to fall below 500° C, the reaction between the carbon and steam gives carbon dioxide and hydrogen.

$$C + 2\,H_2O \longrightarrow CO_2 + 2\,H_2 - 19{,}000 \text{ cal/g mol (2850 Btu/lb of C)}$$

Another reaction is involved

$$CO + H_2O \longrightarrow CO_2 + H_2 + 9800 \text{ cal/g mole.}$$

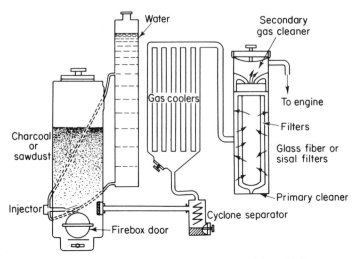

Figure 10-8 Diagram of a gas generator used for vehicles.

The change in composition of the mixed gases with temperature is shown in Fig. 10-9.

The manufacture of water gas is a cyclic process, which is represented diagrammatically in Fig. 10-10. Air is first blown through the coke or other fuel until the temperature of the bed reaches 1200° to 1400° C (2200° to 2550° F). During this time the emerging gases are vented to the stack (#1 in the Fig. 10-10). The air is then stopped, and steam is admitted to the bottom of the fire bed. The stack valve is closed, and the valve to the gas holder opened (#2). The steaming period is divided into up-flow and down or reverse steam (#3) in order to get more uniform reaction and to prevent loss of carbon in the ash. The valves are worked automatically. Steaming continues until the temperature drops to about 800° C. Carman[1] cites a typical schedule: combustion blow, 1 min; up steam run $2\frac{1}{2}$ min; down steam run 1 min; up run purge 10 sec. The air enters at a high velocity, whereas the steam enters at a much lower velocity. About 40 cu ft of air is used for each cubic foot of steam. Both the steam and entering air are preheated by waste heat exchangers.

Carburetted Water Gas

The heating qualities of water gas may be raised by the addition of volatile hydrocarbons. This is done by spraying crude oil into a type of thermal cracking chamber, called a carburetter, during the steaming cycle. The water gas entering the carburetter mixes with the volatilized and low

---

1 P. C. Carman, *The Chemical Constitution and Properties of Engineering Materials* (London: Arnold & Co., 1949).

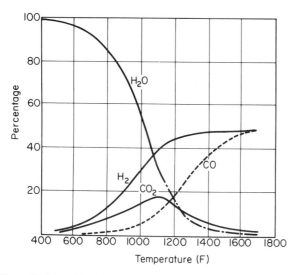

Figure 10-9 Equilibrium concentrations of gases in the reaction of steam and carbon.

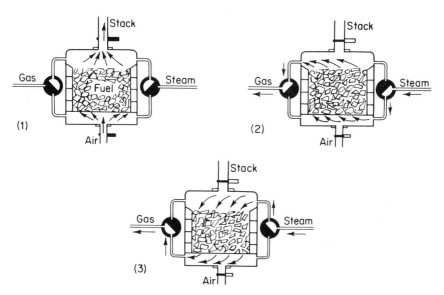

Figure 10-10 The production of water gas: (1) combustion or heating run; (2) steam uprun; (3) steam downrun.

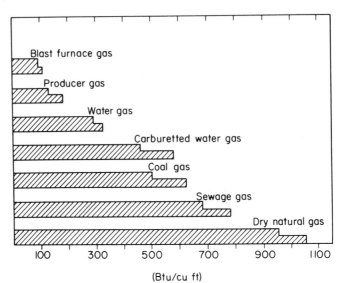

(Btu/cu ft)

Figure 10-11 Heating values of fuel gases.

molecular fractions of the cracked oil to give a gaseous fuel having a caloric value of 500 to 560 Btu/cu ft.

High-Calorie Gas; Lurgi Gas

By using oxygen rather than air, sufficient heat is generated to maintain the water gas reaction as a *continuous process*. Extra steam is used to control the temperature of the fuel bed and to prevent fusion of the ash to the iron grates. A new gasification plant in Australia uses brown coal and oxygen (95 per cent pure) with steam at 28 atm pressure. The resultant fuel gas has a caloric value of 450 Btu/cu ft. In another installation, pulverized or "atomized" coal, oil, or gas is blown by the steam-oxygen mixture into a refractory-lined reaction chamber. These processes make possible the use of lower grade fuel than in the ordinary water gas generator.

Blast Furnace Gas

The smelting of iron consists of the conversion of iron ore, usually iron oxide, to metallic iron by a reducing agent and its separation from the other materials in the blast furnace.

Most of the reduction of the ore is brought about by carbon monoxide

$$3\,CO + Fe_2O_3 \longrightarrow 3\,CO_2 + 2\,Fe^0$$

The carbon monoxide comes from the two reactions represented by the equations.

$$2\,C + O_2 \longrightarrow 2\,CO \quad \text{and} \quad CO_2 + C \longrightarrow 2\,CO$$

Not all of the reducing gas is used, indeed the stack gas is approximately 30 per cent CO, with a small concentration of hydrogen. These give the waste blast furnace gas a heating value of around 100 Btu/cu ft.

Sewage Gas

Sewage gas is produced during the anaerobic digestion of sewage sludge; it contains from 65 to 80 per cent methane and is therefore a good fuel. Many municipalities use it for the generation of electrical power.

A comparison of the heating values of common gaseous fuels is shown in Fig. 10-11.

10-8 Calculation of the Heating
Value of Gaseous Fuels

The heating value of any fuel is normally expressed as cal/g or Btu/lb. If it is a pure substance, the value may be given as cal/g mole or Btu/lb mole. Since cal/g $\times$ 1.8 = Btu/lb,

$$\frac{\text{cal/g-mole} \times 1.8}{\text{molecular weight}} = \text{Btu/lb}$$

For hydrocarbon fuels Kharasch[1] found that the heating value Q, in kg cal/g mole could be approximated by multiplying the number of valence electrons in the molecule by a factor of 26.05. Thus, ethane, C_2H_6 with $8 + 6$ valence electrons, would give an estimated Q of 14×26.05 or 364.7 kg cal/mole. The experimental value is 368.4. The calculated and observed values for a series of paraffins are found in Table 10-3.

Since each successive hydrocarbon in the series contains an additional —CH_2— group which adds six valence electrons to the molecule, the molar heat will increase by increments of 156.3 kg cal. The average increase in the

Table 10-3. Comparison of Heats of Combustion of Alkanes
Q calculated kg cal/g-mole[a]

Substance (Normal)	CH_4	C_2H_6	C_3H_8	C_4H_{10}	C_5H_{12}	C_6H_{14}	C_7H_{16}	C_8H_{18}	C_9H_{20}
Kharasch's formula	208.4	364.7	521.	677	838	991	1146	1303	1459
Observed	210.8	368.4	526.	684	834	990	1149	1305	1456

[a] Kg cal = 1000 (15°) cal.
   K cal = 1000 mean cal = 1000.17 Kg cal. Since these quantities differ by only 0.017% and the heats of combustion are not known with that degree of accuracy, Q values are commonly given as K cal.

1 M. S. Kharasch, and B. Sher, *Journal of Physical Chemistry*, **29** (1925), 625–88.

experimental heats from one hydrocarbon to the next is 155.9 kg cal. The additive effect is also seen in the measured caloric values for primary alcohols, given in Table 10-4.

The heating value may also be estimated from the percentage composition by weight, as with the solid fuels. The values of Q, so calculated for gaseous fuels, are somewhat higher than the experimental values.

EXAMPLE

Ethane, C_2H_6, has a molecular weight of 30. The percentage of carbon is $\frac{24}{30} \times 100 = 80$. The percentage of hydrogen is 20.

$$Q = \frac{14,600 \times \%C + 62,000 \times \%H}{100} = 11,680 + 12,400 = 24,080 \text{ Btu/lb}$$

Table 10-4. EXPERIMENTAL HEATING VALUES FOR SOME PRIMARY ALCOHOLS

Alcohol	Formula	Q, kg cal/mole	Increment	
Methanol	CH_3OH	170.9		
Ethanol	C_2H_5OH	327.6	156.7⎫	
n-Propanol	C_3H_5OH	480.5	152.9⎪	
n-Butanol	C_4H_9OH	638.6	158.1⎬	Average 155.7
n-Pentanol				
(Amyl alcohol)	$C_5H_{11}OH$	793.7	155.1⎭	

The experimental value is 22,280 Btu/lb. Calculated by Kharasch's formula, it is 21,880 Btu/lb.

The Heating Value in Btu/cu ft

One gram molecular weight of a gas occupies 22.4 liters at standard temperature and pressure. It so happens that if one has a molecular weight of the gas in *ounces* (instead of *grams*), it will occupy 22.3 *cubic feet* under the standard conditions. At 60° F, this "ounce molecular volume" is 23.5 cu ft. Heating values of gases are usually given in Btu/cu ft at this temperature. They may be calculated as follows:

Determine the heating value of ethylene in Btu/cu ft at 60° F, if Q/lb is 22,080 Btu. The molecular weight of ethylene, C_2H_4, is 28.

28 oz occupies 23.5 cu ft at 60° F

16 oz occupies $23.5 \times \frac{16}{28}$ cu ft giving 22,080 Btu

1 cu ft of the gas will therefore give

$$\frac{22,080 \times 28}{23.5 \times 16} = 1640 \text{ Btu}$$

In Table 10-1 the composition of representative fuel gases is given as percentage by volume. The heating value of a mixed gas is obtained by summation of the heat evolved by the given amounts of the components. The heat of combustion of carbon monoxide is 323.6 Btu/cu ft; hydrogen gives 324.5 Btu/cu ft; methane gives 1012 Btu/cu ft, and ethane, 1762.

EXAMPLE

Calculate the heating value of the coal gas listed in Table 10-1. One hundred cu ft of the gas contains:

$$
\begin{array}{lll}
7.4 \text{ cu ft of CO} & \text{to yield} & 7.4 \times 323.6 = 2,386 \text{ Btu} \\
52.1 \text{ cu ft of H}_2 & \text{to yield} & 52.1 \times 324.5 = 16,900 \\
29.2 \text{ cu ft of CH}_4 & \text{to yield} & 29.2 \times 1012 = 29,550 \\
7.9 \text{ cu ft of C}_2\text{H}_4 & \text{to yield} & 7.9 \times 1640 = \underline{1,296} \\
& & 50,132
\end{array}
$$

or 501 Btu/cu ft.

Percentage by volume may be converted to percentage by weight. Thus for the sewage gas in Table 10-1, the composition may also be expressed as 46.7 per cent CO_2, 50.6 per cent CH_4, 0.9 per cent H_2S, and 1.8 per cent N_2 by weight.

10-9 Oxygen Requirements

The oxygen necessary for combustion is determined by use of equations for the combustion reactions.

Air contains 21 per cent oxygen by volume, or 23.3 per cent by weight. The volume or mass of air necessary to burn a given amount of fuel can be calculated from the corresponding oxygen requirement. For example, what volume of air is necessary for the combustion of 1000 cu ft of a sewage gas which contains 73.3 per cent CH_4 and 0.6 per cent H_2S by volume?

(a) $$CH_4 + 2 O_2 \longrightarrow CO_2 + 2 H_2O$$

(b) $$2 H_2S + 3 O_2 \longrightarrow 2 SO_2 + 2 H_2O$$

In 1000 cu ft there are 733 cu ft of CH_4 which require 1466 cu ft of oxygen. In 1000 cu ft there are 6 cu ft of H_2S which require 9 cu ft of oxygen.

$$
\begin{array}{l}
\text{Total} = 1475 \text{ cu ft of oxygen} \\
 = 1475 \times \frac{100}{21} \text{ cu ft of air} = 7024 \text{ cu ft of air}
\end{array}
$$

10-10 Flame Speed and Explosive Limits

Two important factors in the use of fuel gases and vapors are flame speed and "explosive limits." A flame is a zone of combining gas giving out light and heat.

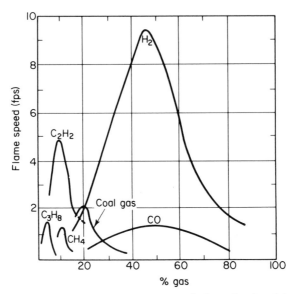

Figure 10-12 Flame speeds *vs* per cent fuel gas in air mixture.

Flame speed is the distance the flame front travels per second in an open tube containing the combustible mixture. Ignition of gas in an enclosed space causes increasing pressure. The explosion time is the time required for the flame to spread through the whole volume. The speed of combustion depends on the nature of the fuel, the temperature and concentration of the gas, and certain surface characteristics. Figure 10-12 shows the flame speed of various gases.

Table 10-5. EXPLOSIVE LIMITS OF SOME GASES AND VAPORS IN AIR AS VOLUME PER CENT

Substance	Per cent	Substance	Per cent
Acetaldehyde	4–57	Gasoline	1.3–6
Acetylene	22.5–80	Hexane	1.2–6.9
Benzene	1.4–8	Hydrogen	4.1–74
Blast-furnace gas	35–74	Methane	5.3–14
Butane	1.8–8.4	Methanol	7.3–36
Carbon monoxide	12.5–74.2	Methyl chloride	10.7–17.4
City gas	5–31	*n*-Octane	0.8–3.2
Cyclohexane	1.3–8.3	Pentane	1.4–7.8
Ethane	3.2–12.5	Producer gas	35–75
Ethanol	3.3–19	Propane	2.8–9.5
Ethylene	3–29	Propylene	2–11
Ethyl ether	1.9–48	Water gas	(6–9)–(55–70)

It is a common observation that if a gasoline-air mixture is too "rich," the engine is choked and "killed." Combustion will also cease if the mixture becomes "too lean." There are definite limits of concentration outside of which no rapid combustion takes place. These explosive or explosion limits vary markedly with the chemical composition of the gas or vapor. The explosive limits for a number of gases and vapors are shown in Table 10-5 and Fig. 10-13. It will be noted that almost any mixture of acetylene or hydrogen with air will explode, whereas propane gas will not form an explosive mixture with air if the concentration of the gas is greater than 9.5 per cent or lower than 2.4 per cent by volume.

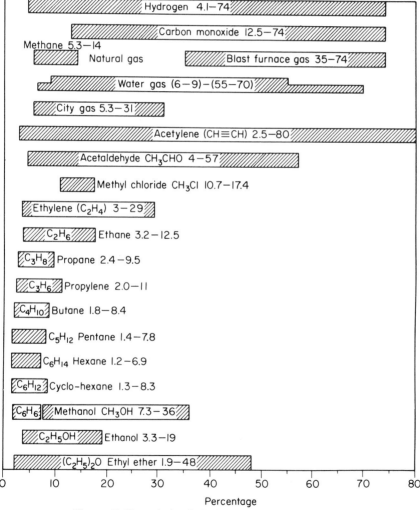

Figure 10-13 Explosive limits in air (% by volume).

The limits of concentration which define the flammability also depend on temperature, pressure, and sometimes on the shape, dimensions, and nature of the containing vessel. Figure 10-14 shows how the explosion limits of carbon monoxide and hydrogen widen with an increase in temperature.

The tendency of a gas to give an explosion depends on its ignition temperature, its flame speed, and the explosive limits. The design of the burner for a gaseous fuel depends on the factors mentioned above. The flame stays at the top of the burner tube when the rate of combustion or flame speed is

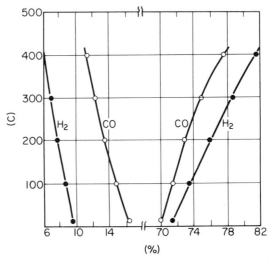

Figure 10-14 The effect of temperature on the explosive limits of hydrogen and carbon monoxide (downward propagation of flame). (Data from H. F. Coward and G. W. Jones, *U.S. Bureau of Mines Bulletin* 279.)

equal to the linear rate of flow of the gas in the tube. Flame height depends on the rate ratio.

If the flow of gas is reduced so that the velocity becomes less than the flame velocity, the burner "strikes back," the flame moving down the burner tube to the jet in the base. There, because of the smaller opening, the gas has a much higher velocity, and the flame persists.

Because of its relatively low combustion velocity, a propane flame is more easily "blown off" the burner than a flame of water gas or coal gas. Because of its narrow combustion limits, the propane flame is also easily extinguished by improper adjustment of the burner. In changing from manufactured or "city gas" to propane or natural gas, adjustments of the jet orifice and air inlet of the burner must be made.

Flame temperatures depend on the caloric value of the fuel, on the combustion rate, and radiation losses.

All tanks or other spaces which contain combustible gases or low-boiling liquids should be tested before welding or cutting by torch is permitted. The explosimeter is an instrument for the detection of combustible gases or vapors, and the measurement of their concentration. A sample of the atmosphere in the tank or space under test is pumped through the instrument, where it comes in contact with a heated filament. Any combustible gas is burned catalytically on the surface of the wire, and the change in conductance of the wire in a balanced bridge arrangement is used to measure the relative concentration of the gas. Dangerous or explosive concentrations are indicated on the instrument scale. Mobile units for detecting leaks in gas mains employ infra-red spectrometers. Continuous sampling of the air near the road surface is obtained through "sniffer" tubes. The spectrometer contains two identical infra-red sources and two gas cells, one of which holds a standard sample

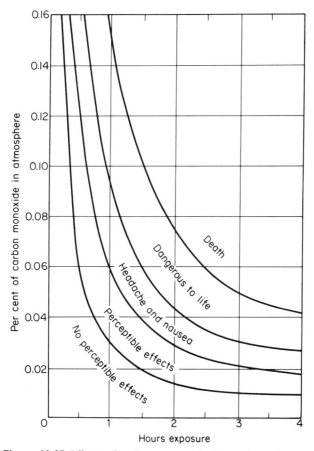

Figure 10-15 Effects of carbon monoxide for a given time on human beings. [Data from Bureau of Standards Tech. Paper 212.]

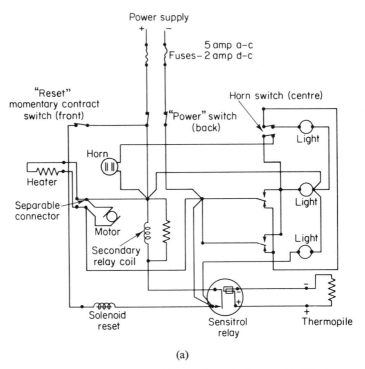

(a)

Figure 10-16 A schematic diagram (a) and photograph (b) of a carbon monoxide alarm, which gives prompt warning when CO reaches a concentration as low as 0.02 per cent. [Courtesy Mine Safety Appliance Co.]

of the comparative gas. When the air sample enters the second cell, any gas present absorbs some of the infra-red of the second source. The two transmitted beams are unequal in energy and the variation generates an electric signal which is related to the concentration of the gas component of the sample.

Concentrations of carbon monoxide much below the minimum explosive limit are dangerous because of the toxicity of the gas. Even very low concentrations are harmful if the exposure to the gas is prolonged. Figure 10-15 indicates the relation of the exposure period and concentration to the toxic effect. The exhaust from internal combustion engines contains appreciable quantities of carbon monoxide, which constitutes a health hazard in many commercial garages. The gas can diffuse through hot iron. Appreciable quantities of carbon monoxide can spread by diffusion or through leaks into furnace rooms, cars, trucks, inboard motorboats, and other enclosed spaces.

Some instruments for determining carbon monoxide are based on the

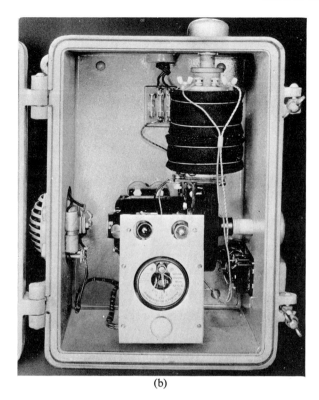

(b)

combustion principle (see Figure 10-16 a-b). The gas is burned in a catalyst tube, the resulting rise in temperature being measured by thermocouples. A typical instrument of this type detects concentrations from 0.02 to 0.150 per cent $\pm$ 0.001 per cent.

Another instrument determines the CO colorimetrically, use being made of the reaction between the gas and a silico-molybdate. Air is drawn through silica gel impregnated with the yellow reactant, which changes to various shades of green depending on the amount of CO. The concentration is determined by comparison with a given color chart. Safety discs which change color if carbon monoxide is present have been devised for use in trucks and cars. The molybdate tester will detect 0.001 per cent CO.

Review Questions

1. Name two ways by which the heat value of hydrocarbon gases may be calculated.

2. Use each of the methods to calculate the caloric value of octane.

3. Determine the Btu/cu ft of propane gas at 60° F and the Btu/lb of liquefied gas.

4. What volume of air is required to burn a gallon of hexane (sp gr 0.6630)?

5. Calculate the heating value of ethanol from the percentage composition as indicated by the formula.

6. The sp gr of ethanol is 0.7893. Which would supply the more energy; a gallon of ethanol or a gallon of hexane?

7. If the heats of combustion of carbon monoxide, hydrogen, and methane are 343, 344 and 1068 Btu/cu ft respectively, calculate the heating value of the water gas and Lurgi gas given in Table 10-1.

8. What is the theoretical weight of steam necessary to convert one ton of coke containing 2 per cent ash into water gas at 900° C?

9. Comment on the statement "Natural gas is more explosive than manufactured gas."

10. Write equations for the recovery of sulfur from natural gas.

11. What burner adjustments would have to be made in changing from a carburetted gas to natural gas?

Further Readings

Carman, P., *Chemical Constitution and Properties of Engineering Materials* (London: Ed. Arnold, 1949).

Goldstein, R., *The Petroleum Chemicals Industry* (2 ed.; London: Spon, Ltd., 1956).

Purdy, G., *Petroleum* (Toronto: Copp Clark, 1958).

Also see current issues of *Industrial and Engineering Chemistry, Oil and Gas Journal, Chemical and Engineering News, Chemical Age,* and *Journal of Applied Chemistry.*

11

Atmospheric Pollution

11-1 Air Pollution

The products of oxidation from the combustion of fuels are usually discharged into the atmosphere. Although in rural areas this presents no problem, in urban centers this practice causes serious pollution of the air.

Air pollution is not a new problem. In 1661, John Evelyn published a treatise on "The Smoake of London." The title page, Fig. 11-1, carries a quotation from Lucretius (97–53 B.C.) which indicates that even 2000 years ago smoke nuisance was not unknown. Seneca (4 B.C.–65 A.D.), a Roman Stoic, was not very stoical regarding air pollution. In a letter to a friend he wrote, "As soon as I got away from the stench of the smoky chimneys [of Rome] which poured forth whatever pestilent vapors and soot they held in them, I felt a change in my disposition" (for the better). Sixteen centuries later John Evelyn complained, "the cole Smoake from Brewers, Limeburners, Salt and Sope-Boylers and other private trades does manifestly infest the Aer . . . , Sullies all her [London's] Glories, superinducing a Sooty Crust or Furr upon all that it lights, soyling the Moveables, tarnishing the Plate, Gildings and Furniture and corroding the very Iron-Bars and hardest Stones . . . , corrupting the Lungs, so that Catharrs, Coughs and Consumptions rage more in this one city than in the whole earth besides."

Evelyn's treatise was rediscovered a hundred years later and reprinted in 1772. Apparently nothing had been done during the intervening century;

F U M I F U G I U M:

O R,

The Inconvenience of the A E R,

A N D

S M O A K E of L O N D O N

D I S S I P A T E D.

TOGETHER

With fome R E M E D I E S humbly propofed

By J. E. Efq;

To His Sacred M A J E S T I E,

A N D

To the P A R L I A M E N T now Affembled.

Publifhed by His Majefties Command.

Lucret. l. 5.

Carbonumque gravis vis, atque odor infinuatur
Quam facile in cerebrum?———

L O N D O N:

Printed by W. G O D B I D, for G A B R I E L B E D E L, and T H O M A S
C O L L I N S ; and are to be fold at their Shop at the Middle
Temple Gate, neer Temple Bar. M.DC.LXI.
Re-printed for B. W H I T E, at Horace's Head, in Fleet-ftreet.
M DCC LXXII.

Figure 11-1 Title page from J. Evelyn F.R.S., *The Smoake of London*. [Courtesy A. E. Gunther and the University Press, Oxford.] The Latin quotation is from the Roman poet Lucretius, 97–53 B.C. It may be translated, "How easily the heavy potency of carbons and odors sneaks into the brain!" The title of his didactic poem, *De Rerum Natura* (Concerning the Nature of Things) is not inappropriate to our present studies.

indeed, conditions were worse. The editor of the reprinted edition states in his preface, "Since his time we have a great increase in Foundries, Sugar-bakers, Glass-houses to add to the black catalogue, at the head of which must be placed the Water Works which leaves the astonished spectator at a loss to determine whether they do not tend to poison and destroy more inhabitants by their Smoke and Stench than they supply with water."

Aerosols

Any suspension of colloidal or near-colloidal particles in a gas is called an *aerosol*. The particles may be liquid, as in mist, fog, clouds, or haze; or solids, as fumes, dust, fly-ash, or solar smoke. Gases mix with the air, are dissolved in liquid droplets, or are adsorbed on the surface of the sus-pended particles. Aerosols differ in several respects from other colloidal dispersions or sols. These differences are of importance in the destruc-tion or stabilization of smoke, smog and fumes.

1. In an aqueous sol or colloidal solution, the particles all carry the same kind of charge. In an aerosol some of the particles may be positive, some negative, and some may be uncharged.

2. Aerosol particles are suspended in a low-viscosity medium and have longer "mean free paths" than other colloidal suspensions. An average smoke particle settles 4 in./hr in still air.

3. The optical and thermal properties of aerosols are distinctive. The particles in some aerosols move toward the light; in others, the particles move away from the source of illumination. This phenomenon is called photo-phoresis. Soot and other solids, such as iron dust, dyes, such as methylene blue, and even solar or cosmic dust move away from the light. Some smoke, for example, cigarette smoke, aerosols containing transparent liquid droplets, sulfur and selenium aerosols, and others, move toward the incident beam. The photophoresis of a carbon black aerosol is so marked that the smoke can be made to flow around corners by subjecting it to cross lighting.

4. All aerosols are repelled by a hot object, but tend to adhere to a cold surface. This can be seen from the pattern of deposited dust and dirt on interior walls of a building. When a room is warmed by heating the air, the dust collects on the cooler furniture. If radiant heating is used, the objects in the room are warmer than the air and there is less tendency for dust to settle.

5. The particles in an aerosol adsorb and concentrate gases and vapors on their surface. A liter of acetylene black may only contain 50 ml of solid carbon. The particles are separated by thick cushions of adsorbed air.

Smoke

Smoke is an aerosol produced by incomplete combustion. It varies in composition and properties with the fuel and oxidation conditions. Smoke from a domestic fire is quite different from the smoke of a mechanically fired industrial plant. Cigarette smoke is largely a suspension of liquid droplets, aqueous solutions, oils, and tars. Soft coal and heavy oils, when burned with insufficient oxygen, produce the dirtiest and most corrosive type of smoke. The large particles of soot adsorb moisture and acid gases amounting to 15 per cent of their weight.

The complex aerosol known as smoke may contain toxic gases, carbon monoxide and hydrogen sulfide under poor oxidizing conditions, and sulfur

Table 11-1. FUEL CONTRIBUTION TO ATMOSPHERIC POLLUTION IN METROPOLITAN TORONTO, 1958[a]

Fuel	Amount used	SO_2	Fly-ash	Smoke	
Coal	Tons	Tons	Tons	Tons	%
Bituminous	500,000	20,000	1,750	500	0.5
	60,000	2,400	2,100	3,000	3.0
	1,000,000	40,000	500	25,000	26.5
Anthracite	110,000	550	100	550	0.5
Oil	Imp gallons $\times 10^6$				
Heavy fuel oil	92	17,400	1,750	14,500	15.5
Medium	19	1,600	...	1,400	1.5
Domestic	340	28,000	...	46,300	50.0
Diesel	16.5	350	...	1,200	1.0
Gasoline	286	5,700	...	?	
Lube oils	1			1,500	1.5
Total annual pollution, tons		116,000	6,200	93,950	100.0

[a] From a report by the Board of Works, Industrial Waste Conference, June 15, 1958.

dioxide and trioxide, oxides of nitrogen and carbon dioxide in normal combustion, as well as unsaturated hydrocarbon vapors and droplets, aldehydes, peroxides, tars, organic acids, soot, dust, fly-ash, and other solids.

Table 11-1 shows approximate amounts of three types of pollutants introduced into the Toronto atmosphere in 1958. These figures were calculated from the known amounts of the different types of fuel used, the average sulfur content of each type, and from experimental studies of smoke production. The table contains no estimate of other common contaminants, nor does it include the amounts of fumes, dusts, and other aerosols from industry. It is obvious that the total pollution when nonfuel sources are considered will be in excess of these amounts.

The deposition of contaminants from the air amounts to 45 tons/sq mile/

month in Toronto. Table 11-2 gives figures for some other North American cities, as cited by M. Katz. While improvement has been reported in some areas, heavy contamination of urban atmosphere is still present.

Table 11-2. AEROSOL PRECIPITATION
tons/mi²/month

Chicago	61.2	Los Angeles	33[a]
Detroit (1953)	72.1	Pittsburgh[b]	45.7
New York (1953)	67.5	Windsor, Ont.[c]	64

[a] Pollution Control Los Angeles District Report 1961 gives 20 to 36.9 as the 1957 range of mean values for the area.
[b] Insolubles only.
[c] Found to contain 18 different metals.

The aerosol formed by the reaction of some of the components of smoke with fog or water vapor has been dubbed *smog*. It reduces visibility and cuts off the ultra-violet radiation. It causes eye and throat irritation. In the prolonged spell of smog in London in 1952, health authorities attributed the death of some 4000 people to lung congestion aggravated or induced by the smog. Figure 11-2 shows the greatly increased death rate following the onset of the smog and the very slow return towards normal values. Pollution of the air and smog caused many deaths in the Meuse Valley, Belgium, in 1930 and in Denora, Pa., in 1948.

The Air Pollution Board of Los Angeles County has found that the

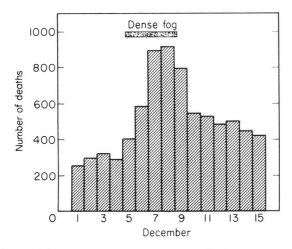

Figure 11-2 Deaths in Greater London each day from December 1 to 15, 1952. Some 4000 deaths were attributed to the dense four-day fog. [Courtesy *Industrial and Engineering Chemistry* **45**, No. 5 (1953),105A.]

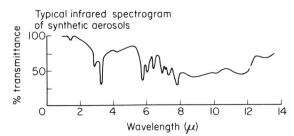

(a)

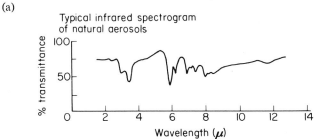

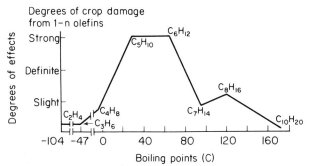

(b)

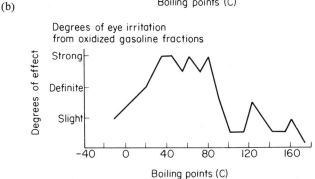

Figure 11-3 (a) Comparison of synthetic and natural ether-soluble aerosols; (b) comparison of the effect of various compounds in motor exhaust on eye irritation and crop damage. [Courtesy of the Los Angeles Air Pollution Control Officer.]

automobile is the chief source of the smog in that area. Doubtless, the automotive and diesel engine are important contributing factors in the air pollution of any city. In 1951 chemists succeeded in duplicating in the laboratory the smog which plagues the city at times. The "artificial" and "natural" aerosols were shown by infrared-spectroanalysis to be very similar (Fig. 11-3a). Studies on the effects of individual components of the synthetic smog indicated that there was a close correlation between eye irritation and the concentration of certain unsaturated hydrocarbons which are found in automobile exhaust fumes. The same substances also cause crop damage (Fig. 11-3b). The investigators found that organic peroxides, ozone, nitrogen oxides, and other oxidation products also cause tissue irritation and the deterioration of rubber, textiles, and paint films. Table 11-3 gives a proximate analysis of the contaminating gases or vapors in downtown Los Angeles' atmosphere on a clear day when the visibility was seven miles, and on a day when smog reduced the visibility to one mile.

Table II-3

Pollutant	Concentration in p.p.m., i.e., cc vapor/cu meter		
	Clear day	Hazy day	Increase
Carbon monoxide	3.5	23.0	× 6.5
Hydrocarbons	0.2	1.1	× 5.5
Peroxides	0.1	0.5	× 5.0
Oxides of nitrogen	0.08	0.4	× 5.0
Lower aldehydes	0.07	0.4	× 6.0
Ozone	0.06	0.3	× 5.0
Sulfur dioxide	0.05	0.3	× 6.0

There are other kinds of smoke, such as chemical smoke or fumes, and smokes produced for military purposes, for example, black smoke screen from banked or low air combustion of fuel oil, stannic or titanium tetrachloride, oleum, silicocalcium $CaSi_2$, zinc and hexachlorethane, and so on.

Many cities and municipalities have bylaws which forbid the emission of "dense" smoke for more than a very brief period. A dense smoke is defined by the United States Weather Bureau as one which obscures objects 100 feet away. A light smoke is one which obscures the distant view but not near objects. A better method of determining smoke density is by *Ringelmann numbers*, as illustrated in Fig. 11-4. A No. 1 smoke cuts out 20 per cent of the incident light; No. 2 smoke cuts off 40 per cent of the light; No. 3 smoke, 60 per cent; and No. 4, 80 per cent or more. Photoelectric devices and extinctometers may also be used to determine the exact percentage of the light transmitted through the smoke.

Accurate measurements of smoke density are expressed as the reciprocal

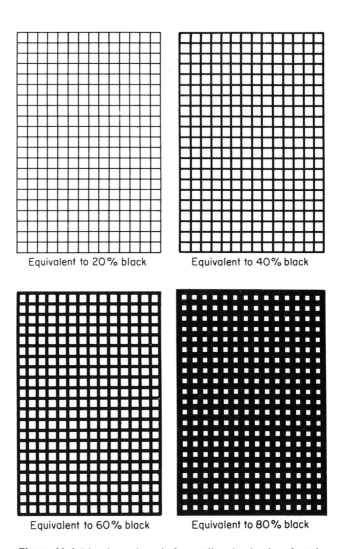

Figure 11-4 Ringelmann's scale for grading the density of smoke (reduced above to about one-fourth normal size) is hung on a level with the eye, about 50 ft from observer, as nearly as possible in line with chimney. Observer glances from smoke to chart and notes corresponding number. No smoke is recorded as No. 0; 100 per cent black smoke as No. 5. (Further information available in U.S. Dept. of Interior Bureau of Mines Circular 6888.)

of the depth of smoke necessary to obscure the filament of a standard 40 watt lamp. Thus if a 1 ft layer of smoke just obscures the filament, the density index is 1. If a thickness of 2 ft in the layer of smoke is necessary, the index is 0.5. For evaluating smoke-producing chemicals, the smoke density is multiplied by the number of cubic feet of smoke produced per pound of material. This is called the Total Obscuring Power. Chemicals for producing smoke screens should have a high TOP.

Prevention and Cure of Air Pollution

Much of the pollution of city air could be prevented by proper combustion methods. Even tar and rubber can be burned without smoke. To establish proper combustion conditions, the proportions of air and vaporized fuel must be regulated. In addition there are four factors which may be controlled to give smokeless combustion. These are temperature, time, turbulence, and treatment of the issuing gases. A high *temperature* makes for rapid oxidation. The *time* of sojourn of the vapors in the high-temperature region should be as long as possible. Hence a long fire chamber is desirable. *Turbulence* increases the chance of the hot gases and any suspended particles coming into intimate contact with the hot oxygen. If these three conditions are met, the exhaust gases will not contain any unburned combustible matter. Smokeless incinerators are based on these principles. Suspended particles, ash, salts, or droplets of acids in smoke can be removed by *treatment* based on the properties of aerosols. Furthermore, dusts and fumes from smelters, cement plants, metal fabricators, and so on, may be prevented from contaminating the atmosphere. Their removal is brought about by the following:

1. Electrostatic precipitation, for example, Cottrell (Figs. 11-5 and 5-5).

2. Filtration, for example, glass fiber or silicone-treated textile bags for hot exhaust gases, or other textiles or felts for cold aerosols (Fig. 11-6).

3. Centrifugal separators. In these the fast-moving effluent suspension is made to change direction, and the particles are thrown to the wall by centrifugal force. Such an installation is used to separate fine particles of catalyst from exhaust gases of a cat-cracker regenerator. A mechanical separator for removing fly-ash is indicated in Fig. 5-5.

4. Mutual precipitation or solution by spray treatment. This method is utilized by the petroleum industry, where the smoke from a waste gas burner is suppressed by several small spray nozzles set a few inches above the tip of the burner.[1]

5. Ultrasonic vibration. Ultrahigh-frequency vibrations cause increased collisions and adherence of the suspended particles.

The elimination of the smog-producing products from the exhaust of millions of motor vehicles is a more difficult problem. Indeed, this source of pollution is growing year by year. It has been found that more unburned

---

1 C. F. Daly, *Industrial and Engineering Chemistry* **48,** 2 (1956) 101A.

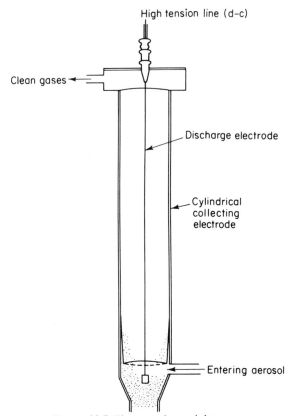

Figure 11-5 Electrostatic precipitator.

or partially burned hydrocarbons are emitted during deceleration than in other phases of driving. Several devices have been designed to cut off the fuel during deceleration, but none has proved entirely satisfactory. Afterburners, in which any combustible products are reignited and burned, are more successful, particularly for local buses. Such vehicles operate for a greater portion of their driving time on the deceleration, idling, and acceleration cycles than do automobiles.

Low-temperature catalytic reburners, although still expensive ($175.00 to $200.00) may eventually prove to be the solution to the elimination of smog-producing exhaust. One of the difficulties in the development of this type of burner has been the poisoning effect of the lead compounds from the gasoline on the catalyst. Buses and trucks in Los Angeles are now required to install afterburners. These are reported to be 95 per cent efficient.

Research and control of fuel composition, the addition of smoke-reducing additives (see Diesel Fuels), the reduction of nitrogen oxides, and other factors may further speed the elimination of smog from our cities.

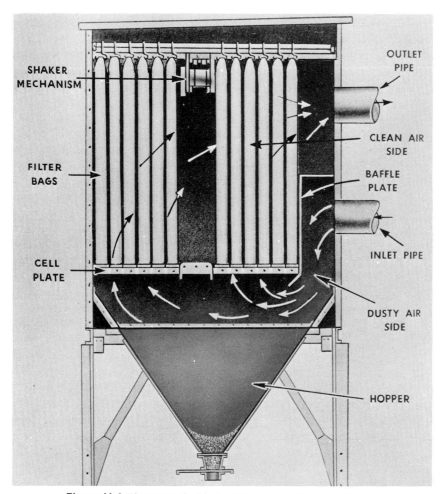

Figure 11-6 The removal of industrial dusts by filtration. [Courtesy American Wheelatrator and Equipment Co.]

11-2 Explosive Aerosols

Various metal dusts (for example, aluminum, magnesium, zinc, iron, and titanium), wheat dust, flour, starch, bakelite and other resins and plastics, lignin, wood dust, oil mist, and lacquer spray have been the source of many expensive and often fatal explosions. A published summary records 840 such explosions in 20 different industries, resulting in 541 deaths, 1294 persons injured, and plant damage of over $73 million.

The tendency for a dust suspension to explode depends on its chemical nature, its ignition temperature, the concentration and size of the particle, and the relative humidity. For a nitrocellulose dust the ignition temperature is relatively low, and its minimum explosive concentration is only 24 mg/1. The flame velocity for an aluminum dust has been reported as 265 cm/sec. This is of the same order as that for a mixture of hydrogen and air. For a lignin aerosol the velocity was 190 cm/sec.

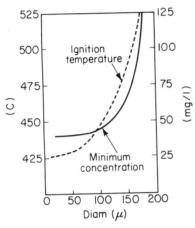

Figure 11-7 The effect of particle size on the ignition temperature and the critical or minimum concentration of starch dust to give an explosion.

Below certain sizes the ignition temperature depends more on the nature of the material than on particle diameter. Coarser dispersions require higher temperatures. The relation of particle size to ignition temperature and the critical concentration at which a starch dust will explode is shown in Fig. 11-7.

High humidity decreases the explosibility of the aerosol. The adsorbed water vapor demands an increased amount of heat to raise the particles to the ignition point. Moisture tends to dissipate static electricity produced by the movement of the aerosol particles.

The minimum energy required of an electric spark to start combustion also depends on the factors listed above.

Noncombustible dusts may decrease the tendency of a mixture of gases or an aerosol to burn explosively by terminating any energy chains and blocking the chain reaction. This is the reason for placing rock dust on ledges and shelves in coal mines. Any minor "bump" would dislodge the dust and prevent a major secondary blast. However a noncombustible dust may act as a catalyst for some gaseous reactions, for example, platinum dust for hydrogen and oxygen, or hydrogen-air mixtures.

Dust explosions may occur in gas mains. The particles, which become charged as they flow along, have been identified as FeO, free sulfur, tar, and oil droplets. Some dusts in gas mains are due to corrosion of the steel pipes by water vapor, hydrogen sulfide, and oxygen in the gas.

Dust explosions may be prevented by good housekeeping in the plant, by adequate ventilation and dust collection, by grounding all grinding equipment, and by the exclusion of flames or conditions which might produce a spark in the presence of any such aerosol.

Aerosols from Cans

Many substances can be applied more conveniently and efficiently in the form of an aerosol than by "bulk" methods. Pressurized containers which produce an aerosol on the sudden release of the propellant gas, are now made by the millions. The greater proportion of these contain cosmetic products or insecticides. In 1961, lacquers, enamels, and other protective coatings amounted to 77 million units. Penetrating lubricants, anti-foamers, special cleaners, fire extinguishers, and many other products of interest to the engineer, marketed as a miscellaneous group of push-button aerosols, amounted to 42 million cans. By 1962 sales in Canada and the United States totalled over 870 million units. It is predicted that more than a billion units will be used in 1964.

Review Questions

1. Indicate the correct statement: The air over metropolitan Toronto is polluted by sulfur dioxide in amounts averaging 95,000 lb, 950,000 lb, 9,500 lb per day.

2. Define smog, mist, fog, fly-ash, haze, radioactive fallout, cloud.

3. Why is the sky blue? What makes distant green hills appear blue or purple?

4. What is the Dorn effect? Where is it important?

5. Why are aerosols of certain dusts explosive?

6. Indicate the effect of particle size on (a) the ignition temperature, (b) the increase in pressure on combustion, (c) the ease of ignition by a spark.

7. What are some of the components of exhaust fumes which cause smog?

8. Indicate the effect of moisture on (a) the corrosive effect of soot, (b) the explosion of a dust suspension.

9. What is the chemical nature of the corrosion product when copper corrodes in moist air (a) containing CO_2, (b) SO_2, (c) near the sea?

10. In what ways may auto fumes be eliminated?

11. What is the nature of fallout?

12. How can fallout be dealt with?

13. Explain Ringelmann's numbers.

14. A certain military screening reagent gives 2000 cu ft of smoke per pound with a density of 2.5. What is its total obscuring power (TOP)?

Further Readings

Evelyn, J., *The Smoake of London* (Oxford: Ashmolean Reprint VIII).

Faith, W., "Air Pollution Review," *Industrial and Engineering Chemistry*, **52** (1960), 967.

Green, H., and Lane, W., *Particulate Clouds: Dusts, Smokes and Mists* (London: E. & F. N. Spon, Ltd., 1957).

Katz, M., "Atmospheric Pollution and Its Control, *Water and Sewage*, **87** (1949), 29.

Magill, P., Holden, F., and Ackley, C., *Air Pollution Handbook* (New York: McGraw-Hill, 1956).

Air Pollution and Smog (San Marino, Cal.: The Air Pollution Foundation, 1960).

"Symposium on Air Pollution Control," *Industrial and Engineering Chemistry*, **47** (1955), 931–81.

12

Power from Nuclear Fuels

12-1 Nuclear Fission

It is assumed that the reader is familiar with the general structure of the atom, isotopes, and the changes that take place during the natural decay of radioactive atoms.

Nuclear reactors for the production of power are at present based on the energy released by the disappearance of mass during the splitting or fission of certain heavy nuclei. The amount of energy obtained can be calculated from the Einstein equation $E_{ergs} = mC^2$, where m is the mass in grams "lost" or converted into energy during fission, and C is the velocity of light.

The history of artificial or induced disintegration of matter may be considered to have begun in 1919 when Sir E. Rutherford knocked H out of nitrogen by using alpha particles as projectiles. The equation for the reaction may be written:

$$_7N^{14} + {_2}He^4 \longrightarrow {_1}H^1 + {_8}O^{17} \tag{1}$$

$$\begin{array}{cccc} \text{Nitrogen} & \alpha\text{-particle} & \text{Proton or} & \text{Isotope of} \\ & & \text{H nucleus} & \text{oxygen} \end{array}$$

Neutrons, the projectiles responsible for the fission of nuclear fuels, were discovered in 1932. They too can be obtained by bombardment of certain light elements with α-particles, for example,

$$_4Be^9 + {_2}He^4 \longrightarrow {_6}C^{12} + {_0}n^1 \tag{2}$$

$$_3Li^7 + {_2}He^4 \longrightarrow {_5}B^{10} + {_0}n^1 \tag{3}$$

Neutrons, being uncharged, can approach and penetrate the positively charged nucleus of the target atom more easily than can an alpha particle. The probability of a neutron being absorbed or scattered or deflected depends on a quantity called the *cross section*, which is related to the apparent target diameter, and inversely to the neutron velocity. The rate of absorption of neutrons is determined by the cross section and the neutron "flux"; the latter is defined as $_0n^1/cm^3/sec$.

When a neutron enters the nucleus, it forms an isotope of the target atom with a weight number one unit greater. The new isotope may be unstable and decompose by ejecting a proton, an alpha or beta particle, an additional neutron, or if the nucleus is very large, it may explode into two or more nuclear fragments representing other elements, as shown by equations (4) to (8),

$$_{11}Na^{23} + _0n^1 \longrightarrow _1H^1 + _{10}Ne^{23} \tag{4}$$

$$_{19}K^{39} + _0n^1 \longrightarrow 2\ _0n^1 + _{19}K^{38} \tag{5}$$

Reaction (5) is remarkable in that the return in neutrons is double the expenditure.

Natural uranium, element 92, is a very large, heavy element. It is a mixture of three isotopes, 99.27 per cent having mass 238, 0.72 per cent U^{235}, the other isotope, 234, being present in a few parts per million. When a neutron enters the nucleus of U^{235}, disruption or splitting of the nucleus occurs, with the production of two heavy fragments and an average of 2.5 neutrons. In the disintegration, a portion of the mass is converted to energy.

The fragments are not always the same—in fact fission of different U^{235} atoms may yield 20 to 30 varieties of progeny. However 99 per cent of these fission products fall into two groups; one of the resulting atoms will have a mass number between 85 and 105, and a second product will have a mass number between 130 and 150, that is,

$$_{92}U^{235} + _0n^1 \longrightarrow A^{85-105}B^{130-150}1 - 3\ _0n^1 + 200\ Mev \tag{6}$$

e.g.,
$$\longrightarrow _{36}Kr^{90} + _{56}Ba^{144} + 2\ _0n^1 + energy \tag{7}$$

or
$$\longrightarrow _{38}Sr^{95} + _{54}Xe^{139} + 2\ _0n^1 + energy \tag{8}$$

The initial products form new products by radioactive decay. Thus

$$_{54}Xe^{139} \xrightarrow{\beta} _{55}Cs^{139} \xrightarrow{\beta} _{56}Ba^{139} \xrightarrow{\beta} _{57}La^{139}$$

and $_{38}Sr^{95}$ undergoes four successive beta-ray emissions becoming molybdenum, $_{42}Mo^{95}$.

Physicists usually express the energy released in Mev, million electron volts. An electron volt (ev) is the energy required to raise an electron through a potential of 1 volt. One Mev $= 1.601 \times 10^{-6}$ erg. Einstein's equation gives the energy in ergs. When the mass transformed is 1 gram,

$$E = (2.99776 \times 10^{10}\ cm/sec)^2 = 8.978 \times 10^{20}\ ergs$$

In the fission of 1 lb of U^{235} (about 1 cu in. of metal), energy equivalent to approximately 3.6×10^{10} Btu, or 9.1×10^{12} cal, is released. Expressed in other units this is 1.0×10^7 kwhr, or 2.8×10^{13} ft lb.

Calculation of the energy obtained, may be made by use of the data in Table 12-1.

Assuming that fission of U^{235} followed equation (8), giving the final products $_{57}La^{139} + _{38}Sr^{95} + 2\ _0n^1$, the loss in mass comes to 0.22507 amu. This is 0.953 per cent of the reactants, or 9.57 g per 1000 g of U^{235}. Since the

Table 12-1

Particle	Atomic mass units[a]	Particle	Atomic mass units[a]
Electron, $_1e^0$	0.0005486	U^{235}	235.124
Proton, p, $_1H^1$	1.00758	Mo^{95}	94.945
Neutron, $_0n^1$	1.00893	La^{139}	138.945
Deuteron, D, $_1H^2$	2.01473	O^{16}	16.00000
α-particle, $_2He^4$	4.00389	1.6597×10^{-24} g = 1.000 amu.[a]	

[a] The atomic mass unit is based on the mass of the O^{16} isotope. Atomic weights used in ordinary chemical calculations are based on the average weight of oxygen atoms = 16.00. Owing to the presence of some heavier oxygen isotopes, the chemical atomic weight = atomic mass units × 1.00027.

transformation of 1 g of matter into energy gives 8.987 ergs $\times 10^{20}$, the fission of 1 g of the atomic fuel in this case yields

$$8.987 \times 10^{20} \times 9.57 \times 10^{-3}\ \text{erg} = 8.60 \times 10^{18}\ \text{ergs}$$

or $\qquad 8.60 \times 10^{18} \times 2.3889 \times 10^{-11}\ \text{kcal} = 2.055 \times 10^8\ \text{kcal}$

or $\qquad 2.055 \times 10^8 \times 3.968\ \text{Btu} = 8.154 \times 10^8\ \text{Btu}$

For 1 lb of U^{235} this fission produces

$$8.154 \times 10^8 \times 453.59 = 3.698 \times 10^{10}\ \text{Btu, or } 1.084 \times 10^7\ \text{kwhr.}$$

These calculated values are based on one particular fission path, whereas many different products are formed with an average of 2.5 neutrons. Taking the average heating value of North American bituminous coals from 30 different localities as 13,100 Btu/lb, and the average Btu/lb of nuclear fuel as 3.6×10^{10}, it is apparent that 1 lb of the latter is equivalent to $2\frac{3}{4}$ million lb, or approximately 1400 tons, of coal.

12-2 Energy from Synthetic Nuclear Fuels

Although U^{238} is not itself a nuclear fuel, it will absorb fast neutrons to form an unstable radioactive isotope $_{92}U^{239}$ with a half-life of 23 min. A beta particle is emitted, so that the resulting element has atomic number 93.

This has been named *neptunium*. A further loss of a beta particle gives rise to element 94, *plutonium*, a relatively long-lived atom unless struck by a neutron which causes fission.

$$_{92}U^{238} + _0n^1 \xrightarrow[\text{fast}]{} _{92}U^{239} \xrightarrow[\text{23 min}]{\beta} _{93}Np^{239} \xrightarrow[\text{2.3 days}]{\beta} _{94}Pu^{239} \text{ (fissionable)} \qquad (9)$$

This is called a *breeder reaction*.

The element thorium can also be used to breed nuclear fuel.

$$_{90}Th^{232} + _0n^1 \xrightarrow[\text{fast}]{} _{90}Th^{233} \xrightarrow{\beta} _{91}Pa^{233} \xrightarrow{\beta} _{92}U^{233} \text{ (fissionable)}$$

Both of these materials emit neutrons upon fission.

12-3 Critical Mass and the Original Atomic Bomb

Obviously, if each of the neutrons produced in the fission reaction were picked up by additional U^{235} atoms, and each in turn produced two or three neutrons, an explosive chain reaction would occur. This is essentially what happens in the atomic bomb of the conventional type. It cannot happen if all but one of the several neutrons produced are lost (1) by escaping from the lump of active material or (2) by absorption by nonfissionable atoms. The first condition in producing the bomb is to have a sufficient concentration of U^{235} or Pu^{239} to provide a good neutron flux; the second is to bring together a sufficient amount of the enriched material so that only a small proportion of the neutrons escape and a multiplying chain reaction occurs, with the instantaneous release of tremendous energy. The mass of fissionable material required to initiate this chain reaction is called the *critical mass*.

12-4 Power Reactors

To produce power from nuclear fission, the rate of the chain reaction must be controlled so that the net result is that each fission passes on, or activates, only one atom. The mechanism is then a straight but continuous energy chain, rather than the multiple-branching energy chains of the bomb. This control may be achieved by inserting elements which absorb neutrons, such as cadmium, cobalt, or boron. Withdrawal of the control rods increases the neutron flux. The reactor may be shut down or stopped by dropping the entire control rods into their tubes in the reactor. A controlled atomic reaction may be represented by Fig. 12-1.

There are several types of nuclear power reactors. Classification is based on the type of fuel, control method, moderator, coolant, and heat-transfer agent. All nuclear reactors are surrounded by shielding consisting of a reflector (graphite, heavy water, or beryllium, among others) to shunt back

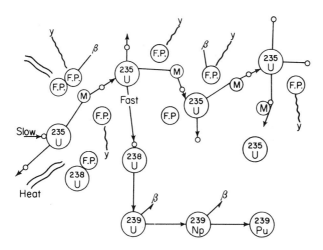

Figure I2-I Reactions in a thermal nuclear reactor. M—moderator; F.P.—fission product; ○—neutron.

escaping neutrons, a thermal shield of water between concentric steel shells, and a biological shield usually of thick concrete to cut out gamma and neutron radiation. The whole reactor in land installations is often surrounded by a large metal sphere. A few specific types of reactors are described later.

Nuclear Fuels

Natural uranium in the form of the metal, its oxides, or salts can be used as nuclear fuel, although only seven out of every 1000 uranium atoms present can undergo fission. This type of fuel has a critical mass and requires the presence of a *modifier* to slow down the neutrons so that they are more easily captured by the relatively few U^{235} atoms present. The neutrons are ejected at speeds of several thousand miles per second. The moderator reduces the speed to a mere crawl, about 1 mile/sec. This is about the average speed of a hydrogen molecule at ordinary temperatures, so a reactor using the slow or "thermal" neutrons is called a *thermal reactor*. (The term has no reference to the capacity of the reactor to produce heat.) Canadian and Indian reactors use natural uranium fuel with heavy water as moderator. Other moderators used are graphite, beryllium, and ordinary water of extreme purity. Heavy water has an advantage as a moderator because it also acts as a control of the neutron flux and hence the rate of the reaction. Dumping the D_2O from the reactor cuts off effective neutron collisions; increasing the level of the heavy water in the reactor increases the absorption and fission.

Enriched fuels are used in reactors in the United States and the United Kingdom. Fuels may be enriched by adding more U^{235} or Pu^{239} obtained from "breeder reactors," or U^{233} obtained from thorium [equation (10)]. The concentration of fuel element is usually from 1.3 per cent to 4.0 per cent, that is, approximately two to six times the fission fuel in natural uranium.

"Fast reactors" are fuelled with highly concentrated or almost pure synthetic elements, or U^{235} separated from U^{238}. The research reactor at M.I.T. uses fuel containing 93 per cent U^{235}.

Enrichment of the fuel with U^{235} requires an expensive separation of this isotope by *physical* methods, since both isotopes have identical *chemical* properties. Uranium oxides are first converted to the fluoride UF_6 which is volatile. According to Graham's law, the rate of diffusion of a gas or vapor through an orifice or porous septum, varies inversely as the square root of the density. In this case the difference in densities is less than 1 per cent, so the diffusion process must be repeated many times to effect a separation of U^{235} of a suitable degree of purity. The cost of such an installation is reported to be around $500,000,000. This is one of the reasons that Canada has developed the "thermal" type of reactor using natural uranium.

A gas ultracentrifuge which rotates at speeds in excess of 40,000 rpm has recently been developed by Professor W. Groth of Bonn University and G. Zippe of the Atomic Energy Commission of the United States. According to press reports this method of separating the isotopic fluorides is much cheaper than the diffusion methods.

As indicated previously, a thermal or slow reactor operating on cheap natural uranium will breed valuable fuel which can be separated and concentrated chemically. A fast reactor may breed more fuel than it burns since

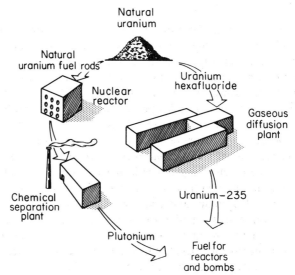

Figure 12-2 Two paths for the production of enriched fuels. [Courtesy A.E.C.L.]

the fission of one U^{235} atom may activate more than one U^{238} or Th^{233} atom in the process.

The used fuel rods in which the U^{235} has been depleted will contain Pu^{239} and U^{233}, as well as unreacted U^{238}. UF_6 is obtained by treatment with F_2—HF or with liquid ClF_3. In the latter method the ClF_3 acts as a catalyst:

$$U \quad + 3\ ClF_3 \longrightarrow UF_6 + 3\ ClF$$
$$3\ ClF + 3\ F_2 \longrightarrow 3\ ClF_3$$
$$\overline{U \quad + 3\ F_2 \longrightarrow UF_6}$$

The PuF_4 can be readily separated from the uranium fluorides.

In another process, the fuel residues, for example, zirconium-uranium alloy, aluminum-uranium alloy, stainless steel, UO_2 ceramic, and the other "unburned" fuels are treated with a solution of NO_2 and HF at 200° to 350° C. Soluble salts of uranium next react with BrF_3 to give UF_6 which is separated from TeF_6 by distillation. The addition of F_2 converts the plutonium to PuF_4 at 700° F. The process equipment is made of monel metal and fluoplastics (see Chapter 17). The cladding and alloying metals and the insoluble and non-volatile fluorides of the fission products are discharged as a slurry.

Figure 12-2 indicates the two paths for the production of enriched fuels.

Coolants

The kinetic energy of the fragments of the fuel atom is converted to heat by their jostling of other atoms in the fuel rod. A significant amount of heat is also created by the action of gamma rays and neutrons on the reactor components and structure. The heat is removed by the coolant circulated between the rods and the "cans" or containers. This serves two purposes: (1) to keep the fuel elements from melting or reaching allotropic transition points and to protect the containers, and (2) to provide the heat source for steam for the turbogenerators.

Various coolants are in use: ordinary water, pressurized water, deionized water, heavy water (D_2O), gases under pressure, liquid metals and alloys, and stable organic liquids. The choice of coolant is dependent not only on the thermal conductance and specific heat of the coolant, but also on whether it will react with or corrode the alloying elements, the metal cladding, or the sheathing of the fuel rods or their containers. Another consideration is the tendency of the coolant to absorb neutrons.

Fast reactors using rich fuel may be cooled by liquid metals such as bismuth, or a sodium-potassium alloy. The Na-K amalgam absorbs neutrons and soon becomes radioactive, so that the primary heat exchanger in which the heat is transferred to a second Na-K loop or circuit, has to be heavily shielded. The secondary loop, which is not radioactive, provides the heat for the high-pressure steam boiler.

When water is used as the coolant, it is carefully purified to remove all dissolved materials and thus reduce the possibility of becoming radioactive. The water is demineralized by ion-exchange resins. The electrical resistance of the pure water is around 18,000,000 ohms. Ordinary distilled water has a resistance of 500,000 ohms.

High-pressure steam may be produced directly by the coolant in the reactor, or the water may be kept from boiling by pressure. The temperature of the pressurized water is 540° F.

The purity of the water is maintained by continuous passage of a fraction of the condensate through deionizing resins. These remove any corrosion products or radioactive ions picked up during use.

Figure 12-4 is a diagram of a power reactor using heavy water as coolant. The moderator in this installation is also a separate heavy-water system. Heavy water has very low neutron absorption and is a good neutron reflector. A reactor, which is cooled and moderated by D_2O, has a very high utilization, or "burn up" of the U^{235} of the fuel.

Other coolant systems are indicated in the following description of some typical operating reactors.

Specific Examples of Operating Reactors

Experimental reactors are designed for research into various phases of nuclear chemistry and physics rather than for the production of power. In the M.I.T. experimental reactor, the fuel is highly concentrated U^{235} (93 per cent) in the form of an alloy of aluminum and U^{235}. The reactor is controlled by cadmium rods, with D_2O used as a moderator and graphite as a neutron reflector. The output is equivalent to 250 kw of electricity.

Canada's first nuclear power station has an output of 20,000 kw. This pilot plant is known as NPD, or Nuclear Power Demonstrator. The layout is shown in Fig. 12-3, and the principles of its operation illustrated in Fig. 12-4. The fuel is natural uranium in the form of uranium oxide pressed into small pellets and sintered. The high-density pellets are put into Zircaloy tubes (ZrAl alloy). A bundle of these tubes, 7 to 19 of them, held together by spiral ribs, constitute a fuel rod. The ribs act as spacers and provide an efficient swirl-type of coolant flow.

Several rods are inserted in each of the aluminum tubes in the reactor core, which in this case is a tank, since the moderator is heavy water. The core, or "calandria," has 132 coolant tube assemblies 15 ft long and 4 in. in diameter. Two of these are shown in Fig. 12-5 and three are indicated in Fig. 12-4. Fuel rods can be added or withdrawn while the reactor is operating at full power. The reactor is controlled by adjusting the level of the moderator in the tank and calandria by helium gas pressure (Fig. 12-4). The reactor can be shut down by immediate discharge of the heavy water into the dump tank below.

Pure light water (H_2O) serves as a neutron reflector in place of graphite used in many other reactors. The horizontal calandria with shielding is 50 ft below ground level.

The CANDU power station, Fig. 12-6, to be completed in 1965, is based on the NPD reactor. It will use 19 tube fuel rods, each containing 33 lb of

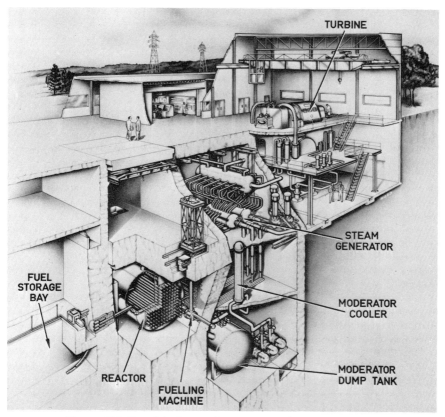

Figure 12-3 Canada's first nuclear power station NPD (Nuclear Power Demonstration). It uses natural uranium in the form of uranium oxide for fuel and heavy water for moderator and coolant. The pilot plant produces 20,000 kw of electricity. [Courtesy A.E.C.L.]

uranium oxide. The total cost of the fuel at $30.00/lb will be $4,605,000. The station will generate 200,000 kw.

The first privately financed, full-scale nuclear power plant in the United States is the *Commonwealth Edison Dresden installation* near Joliet, Ill. The 180,000 kw plant (Fig. 12-7) was completed in 1960. The 190 ft steel sphere houses the reactor (a dual-cycle, boiling-water type) and the primary steam

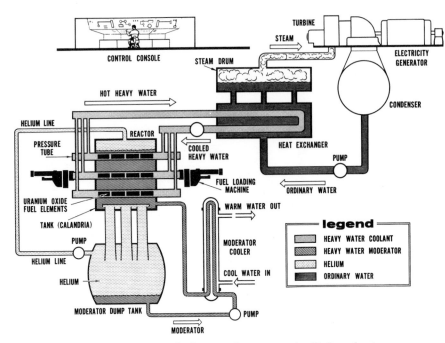

Figure 12-4 Schematic diagram of a reactor using D_2O moderator and coolant. NPD and CANDU reactors. [Courtesy A.E.C.L.]

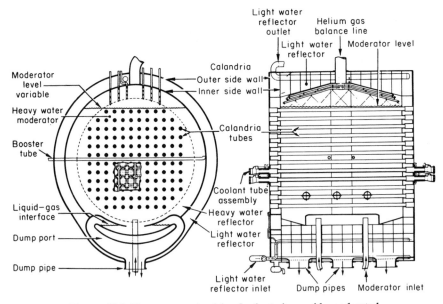

Figure 12-5 The core or calandria of a deuterium oxide moderated reactor. This reactor uses a heavy water and a light water reflector, with heavy water as a coolant. [Courtesy A.E.C.L.]

150

Figure 12-6 The Douglas Point 200,000 kw Nuclear Power Plant (CANDU). The reactor is in the domed building. [Courtesy A.E.C.L.]

Figure 12-7 Commonwealth Edison Dresden Nuclear Power Plant: (A) a 3000 ton, 190 ft sphere contains the reactor, primary steam condensers, and secondary steam generator; (B) is the fuel storage vault; (C) the fuel-handling building; (D) houses the turbines and generators, and is provided with movable shielding; (E) contains condensers, feed water heater, and de-mineralizers; (F) is the administration building. Cost of the plant: $51,000,000; output: 180,000 kw. [Courtesy Commonwealth Edison.]

151

drum and condensers. The reactor is 41 × 12 ft with 5 in. thick steel walls lined with $\frac{3}{8}$ in. stainless steel. Ventilating air and gases are discharged after suitable delay and dilution through the 300 ft stack.

The reactor uses enriched uranium fuel, U^{235} 1.5 per cent, in 452 fuel rods clad with Zr. The control is by 80 rods containing boron in stainless steel. Primary steam coming directly from the reactor is at 545° F; it is piped to shielded turbines at 1000 psi. Secondary steam generators receive steam at 500 psi. The 66 tons of enriched fuel will run the plant for 3 years.

The Shippingport reactor near Pittsburgh is a pressurized, nonboiling, light-water cooled reactor. The fuel is enriched uranium, U^{235} 1.4 per cent.

Figure 12-8 NS Savannah immediately after launching, July 21, 1959. [Courtesy N.Y. Shipbuilding Corp.]

The purity of the coolant is maintained by use of a special monobed containing a lithium resin and an anion hydroxyl resin. The resulting treated, or "polished," water contains a trace of LiOH, which keeps the coolant slightly alkaline and reduces corrosion. When the resins become highly radioactive or inefficient, they are removed. The initial power production was 60,000 kw, with a scheduled increase to 100,000 kw. The smaller nuclear reactors at Camp Century in Greenland and at McMurdo and other bases in Antarctica also employ water as coolant and radiation shield.

The *Nautilus*, other nuclear submarines, and the *Savannah* (Fig. 12-8), also have pressurized water-cooled reactors. The active core of the *Savannah* is approximately 5 × 5 ft. The outlet temperature of the primary coolant is 521° F at 1750 psi. The ship is expected to cruise 300,000 miles without refuelling.

It is estimated that by 1965 there will be 50 nuclear power reactors in operation in Great Britain, generating from five to six million kilowatts. The

Calder Hall reactor is typical of several British reactors. It is cooled by carbon dioxide gas under pressure, moderated with graphite, and controlled by boron-steel rods. The fuel is enriched uranium. The reactor consists of a 1000 ton cylinder of graphite with cylindrical holes for the fuel elements and control rods. The pressure vessel enclosing the core is 60 × 30 ft with walls of 2 in. welded steel. The CO_2 emerges at 560° F and 100 psi, generating steam at 200 psi and in a secondary exchanger at 52 psi. The thermal shielding is 6 in. steel plate, with a biological shield of high density concrete 7 ft thick. Ventilation is provided by a 200 ft stack.

Modifications of this type of reactor include the use of uranium carbide (UC) or plutonium carbide, which are molecular combinations of fuel and modifier atoms. Higher gas pressures, and therefore greater efficiency, are obtained by increasing the strength of the pressure shell.

An organic cooled deuterium oxide moderated reactor, designed for Atomic Energy Canada Limited, is fuelled with natural uranium. A tank of organic liquid placed above the calandria or reactor tank acts as a shield and reservoir. The organic liquid is called *terphenyl*

or *diphenyl benzene*. It has low neutron absorption and is much cheaper than heavy water. It is also thermally stable, resembling its relative diphenyl or "Dowtherm." Fuel rods are inserted into vertical coolant tubes. Control of the reaction rate is the same as for the CANDU or NPD reactors. A flow diagram of the organic-cooled reactor is shown in Fig. 12-9.

Small power generators can be made by using the heat developed by synthetic radioactive materials. In a nuclear reactor, heat from the radiations of such atoms is largely responsible for the necessity of cooling the thermal shield. A "portable" atomic generator, using radioactive strontium 90, has been developed by the United States Atomic Energy Commission. A power unit weighing about one ton when equipped with steel and lead shielding is so rugged, it can survive a plane crash without releasing any of its radioactive fuel. The power unit itself weighs only 55 lb.

One of the most immediate uses of this Sr^{90} power generator is for automatic weather stations in remote areas. A unit was recently established on Graham Island in the Canadian Arctic 750 miles south of the Pole. It is expected to operate on its charge of radioactive fuel for over two years, transmitting weather data every three hours.

12-5 Radiation Dangers and Their Evaluation

It is obvious from the discussion of shielding that every precaution is taken to protect the operators of nuclear power plants and the public from

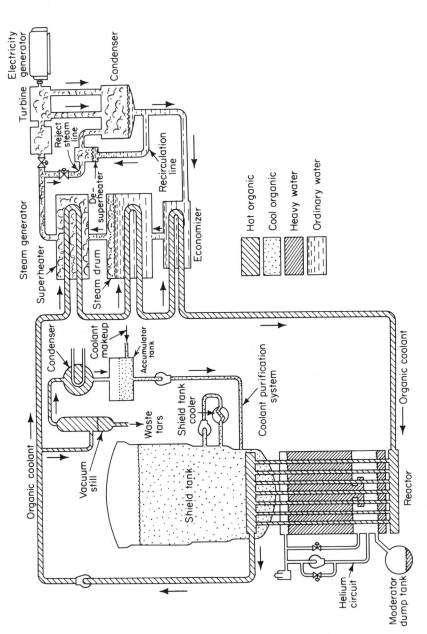

Electricity generator

Turbine

Condenser

Steam generator

Superheater

De-superheater

Steam drum

Reject steam line

Recirculation line

Economizer

Hot organic

Cool organic

Heavy water

Ordinary water

Condenser

Coolant makeup

Accumulator tank

Shield tank cooler

Coolant purification system

Waste tars

Vacuum still

Shield tank

Organic coolant

Organic coolant

Reactor

Helium circuit

Moderator dump tank

harmful radiation. All radioactive material is hazardous. If taken into the body as radioactive dust or gas, or as contaminants in food or drink or by absorption on the skin, serious tissue changes will take place. Ordinary clothing will stop alpha and beta radiation, but gamma radiation and neutrons are much more penetrating and are only stopped by inches of lead or several feet of soil, rock, or cement.

Radiation is measured in a number of ways. The unit used to indicate the radioactivity of a material is the *curie*. It originally represented the number of atoms disintegrating per second using one gram of radium as standard, 3.7×10^{10}/sec. Since this is a very large number, millicuries (mc), and microcuries ($\mu c = 3.7 \times 10^4$/sec) are in more general use. Thus, if a sample was found to emit 74,000 beta particles/sec, its radioactivity would be 2 microcuries.

The unit for measuring amounts or intensities of X rays or gamma radiation is the *roentgen* (r). It is defined as the amount of such radiation which will produce 1 esu charge in 1 cm^3 of dry air at standard temperature and pressure (STP). This charge is of course due to the ionization of the air molecules by the radiation. One roentgen corresponds to 1.61×10^{12} ion pairs per gram of air and represents the absorption of 83.8 ergs of energy. The maximum daily exposure to X or gamma radiation should not exceed 0.06 r.

The *rad* represents an amount of radiation that gives an absorption of 100 ergs per gram of target material. The letters stand for roentgen absorption dose. In biological tissue 1 r is equivalent to from 0.95 to 1.5 rad, depending on the type of tissue and energy of the radiation. A new unit, the *rem* (r equivalent, man), is the amount of radiation which is biologically equivalent to 1 r in human tissue, approximtely 100 ergs/gram.

12-6 Engineering Uses of Radioactive Elements

Many varieties of radioactive atoms can be obtained as by-products of nuclear reactors. Each has its characteristic rate of decay, usually expressed as time to half value or "half life." Most of the active isotopes in use give beta and gamma radiation.

When mixed with their ordinary inactive brothers, they do not become separated by any chemical reaction, and the proportion of radioactive to stable isotope of the element remains constant. Since the concentration of radioactive atoms may be readily determined because of the emitted radiation, such isotopes are used in engineering to determine metal wear, the rate and extent of corrosion, the efficiency of lubricants (see Fig. 13-1), the solubility of pigments, and for many other purposes. Dumbbell-shaped separators, carrying specific radioactive material, are used to separate different grades of petroleum products or those belonging to different companies in the same pipeline. The progress of each sample can thus be monitored. Since the absorption of radiation varies inversely with the thickness of the medium, radioactive isotopes are used as thickness gauges in the production of foils and films. Gamma-ray emitters are also employed to detect flaws in castings and welds.

Table 12-2 indicates the half-life and the type of radiation of common radioactive isotopes.

Table 12-2. COMMON RADIOACTIVE ISOTOPES OF SERVICE IN ENGINEERING

Element	Atomic number	Half-life	Type of radiation
Br^{78}	35	6.4 min	beta and gamma
Bi^{212}	83	60.5 min	beta
Pb^{212}	82	10.6 hr	beta
Na^{24}	11	14.8 hr	beta and gamma
P^{32}	15	14.3 days	beta
S^{35}	16	87.1 days	beta
Co^{60}	27	5.3 years	beta and gamma
Sr^{90}	38	25.0 years	beta and gamma
C^{14}	6	5,570._ years	beta

12-7 Nuclear Fusion

If two or more light atoms are made to collide with sufficient force, the nuclei may fuse, producing one or more heavier atoms. The fusion can only be achieved at collision speeds corresponding to temperatures in millions of degrees centigrade, such as occur in the atomic fission bomb (10^8 °K). An atomic fusion is therefore called a *thermonuclear reaction.*

During fusion of the nuclei, mass is lost or rather converted to energy. Reference to Table 12-1 will indicate that, should an alpha particle or helium nucleus be produced by the fusion of two neutrons and two protons, a considerable proportion of the mass would disappear.

$$2\,_0n^1 + 2\,_1H^1 \longrightarrow\ _2He^4$$

$$2.01786 + 2.01516 \longrightarrow 4.00389$$

The loss is 0.02913 amu, or 27 Mev.

Thermonuclear reactions such as the fusion of two deuterons or a deuterium and a tritium nucleus, furnish the source of energy in the hydrogen bomb with its explosive power equivalent to megatons (millions of tons) of TNT.

$$_1H^2 + \,_1H^2 \longrightarrow\ _1H^3 + \,_1H^1 + 4 \text{ Mev}$$

$$_1H^2 + \,_1H^3 \longrightarrow\ _2He^4 + \,_0n^1 + 17.6 \text{ Mev}$$

Tritium can be produced by the action of fast neutrons on a lithium blanket.

$$_0n^1 + _3Li^7 \longrightarrow 2\,_1H^3 + _1H^2$$

The production of industrial power from thermonuclear reactions seems to be some distance in the future.

Review Questions

1. Translate $_7N^{14} + _2He^4 \rightarrow _8O^{17} + _1H^1$.

2. What is the significance of the reaction above?

3. What was the first source of neutrons?

4. Complete $_{19}K^{39} + _0n^1 \rightarrow$

5. If strontium 90 and three neutrons were produced during the fission of a U^{235} nucleus, what would you expect to be the other product of the fission?

6. From Einstein's formula, calculate the energy released (in ergs) when 1 gram of matter is destroyed.

7. When a gram of U^{235} undergoes fission, approximately 5.3×10^6 kwh of energy is released. What percentage of the original mass has been converted?

8. When strontium 90 gives off a beta ray, what element does it become?

9. Tritium, the isotope of hydrogen of mass 3 is radioactive. What element is formed when it ejects a beta ray?

10. What are the essential components of a power reactor?

11. What are the advantages and disadvantages of natural uranium fuel?

12. How is the thermal-type reactor controlled?

13. In what type of reactor does one substance serve as control agent, moderator, and coolant?

14. Cite three types of industrial reactors in use.

15. What is the major source of heat in the reactor: the energy of the heavy fragments of the fission, the stopping of neutrons by the coolant, electromagnetic radiation, alpha and beta particles, or the energy of the atoms of the reflector when hit by neutrons?

16. Distinguish between a thermal nuclear reactor and a thermo-nuclear reaction.

17. Discuss the reaction

$$_1H^2 + {}_1H^3 \rightarrow {}_2H^4 + \text{energy} \quad \text{or} \quad ({}_1D^2 + {}_1T^3).$$

18. Show by equations how synthetic nuclear fuels are produced.

Further Readings

Benedict M., and Pigford, T., *Nuclear Chemical Engineering* (New York: McGraw-Hill, 1957).

Dufek, Rear Ad. G., "Nuclear Power for Polar Regions," *National Geographic* **121**, No. 5 (1962), 712.

Putman, J., *Isotopes* (Middlesex, G.B.: Penguin Books, Inc., 1960).

Proceedings of International Conferences on the Peaceful Uses of Atomic Energy (New York: United Nations, 1956, 1959).

13

Lubrication and Lubricants

Lubrication involves the addition of some substance to reduce the friction between moving surfaces. Proper lubrication depends primarily on the chemistry of the lubricant. This is shown by the data in Tables 13-1 and 13-3. The ability of the oil to spread over the bearing, to resist displacement by heat or pressure, its stability against cracking and oxidation, its viscosity, and many other important qualities are determined by its chemical nature. Modern improvements in lubricants have been the result of chemical research. The *chemical* as well as the *physical* properties of the bearing surfaces are also of major importance.

Friction: Thief of Power and Destroyer of Bearings

Friction wastes power—almost 20 per cent in a modern car. It is the chief cause of wear in any machine. The chief cause of friction is the chemical bonding or van der Waals attraction, where a few atoms or molecules come into contact. Such contacts may result in dislodgement of particles of colloidal size or larger from one surface by the other. Sometimes fusion of a tiny peak or asperity may take place. The introduction of a lubricant lessens the amount of dislodgement or pickup. This is illustrated by Fig. 13-1 and Table 13-1.

It will be seen from the table that a good lubricant reduces but does not completely eliminate pickup. It also appears that two lubricants giving the

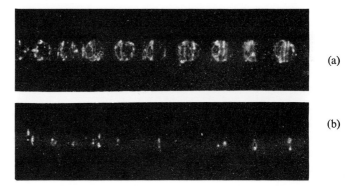

Figure 13-1 Autoradiograph showing the transfer of radioactive lead particles from a lead slider to a steel plate (a) when no lubricant is present, (b) when lubricant is added. The area and intensity of the spots on a photographic film when placed on the steel plate indicate the number and size of the particles of metal transferred from the slider. A lubricant reduces, but does not eliminate, pickup or friction. [From F. Bowen and D. Tabor, *Friction and Lubrication*, Methuen and Co., Ltd., 1956, by permission.]

same coefficient of friction may permit very different amounts of wear. The amount of pickup will, of course, differ with different surfaces. Perfectly clean metallic surfaces will show greater friction and pickup than contaminated surfaces. In engineering practice, every metal surface is covered by a molecular layer of oxide which has a lower *coefficiency of friction than the pure metal in vacuo*. Many substances can act as lubricants. They may be gases, liquids, or solids. The most widely used lubricant is oil.

The lubricating oil of today is basically a mixture of hydrocarbons derived from crude oil. Before the advent of crude oil refining, liquid lubricants

Table 13-1. FRICTION AND PICKUP WITH COPPER ON COPPER
(2 kg load)

Condition	Coefficiency of friction[a] C_f	Pickup per cm track	Average mass of lump picked up
		in micrograms	
Unlubricated	1.2	20.0	0.1
With silicone	1.0–1.2	10.0	0.1
Paraffin oil	0.2–0.3	0.5	1×10^{-3}
Paraffin wax	0.1–0.3	0.10	5×10^{-4}
Solid alcohol	0.65	0.05	3×10^{-4}
Fatty acid	0.01		
Copper soap	0.05	0.001	1×10^{-5}

[a] Coefficiency of friction C_f = pull/weight or tangent of sliding angle.

were chiefly fatty oils such as olive oil or lard oil. Such oils had a marked tendency to oxidize and to form sludges and emulsions. Paraffin or mineral oils are better in this respect and are much cheaper. Almost a century ago the locomotive engineers on the French railroads went on strike to protest the change from olive oil to mineral oil. They couldn't use the new lubricating oil to fry their dinners!

13-1 The Manufacture of Lubricating Oil

Lubricating oils are obtained from the petroleum fraction called "reduced crudes." The boiling points of the compounds in these fractions are too high ($\sim$600° F) for distillation at room temperature, so fractionation is carried out under reduced pressure. Thus a hydrocarbon called *eicosane*, $C_{20}H_{42}$, with a boiling point of 325° C at atmospheric pressure (15 psi) will boil at 170° C at 0.01 psi. In practice, the separation of the lubricating oil is effected at external pressures of about 0.75 psi.

Vacuum, or reduced pressure distillation, produces three main lubrication fractions, light, medium, and heavy stocks. Each of these is subjected to various procedures, depending on the quality desired and the source of the oil. The usual refining operations are solvent extraction, dewaxing, brightening, or/and finishing (Fig. 13-2).

Solvent extraction improves the lubricating, the flow properties, and stability of the oil by removing asphaltic compounds which tend to form acid sludges and have low viscosity index numbers (see page 168). The solvents most commonly used are phenol,

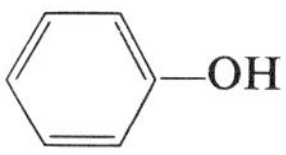

with a melting point of 59° C; the methyl derivatives of phenol, called *cresylic acid*, for example,

p-cresol,

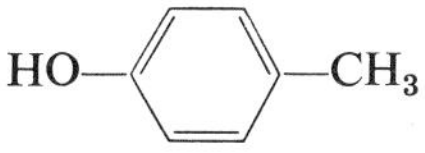

nitrobenzene,

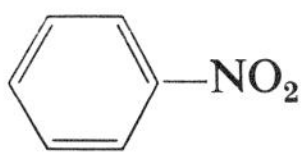

furfural,

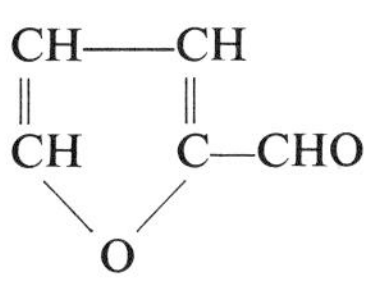

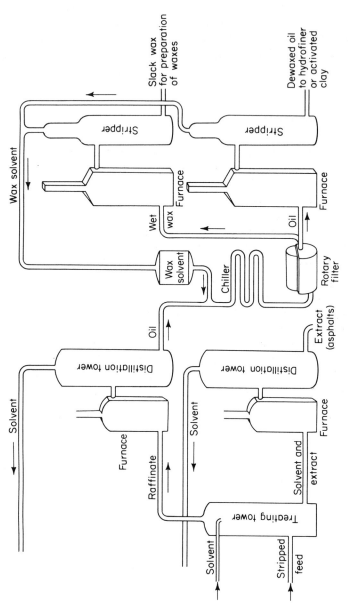

Figure 13-2 Preparation of lubricating oil.

liquid propane, liquid sulfur dioxide and benzene, and chlorinated solvents, such as *sym*-dichlorethylether $(CH_3CHCl)_2O$. A phenol extraction unit is shown in Fig. 13-3.

In the first process the molten phenol flows by gravity through an ascending column of oil, dissolving asphalts and gum-forming olefins and extracting

Figure 13-3 A phenol extraction unit. The phenol dissolves asphalts and other compounds which tend to form sludge in the engine. [Courtesy Imperial Oil Ltd.]

various sulfur compounds. The out-flowing treated oil is called *raffinate*. The raffinate is contaminated by some phenol, which is removed by heating the mixture to 250°–260° C (500° F) and passing the vapors to a stripping tower. The phenol which has a boiling point of 182° C (361° F) is distilled off and recovered. The oil is pumped to another part of the plant for further treatment.

The "bottoms" from the phenol treatment contain approximately 85 per cent phenol. This solvent is recovered also and united with the phenol from the raffinate for reuse.

Furfural is a by-product from oat hulls, corn cobs, and other sources. It is an amber-colored liquid with a boiling point not very different from phenol, namely 161.5° C. It has certain advantages over phenol as an extractive: (1) not as much of it is left in the raffinate or extracted oil, (2) it can be easily removed from the oil by steam, (3) it is not as corrosive as phenol.

Asphalts are not soluble in liquid propane, whereas paraffins and naphthenes are. If the heavy untreated oil is mixed with liquid propane under pressure by a counter-flow arrangement, the asphalt components settle out, and the propane raffinate is removed from the top of the extractor. The propane can be easily removed from the oil by steaming, but if the oil is paraffinic, the raffinate is treated to remove the wax.

Figure 13-4 Dewaxing units. Removal of unwanted waxes is one of the three main steps in the purification of oils. [Courtesy Imperial Oil Ltd.]

Dewaxing

Dewaxing is necessary, particularly with nonasphaltic types of crudes, to increase the fluidity of the lubricating oil at low temperatures. Waxes found in oils have melting points from 32° to 71° C for paraffin waxes, to 95° for microcrystalline waxes; thus they tend to crystallize out, forming a gel-like structure when the temperature drops. The temperature at which an oil will no longer flow from a standard test tube is known as the pour point. The removal of wax lowers the pour point of the oil.

Dewaxing is also a solvent-extraction process. The raffinate freed from its initial solvent is treated with approximately twice its volume of a solvent for wax. This solvent may be methylethyl ketone, a mixture of propyl and butyl ketones, chlorinated solvents like trichlorethylene, benzene or mixtures of these. Wax can also be removed by urea.

Liquid propane, which serves to precipitate asphalts, is a good solvent for waxes, so that the propane raffinate may be dewaxed without additional solvent. Pumping off the propane lowers the temperature by the rapid evaporation of the volatile solvent, and the waxes crystallize out. Other raffinate mixtures are passed through cooling coils, and the waxes are removed by sucking the oil through a rotating canvas filter drum. The wax crystals collect on the outside of the canvas and are removed by a scraper blade, whence the material is sent to the wax-recovery unit. The dewaxed oil is retreated and the solvent stripped off in a typical distillation tower.

Figure 13-4 shows a dewaxing unit.

Finishing

The oil may be purified further by filtration through activated clay or bauxite. This step removes color bodies and other compounds by adsorption, as well as some microcrystalline wax.

In the modern refineries, the clay treatment has been supplanted by hydrofining (Fig. 13-5). In this unit, the oil is subjected to hydrogen under pressure and elevated temperatures in the presence of a catalyst. This treatment converts disulfides and other sulfur compounds dissolved in the oil to hydrogen sulfide gas, which is easily removed (see page 82). Unsaturated gum-forming compounds are converted to paraffins and naphthenes. The flow properties of the oil are also improved.

13-2 Testing Lubricating Oils

Viscosity Index

Various tests are made on the finished oils as a control of quality. Probably the best known and least understood by the average motorist is the

Figure 13-5 Hydrofining unit. [Courtesy Imperial Oil Ltd.]

Viscosity Index (V.I.). This index is an indication of the ability of the oil to maintain its fluidity or viscosity over a range of temperature.

Viscosity Measurements

Viscosity may be determined by a variety of methods. The *absolute* viscosity recognized in all scientific laboratories using the C.G.S. system is given in *poises*. Water at about room temperature (22° C or 71.50° F) has a viscosity of 1.0 centipoise (0.010 poise). Another widely accepted system is the *kinematic viscosity*, the unit of which is the *centistoke*. It is related to the absolute viscosity by the expression

$$\text{centistoke} = \frac{\text{centipoise}}{\text{density}}$$

There are several practical but empirical systems used by engineers to compare the fluidity of oils. The one favored on this continent (Fig. 13-6) determines the time in seconds for a standard volume of oil to flow through a standard hole in the bottom of a standard cup at one or more of three arbitrarily chosen temperatures, namely, 100° F, 130° F, and 210° F. The

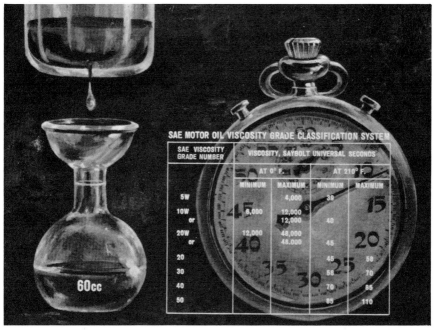

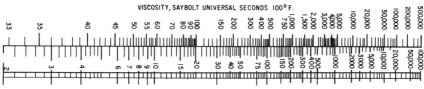

Figure 13-6 Viscosity determination by the Saybolt viscosimeter. On this continent the viscosity of oils is given in Saybolt Universal Seconds (SUS). This is the time required for 60 ml of the oil to flow through the standard hole at a specified temperature. [Courtesy Texaco Co.]

unit is called Saybolt Universal Seconds (SUS), although unfortunately there is little to justify the word "universal"; for in Europe engineers use the Engler viscosimeter, while in Britain and many parts of the Commonwealth the Redwood instrument is preferred. The interrelation between the three empirical units may readily be found.[1]

In North America, an SAE #10 oil has a viscosity between 90 and 120 SUS at 130° F, a #20 oil has Saybolt seconds between 120 and 185, #30 oil between 184 and 255 at the same temperature. The viscosity of a #40 oil has an SUS value greater than 255, at 130° F, but less than 75 at 210° F.

---

1 Viscosity charts are available from the American Society of Testing Materials.

Every oil is more fluid at higher temperatures. Two oils having the same viscosity at 100° F may have very different viscosities at 50° F and still greater difference at 0° F. An ideal oil would remain just as fluid at −40° F as at summer temperatures and would not thin out or reach a low viscosity at high driving temperatures.

As stated above, the viscosity index indicates the ratio of change of viscosity with temperature. If the V.I. is high, the viscosity-temperature curve is flatter than if the index is low.

In determining the V.I., the viscosity of the oil is compared with that of two standard oils of different chemical types but which have the same viscosity at a standard temperature. One of these is a Pennsylvanian or paraffin-type oil, and the other is a Gulf or naphthenic type. In 1932 when this index was suggested, a Pennsylvanian lubricating oil had the most constant fluidity and was arbitrarily given a V.I. of 100, whereas the asphaltic Gulf oil was notoriously poor in this respect and was given a value of zero. The V.I. of an oil under test is calculated from the formula:

$$\text{V.I.} = \frac{\text{visc. Gulf oil at } 100° \text{ F} - \text{visc. } X \text{ at } 100° \text{ F}}{\text{visc. Gulf oil at } 100° \text{ F} - \text{visc. Penn. oil at } 100° \text{ F}} \times 100$$

The V.I. may also be obtained by use of a nomograph. Viscosity temperature curves for typical lube oils and for some synthetic lubricants are given in Fig. 13-7. As in the case of octane numbers, viscosity index numbers above 100 are common now. These are obtained by chemical additives and synthetic compounds.

Other tests which are made on the oil are the flash point, oxidation resistance, carbon residue, precipitation test, neutralization number, specific gravity, and color.

Flash point indicates the volatility of the oil and the tendency of the oil to be burned in the engine.

Oxidation resistance is related to the tendency of the oil to form sludge under operating conditions. A sample of the oil is heated and oxygen is bubbled through it. A readily oxygenated oil soon forms sludge, a thick emulsion of oil and water (from the burning of the hydrogen in the oil). In a car, if sludge accumulates it impedes oil circulation, increasing the coefficient of friction and the amount of engine wear. Comparison of the time before any sludge appears will indicate the relative resistance to oxidation.

The *carbon residue* test indicates the tendency of an oil to deposit carbon. A standard volume of oil is heated in a metal cup to ascertain carbon residue on combustion. Carbon residue is related to the *smoke point* of an oil (see Diesel Fuels).

Both the oxidization resistance and carbon deposit of different oils may be compared by tests run in a standard engine.

The *neutralization number* indicates the concentration and nature of acid or alkali present in the oil.

The *precipitation test* indicates the absence of any suspended solids, such as catalyst particles, clay, or corrosion products. In this test the oil is diluted with naphtha and centrifuged. Any contaminating solids are detected at the bottom of the centrifuge tube.

The *specific gravity* of the oil is determined by a hydrometer. Gravities of oil are expressed on this continent as a number on a scale sponsored by the American Petroleum Institute and are given as *degrees API* (see Fig. 9-2).

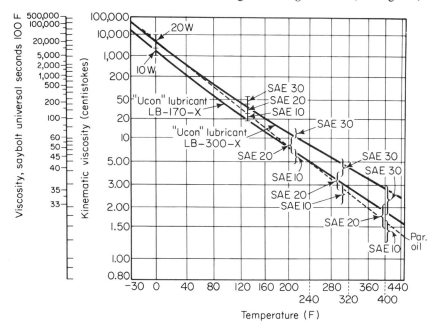

Figure 13-7 Comparison of synthetic lubricants and petroleum oils. The viscosity specification ranges are indicated by numbered bands at 0° F and 130° F. Representative viscosity ranges of SAE 10, SAE 20, and SAE 30 petroleum oils at 210° F and 400° F are shown by numbered brackets. [From "UCON Lubricants," *Carbide and Chemicals*, UCC, N.Y.]

The *color* of the oil is checked against standards. It is controlled for marketing standards and because off-color may indicate deviation in the composition and properties of the oil.

13-3 Some Theoretical and Practical Considerations

When a shaft is separated from the bearing by a uniform film of oil, the resistance to rotation is due solely to the viscosity of the oil. In the ideal case, the torque resisting rotation,

$$F = \frac{2\pi r^2 A}{60l} N\eta$$

This theoretical equation holds for vertical shafts or for very light loads, where r is the radius of the shaft, A is the area of the shaft in oil, l is the thickness of the oil film, N is rpm, and η is the viscosity in poises.

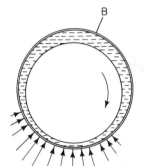

In most cases the film is not of uniform thickness, especially during the initial rotation of the shaft, and there arises an uneven distribution of pressure on the lubricating fluid, as illustrated in Fig. 13-8. Even here $F = KN\eta$ or, if one considers the average pressure per unit of bearing surface P, the friction equals $K'N\eta/P$, i.e., a plot of C_f vs $N\eta/P$ is a straight line.

If the maximum pressure is so great that the oil film is only two or three molecules thick, boundary lubrication replaces hydrodynamic or fluid lubrication. Some of the hills or asperities in the surfaces may be higher than the film thickness, so that some wear or erosion will take place. At extremely high pressures or very low viscosities seizure may occur.

Figure 13-8 Fluid lubrication. Maximum pressure at A, minimum at B. The rotating shaft is supported by the oil pressure. The minimum thickness of the film and the frictional drag depend on the viscosity of the oil, the speed of rotation, and inversely on the pressure.

In an engine the oil not only serves as a fluid or a boundary lubricant, it also functions (1) as a fluid gasket between the cylinder and the piston rings. It should also act (2) as a cleaning agent and (3) as a scavenger to wash off and transport solid particles produced in combustion or wear. In aircraft the lubricating oil may be used as a hydraulic fluid to change the pitch of the propeller or to operate other mechanisms. Here the V.I. is very important.

13-4 Boundary Lubrication

The effectiveness of boundary lubrication depends, even more than it does in fluid lubrication, on the structure and chemical properties of the oil. A lubricant for high-speed gears may be subjected to pressures of 135,000 psi. The thin molecular film must withstand displacement by these high pressures. For boundary lubrication, the molecules should have (1) long hydrocarbon chains, (2) lateral attraction between the chains, (3) polar groups to promote wetting or spreading and orientation over the surface; and for high pressures, (4) active atoms or groups to form chemical bonds with the metal or other surface.

Figure 13-9 illustrates the lubrication of two metal surfaces. True boundary lubrication occurs at points marked *B*. Pickup or surface wear will occur at *A*.

High viscosity index, resistance to heat and oxidation, detergent qualities, adherence, low pour point, "oiliness," and other properties necessary for special uses, are all determined by the chemistry of the lubricant.

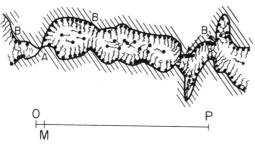

Figure 13-9 Lubrication of a highly polished metal surface. Irregularities on the surface of a machined metal may be 0.1 micron $(1 \times 10^{-4}$ mm) in height or depth. The length of an extended fatty acid molecule such as stearic acid is 2.6×10^{-6} mm or 26 Å, or about $\frac{1}{40}$ of the surface peaks, the ratio of the length of the lines OM and OP above.

True "boundary" lubrication is shown at points marked B. Abrasion and pickup will occur at A.

13-5 Oil Additives or Improvers

It is obvious that an ordinary paraffin or other hydrocarbon cannot possess all these desirable virtues, but with careful refining, mineral oils can be made to behave satisfactorily for most purposes. There are, however, several types of chemical compounds which improve many of the more desirable qualities of the lubricant; several of these additives are given below.

1. *Viscosity index improvers.* These prevent the oil from thinning out at elevated temperatures and from thickening excessively at low temperatures. Such additives are usually hydrocarbon polymers like

$$\left(-CH_2-\underset{\underset{CH_3}{|}}{\overset{\overset{CH_3}{|}}{C}}- \right)_n$$

or Rohm & Haas Acryloid HG especially designed for aircraft oils. Road and laboratory tests published by the Standard Oil Company showed that oils containing a V.I. type of additive gave a large reduction in apparent viscosity at high rates of shear and had significantly lower engine friction or better gasoline mileage. Winter-summer (10–30) oil is an example of lubricant with V.I. improver in it.

2. *Pour-point depressants.* This type of additive enables the oil to remain fluid at lower temperatures. The additive acts as a protective colloid,

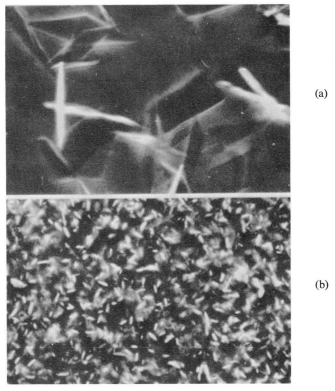

(a)

(b)

Figure 13-10 The effect of a pour-point depressant. The untreated oil (a) forms large interlocking crystals. In the treated oil (b) the depressant induces the formation of very small crystals and the suspension will still flow.

surrounding each wax crystal nuclei as it is formed and thus preventing the growth of large crystals, or a brush-heap, gel-like structure which would immobilize the rest of the oil. The oil pump can still function with the fine suspension of very small "protected" crystals. The effect is shown in the photomicrographs in Fig. 13-10. Pour-point depressants such as *Rislone* and *Paraflow*, among others, are polymeric materials such as

or big molecules like

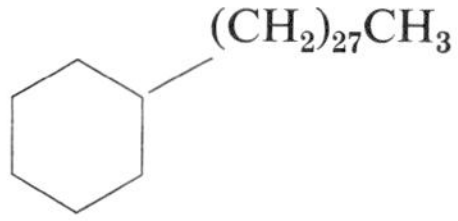

$(CH_2)_{27}CH_3$

or polyesters, for example,

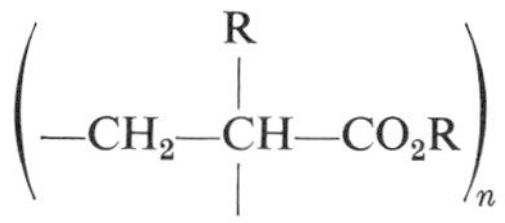

$$\left(-CH_2-\underset{|}{\overset{R}{CH}}-CO_2R \right)_n$$

The alkyl side chains should be at least twelve carbon atoms long.

3. *Detergents.* The octane requirement of an engine increases as the engine becomes dirty. Detergent additions bear a very close relation to their water-soluble counterparts used in domestic laundering. The ideal detergent wets and spreads over the soiled surface, dislodging and suspending the particles of dirt. The wetting or spreading tendency of a compound was found to depend on the nature of its polar end-group and the consequent lowering of the surface tension and interfacial tension. Among the best compounds for cleaning purposes are sulfonates and long organic sulfates. The water-soluble detergents are sodium salts of these, and the oil-soluble derivatives are usually similar heavy metal salts. They have the general formulas:

$$(R-SO_3-)_2M, \qquad (R'-SO_4)_2M \quad \text{or} \quad \left(\underset{}{\overset{O}{\bigcirc}} \right)_2 M$$

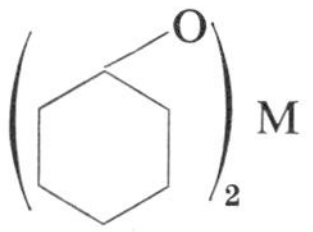

4. *Antioxidants.* Antioxidants increase the resistance of the oil to the effects of oxygen. They are often inhibitors of the substituted amino type, for example,

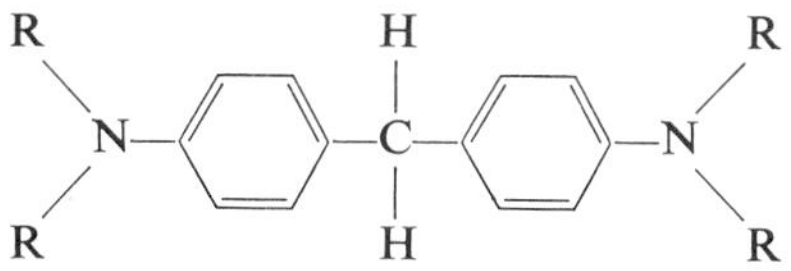

$$\underset{R}{\overset{R}{>}}N-\bigcirc-\underset{H}{\overset{H}{C}}-\bigcirc-N\underset{R}{\overset{R}{<}}$$

Organic phosphorus compounds are also used. Since part of the "dirt" in an engine is due to oil oxidation, the antioxidants help to reduce engine deposits with consequent beneficial effect on the octane requirements.

5. *Corrosion inhibitors.* These compounds may be added to decrease or prevent bearing corrosion. Typical of this group are metallic salts of complex organic thio-phosphoric acids

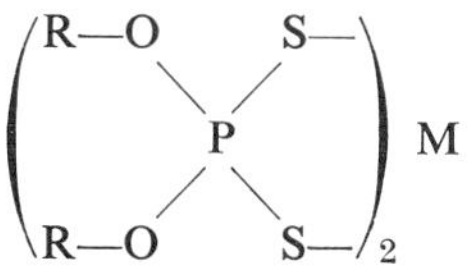

$$\left(\begin{array}{c} R-O \quad\;\; S- \\ \diagdown \;\; \diagup \\ P \\ \diagup \;\; \diagdown \\ R-O \quad\;\; S- \end{array} \right)_2 M$$

6. *Boundary lubrication improver.* Oiliness is related to spreading ability. Fatty acids or their metal soaps containing at least 15 carbon atoms, are better lubricants in many respects than the corresponding hydrocarbons (see Table 13-1). One of the first additives used to improve mineral oils was castor oil in small amounts. The adherence of the fatty esters and reaction of freed fatty acids with the metallic surface to form soaps, gave a long-wearing lubricating film.

7. *Additives for high pressures.* For extreme pressures (that is, high load-carrying properties), substances are added which contain groups that form strong chemical bonds with the surfaces, for example, diphenyl disulfide

or phosphorus derivatives,

and others. Tricresyl phosphate added to gasolines, rather than oils, improves spark plug performance and is reported to diminish wear by producing a mirror-like layer by chemical polishing, which is a chemical reaction with the asperities of the surfaces. Certain chlorine-containing molecules are used as extreme pressure lubricants, the lubricating tassel being bound firmly by combination of the chloride with the metal.

Additives Which Change Bearing Surfaces

The nature of the surfaces is very important in boundary lubrication. While steel on steel is easily lubricated, it is reported to be nearly impossible to run a shaft of inconel (stainless) in an inconel bearing without scoring or seizure, even when a pure petroleum oil is present. Changing the surface, by chemical reaction to oxide, sulfide, or phosphate, lowers the coefficient of friction between the surfaces and improves the efficiency of the oil in boundary lubrication.

13-6 Lubricating Oil Emulsions

Emulsions of oil droplets in water are extensively used under the name of *cutting oils.* These serve several functions. The first is to cool the cutting tool and work, by absorbing the heat of deformation of the chip and the friction against the cutting edge. The second function is to act as a lubricant for the high pressure sliding of the chip over the surface of the tool. The fluid should also remove the smaller particles of the work from the scene of action.

Oil has a poor specific heat, but it is a good lubricant, whereas water is a poor lubricant but has a high specific heat. Hence the combination of the two in the form of an emulsion containing 5 to 45 per cent oil makes use of the good qualities of both liquids.

A good cutting oil increases the accuracy of the cuts and lowers the cost of the work by making possible higher cutting speeds, by prolonging the life of the cutting tool, and by reducing the power demand and the number of rejects.

The preceding discussion on high-pressure lubricants would suggest that a sulfonated or sulfide additive should be present in the emulsified oil droplet in a good cutting oil. For low speeds and light cuts, a chlorinated lubricant may be used. For machining brass, the emulsified oil would be a paraffin oil containing copper oleate or free fatty acid. A sulfurized oil should *not* be used in this instance, as it would discolor the work. For turning aluminum, the emulsion droplets should be of a light, low-viscosity oil (see also Special Lubricants, page 188).

Cutting oils or, more properly, cutting emulsions are often prepared by diluting a so-called "soluble oil" to the desired extent with water. A soluble oil is really not *soluble* in water, but disperses into very small droplets which form a stable milky suspension.

A typical soluble oil can be prepared by dissolving 8 grams of oleic acid in 88 grams of the chosen oil and then adding 4 grams of triethanol amine with stirring. Oleic acid is added drop by drop until the liquid is clear, plus a further two drops in excess. Other weight units may, of course, be substituted.

Emulsions of 50 per cent lube oil and water are used for the lubrication of steam cylinders, giving cooler walls and less oil consumption. Such emulsions are more successful in lubricating compressors handling fuel gases, than all but the best quality bodied-oil.

Concentrated emulsions have much higher viscosity than either of the component liquids. They may behave like soft solids, due to the large amount of surface energy bound up in the interfaces of the two phases and on the resultant structure stabilized by the emulsifying agent.

13-7 Gels and Greases

Greases are semi-solid lubricants designed to "stay put" and to prevent contamination of the bearing by dirt or water. Their structure and behavior indicate that they are typical colloidal systems called gels.

A gel is the semirigid product produced when many colloidal solutions are coagulated. One characteristic of gel formation is the immobilization of all or most of the original liquid. This disappearance of the liquid phase is familiar in the setting of jellies. A solution containing only two parts by weight of gelatin with 98 parts of water will form a soft solid. Another example is the formation of the solid fuel called "canned heat." Such a rather unstable jelly-like solid is obtained by mixing 95 ml of ethanol and 5 ml of a saturated aqueous solution of calcium acetate. In this product the amount of original solid is very small, as is the case with the jellyfish, an example of a living gel, which is 98 per cent water.

Gels consist of a brush-heap structure in which the twigs or branches are colloidal fibers. These fibers may be formed during the coagulation process by polymerization or produced by the linear aggregation of micelles or colloidal particles. Liquid is held in the capillary spaces as in a sponge, but

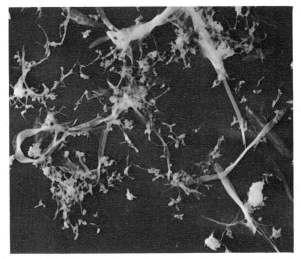

Figure 13-11 Electron photomicrograph of a grease. [Courtesy Imperial Oil Ltd.]

some of the liquid is held more as adsorbed layers around each fibril. Other molecules of fluid, such as water, form quite strong bridges between neighboring fibers. Jellies are gels which can be redispersed by the addition of more solvent or dispersion medium.

Some gels when subjected to shear or stirring will liquefy, but will reset after the stirring has stopped. Such gels are said to be *thixotropic*. This property is often made use of in greases and in paints (see Chapter 19).

In some gels a continuation of the setting process or surface tension forces causes contraction of the brush pile, which results in some liquid being squeezed from the gel. This phenomenon is called *syneresis*. Greases which "bleed" during storage are examples.

Greases are essentially thixotropic gels in which the fibrils or structural elements are metallic soaps, and the entrained liquid is lubricating oil. Figure 13-11 is an electron micrograph of a typical grease. The manufacture of three common types of grease is shown in Fig. 13-12.

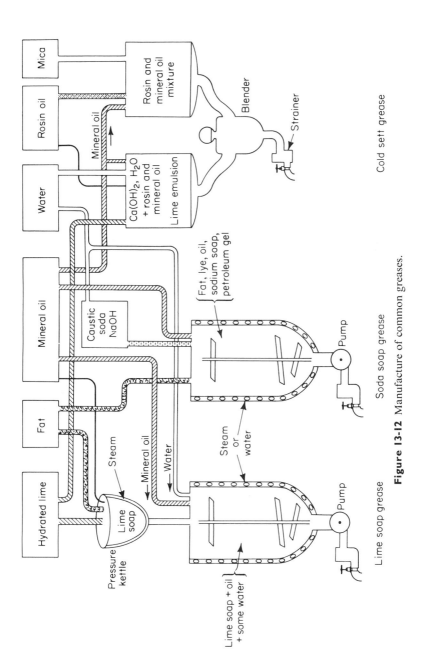

Figure 13-12 Manufacture of common greases.

The shearing of the grease in moving parts causes an increase in fluidity until the viscosity may be only slightly higher than that of the oil component. At the ends of the bearing or shaft, where the grease is not being sheared, the gel structure is maintained. The liquefied lubricant is thus kept in place, and the entrance of water or dirt prevented. Soap fibers having a large ratio of length to diameter give the highest yield or shear values, while the shorter fibers seem to hold the oil more strongly, possibly because of the presence of smaller capillaries in the gel structure.

The soaps used to form the framework of greases are calcium, sodium, lithium, aluminum, and barium salts of saturated and unsaturated fatty acids, containing from 16 to 18 carbon atoms in the chain. In the case of aluminum and lithium greases, the saturated fatty acids are more commonly used. Lead and zinc soaps are also employed in conjunction with other soaps.

The properties of a grease depend on both the metal base and the chemical composition of the fat or fatty acids with which the base is combined. It is known that soaps of unsaturated fatty acids have less bodying power than saturated fatty acids having the same metal cation. Increasing the saturation of the fat used raises the thermal stability of the grease as well as the "dropping point," analogous to the melting point of a pure substance.

In general, in the formulation of lubricating greases, a mixture of fatty acids or glycerides of more than one molecular weight or chain length is used. The fibers formed from such a mixture, not being identical, contribute greater stability to the grease.

Many greases have water incorporated in them. In the case of lime soap grease, this may amount to 10 per cent. While some of the water may be emulsified in the oil, it has been found from photomicrographs that the soap fibril structure breaks down when water of constitution is removed from the grease, with consequent separation of soap and oil.

Water used in the manufacture of calcium base greases is referred to as "tie" water and possesses a wetting ability. Calcium stearate is not wetted by water and poorly wetted by mineral oils. However, if water is poured onto the surface of the calcium stearate and then drained off, the oil will then spread readily over the surface. An alteration of the surface has been brought about by the water.

It has been suggested that the water is present in monolayers between the opposing layers of the polar heads of the soap molecules. This monomolecular water layer favours lateral end-to-end adherence of the micelles, producing the long chains which are responsible for gel structure.

Water, dispersed as a third phase in soap-mineral oil systems, acts as a structural modifier. Water is used to form an emulsion in the manufacture of rosin-based grease.

The presence of water in grease may be detrimental. In aluminum soap products, water will decrease the gel strength of the soap and in some cases completely destroy it. This decrease in strength is no doubt brought about by hydrolysis of the soap by the water present. The fatty acids produced from the soap do not readily recombine with the alumina but are adsorbed on the soap crystallites, probably interfering with polymer growth.

Another theory is that the hydroxyl group of water coordinates with the aluminum atom strongly enough to split some of the polymer chains. However, some water (0.1 per cent) may be present in aluminum-soap greases. Other third-component modifiers are alcohols, phenols, amines, esters, and fatty acids.

Lime-soap Grease

Lime- or calcium-soap-base greases enjoy the largest sale of any type because they are relatively cheap and have good resistance to displacement by water, and are thus suitable for lubricating water pumps, tractors, caterpillar treads, etc. They can be produced in a wide range of consistency, from a soft, semisolid paste, to a hard, smooth solid, by altering the amount of lime soap (10 to 30 per cent). Temperatures above 65° C (150° F) tend to cause deterioration of lime-soap grease due to loss of combined water. The ingredients of lime-soap grease are slaked lime, fats, and lubricating oil.

The first step in preparing lime-soap grease is to make lime soap. The melted fat and some of the mineral oil are mixed with hydrated lime in a closed pressure kettle where a reaction takes place between the glyceride and the alkaline lime at a temperature of about 150° C (300° F).

$$
\begin{array}{ccccc}
& \overset{\displaystyle O}{\underset{\displaystyle \|}{\text{CH}_2\!-\!\text{OC}\!-\!\text{R}}} & & \text{CH}_2\text{OH} & \\[2mm]
2\;\overset{\displaystyle O}{\underset{\displaystyle \|}{\text{CH}\;\!-\!\text{OC}\!-\!\text{R}}} + 3\,\text{Ca(OH)}_2 & \longrightarrow & 2\,\text{CHOH} + 3\,\overset{\displaystyle O}{\underset{\displaystyle \|}{\text{Ca(OC}\!-\!\text{R)}_2}} \\[2mm]
& \underset{\displaystyle \|}{\overset{\displaystyle \text{CH}_2\!-\!\text{OC}\!-\!\text{R}}{O}} & & \text{CH}_2\text{OH} & \\[2mm]
\text{Fat} & \text{Slaked lime} & & \text{Glycerol} & \text{Lime soap}
\end{array}
$$

The exact composition of the soap will depend on the nature of R (that is, on the kind of fat used).

When saponification is complete, the product is dropped or forced by the steam pressure into a jacket mixing kettle. Here the lubricating oil in the desired amount is incorporated. When the kettle is cooled to about 105° C (220° F), the boiling water required to stabilize the grease is added and thoroughly stirred in to give a uniform product. While still fluid, the grease is pumped through a strainer into drums or other containers.

Sodium-soap Greases

Grease based on sodium soaps may be used at higher temperatures than calcium soap greases, due primarily to the higher melting point of this type of lubricating grease and, to some extent, to its fibrous structure. Because sodium soaps are soluble in water, this grease is not suitable for bearings which may be exposed to wet conditions. Soda-base greases contain from 10 to 20 per cent soap. A small amount of water of hydration may be present, although no water is added, as in the manufacture of lime-soap greases. Good dispersions can be obtained under anhydrous conditions.

The manufacture of soda-soap grease is a simpler process than that of lime-soap greases. Saponification takes place in the grease kettle. Concentrated caustic soda and the fat or hydrogenated oil are stirred together at 140° to 150° C (280° to 300° F) until the reaction is complete. The lubricating oil component is mixed into the hot soap and the resulting gel is then packaged.

Aluminum-base Greases

Aluminum-base lubricating greases are very similar to calcium and soda-base greases, but they possess a clarity which gives them a very attractive appearance. They command a premium in price over both soda- or calcium-base greases. They contain about 5 per cent more mineral oil than most calcium-base greases of the same consistency, due to a lower soap content. They are relatively waterproof and have dropping points slightly higher than calcium greases. These dispersions are prepared using aluminum stearate or the mixed soaps obtained on reacting aluminum sulfate with soda soap. In the case of aluminum soaps, the crystals are too small to be resolved microscopically. Studies indicate that the aluminum stearate grease is essentially a metastable jelly at ordinary temperatures, but it changes slowly to a paste on aging. The rate of transformation is accelerated by shear. An aluminum-base grease having a smooth, buttery structure may change to a rubbery type of product at about 200° F or higher and, on cooling at a relatively rapid rate from that temperature level to room temperature, may become a coarse, hard, unsatisfactory lubricant. For that reason, the use of this type of grease is limited to relatively low operation temperatures.

Lithium-soap Gels

Dispersions of lithium soaps in oils are of interest on account of their stability at high temperature and in the presence of moisture. Because the temperature encountered by aircraft at extreme heights can be as low as −67° F, it is very necessary to have lubricants that will permit functioning of controls under such conditions. Properly formulated lithium-base lubricating greases not only meet such conditions, but also have melting points in excess of 300° F; they are also comparatively waterproof. They have high mechanical stability, low oxidation, and are stable in storage. Lithium-base grease may be considered an all-purpose grease. Due to its higher cost, it is only used where extreme conditions exist.

Lithium greases are prepared usually from a fairly pure grade of lithium stearate by heating the cold oil suspension to a temperature in excess of complete solubility (about 200° C). The soap crystals formed on cooling are considerably smaller than those of sodium stearate. The rheological properties of lithium-base greases are similar to those of sodium and calcium soap grease.

Barium-base Lubricating Greases

Barium-base lubricating greases are characterized by extreme resistance to removal from bearings by water, a high melting point, good adhesiveness and cohesiveness, and resistance to change in consistency due to the working action of bearings. The versatility of this type of lubricant has led to its use as a multipurpose grease for automotive and farm equipment and for many other industrial applications.

Rosin Soap Grease

In this type of grease, rosin oil, which contains various saponifiable acids, such as abietic acid, is substituted for fatty acids or fats. The rosin oil is dissolved in the lubricating oil and allowed to react at a relatively low temperature (58° C or 100° F) with a slurry of slaked lime, emulsified oil, and water, called "sett." The resulting grease, commonly known as "cold sett grease," is used chiefly as axle grease for farm wagons and low-speed machinery. It is the cheapest of the greases.

The properties of any of the types of grease described above may be modified by incorporating various additives. These may be other soaps to give a mixed soap base, special fatty acids, or structure-modifying salts, stabilizing agents, inorganic thickeners, and solid lubricants. These increase the usefulness of the product. Copper phthalate is an example of a special additive which decreases the sensitivity of the grease to oxidation. Such a grease maintains its consistency almost unchanged to 150° C (270° F). As the temperature rises beyond this point, to 225° C (405° F), the grease develops a stiffer consistency.

Typical thickeners are silica gel, acetylene black, and modified clays. In the case of clay thickeners, advantage is taken of the base exchange properties by which the sodium cation of the clay is replaced by a tertiary amine or tertiary cation. The colloidal particle of clay is thus covered with hydrocarbon radicals which help to bind the oil component of the grease.

13-8 Synthetic Lubricants

Synthetic lubricants are designed for special jobs. There are 50 commercial fluids now on the market. These include polyisopropylene oxide diesters, fluorinated oil derivatives, and various silicone liquids.

An excellent universal synthetic winter grade (SW) crankcase oil, which has been tested in Alaska, uses polypropylene glycol. The oil is characterized by zero carbonization, low ash, lower starting temperature, and from 60 to 350 per cent greater mileage use. Polyalkylene glycols may be oil soluble or water soluble, liquid or solid. The aqueous lubricating solutions are also used as hydraulic fluids.

A diester formed by the reaction of 2-ethylhexyl alcohol with isosebacic acid gives satisfactory performance from $-65°$ F to $450°$ F for lubrication of turbo-jets. (Isosebacic acid is a mixture of isomers containing 72 to 80 % of 2-ethylsuberic acid, $HOOC(CH_2)_5CH(C_2H_5)COOH$, 12 to 18 per cent of 2,5-diethyladipic acid, $HOOC—CH(C_2H_5)—CH_2—CH_2—CH(C_2H_5)COOH$, and 6 to 10 per cent of sebacic acid, $HOOC(CH_2)_8COOH$.)

Fluolubes

These compounds have high chemical and thermal stability. They are less susceptible to oxidation and cracking. Vapors of diesters containing more than 55 per cent fluorine by weight will not explode when mixed with pure oxygen at $200°$ F. Many of these fluorinated compounds have S.I.T. values of $850°$ F to $1000°$ F. Chlorine derivatives are not as stable but may have good lubricating properties.

One interesting application of such a lubricant is in submarines. These fluorinated fluids have high densities and sink in seawater. Hence the position of a damaged undersea vessel is not betrayed by the presence of an oil slick on the surface.

Silicone Lubricants

For lubrication at elevated temperatures, many silicone fluids are available. The general formula of these is

$$R_3SiO\left(\begin{array}{c} R \\ | \\ Si—O \\ | \\ R \end{array}\right)_n —SiR_3$$

where R is an organic radical.

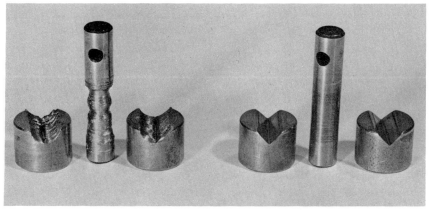

Figure 13-13 Test pieces at the end of Falex test. (Left) specimen showing gross wear when lubricated with dimethylsilicone oil; (right) specimen showing no wear when lubricated with p-bromophenylmethylsilicone oil. [Courtesy G. C. Gainer, Westinghouse Research Center and *Industrial and Engineering Chemistry*.]

Improvement in their properties as boundary lubricants has been made by leaving some unreacted —OH groups and by variation in the type of substituted group. The incorporation in the silicone of phenyl groups bearing halogen substituents increases the load-bearing capacity very considerably. This is shown in Fig. 13-13. The test pieces lubricated with a dimethyl silicone oil exhibit very marked wear, while those lubricated with p-bromo-phenylmethyl silicone oil, show no wear.

Table 13-2. TYPICAL PROPERTIES OF SILICONE OILS

Dow corning fluid	Viscosity cs at 77° F	Viscosity-Temp. coefficient	Flash point, °F	Pour point, °F	Serviceable Temp. Range, °F
200 fluid[a]	20	0.59	450	−76	−75–350
	100	0.60	575	−67	−65–350
	500	0.62	600	−58	−55–350
	12,500	0.58	600	−51	−50–350
510 fluid[b]	50	0.62	525	−80[c]	−70–350
	100	0.62	525	−80[c]	−70–350
	500	0.65	525	−80[c]	−70–350
	1000	0.63	525	−80[c]	−70–350
550 fluid	100–150	0.76	575	−58	−40–350
710 fluid	475–525	0.83	575	− 8	0–500

[a] Available in viscosities from 0.65 to 2,500,000 centistokes.
[b] Available in viscosities from 50 to 100,000 centistokes.
[c] Freeze point, degrees Fahrenheit.

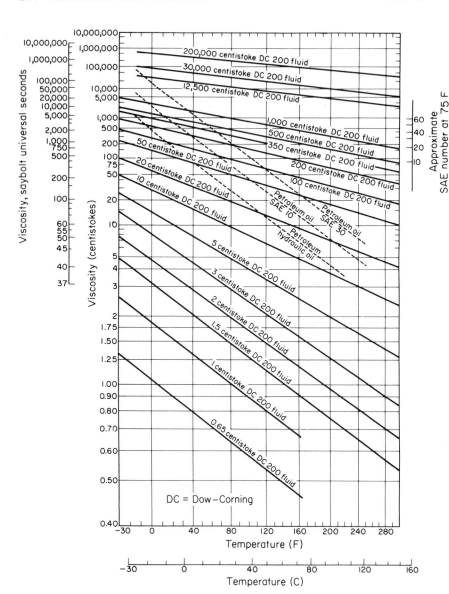

Figure 13-14 A comparison of the effect of temperature on the viscosity of different silicone fluids and standard petroleum lubricating oils. [Courtesy Dow-Corning Silicones Ltd.]

Various silicone oils are available for specific applications in a wide range of viscosity and types. Silicone fluids of the 200 series are recommended lubricants for rubber and plastic surfaces, including moving-picture film, slide rules, gears, bushings, bearings, and as a moisture-repellent, dielectric lubricant for clocks, timers, and other electronic devices. Silicone 510 fluids are suitable for low-temperature lubrication. Silicone 710 fluid is a heat-stable lubricant for oven timers, oven hinges, automatic toasters, and conveyor and dolly wheels or rollers exposed to high temperatures, high humidity, or weathering. It will be apparent from Fig. 13-14 and Table 13-2 that the silicone oils can serve as fluid lubricants over a much greater temperature range than hydrocarbon oils and that the change in viscosity with temperature is much less. Table 13-2 gives some data on different viscosity grades of several types of silicone oils.

Silicone Greases

These greases are made from various silicone oils using lithium soaps or various thickening agents. One of the more-recent types developed for components of space vehicles, missiles, and supersonic aircraft is claimed to be an effective lubricant at temperatures as low as $-100°$ F and to be unimpaired by 1000 hours at 450° F. The upper limit is 600° F (315° C).

The comparison of resistance to oxidation of a silicone and two types of ordinary soap grease is given in Fig. 13-15. In this comparison equal samples of the greases were exposed to oxygen at 110 psi and 210° F for 500 hours.

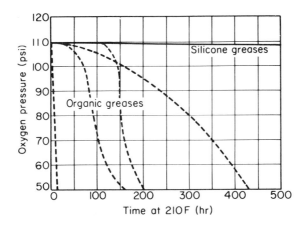

Figure 13-15 Resistance of various soap greases to oxidation as compared with silicone grease. Fall in oxygen pressure vs time is a measure of the rate of oxidation. [Courtesy Dow-Corning Silicones Ltd.]

Reaction of the grease with the oxygen is indicated by the drop in pressure in the bomb.

Greases made with fluorinated diesters also show good stability at elevated temperatures.

13-9 Solid Lubricants

The two solids most widely used as lubricants are colloidal graphite and molybdenum sulfide, MoS_2. Both of these solids have a laminar structure.

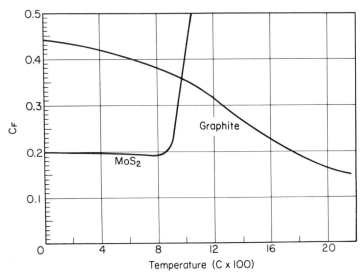

Figure 13-16 Comparison of graphite and molybdenum sulfide as solid lubricants. [From F. Bowden and D. Tabor, *Friction and Lubrication* [London: Methuen and Co., Ltd., 1956] by permission of the authors and publisher.]

Graphite consists of a meshwork of hexagonal carbon rings separated from the top layer of the unit crystal cell a distance of 6.79 Å. The separation of the constituent layers of carbon atoms is two and one-half times the length of the hexagonal rings. Molybdenum sulfide has a sandwich-like structure in which a layer of molybdenum atoms lies between two layers of sulfur atoms. The distance between the sulfur layers is 6.26 Å. Since the constituent atoms are heavier and closer together, it is obvious that MoS_2 will have a higher specific gravity (5) than graphite (2). It is slightly softer than graphite. These materials may be applied as a dry powder, as an aerosol from a freon pressurized container, as a paste, grease, or liquid dispersion. Typical commercial products are "aqua dag" and "oil dag"—aqueous and oil dispersions of graphite; or molykote (MoS_2) products of various types.

Graphite and molybdenum sulfide are particularly valuable as lubricants at extreme pressures and high temperatures. Figure 13-16 shows the effect of temperature on the coefficient of friction of copper when lubricated with these solids. It will be noted that molybdenum sulphide gives a low co-

Table 13-3. COEFFICIENT OF FRICTION C_f BETWEEN VARIOUS SURFACES[a]

Slider	Surface	C_f
Cast iron on steel	Unlubricated	0.4
Cast iron on steel	+Mineral oil	0.1–0.2
Copper on steel	Unlubricated	0.3
Bronze and brass on steel	Unlubricated	0.35
Copper-lead alloy on steel	Unlubricated	0.2
White metal on steel	Unlubricated	0.7
White metal on steel	+Mineral oil	0.2
Graphite on steel	Clean	0.1
Copper on copper	Unlubricated	1.2
	+Liquid silicone	1.0
	+Mineral oil	0.2–0.3
	+Paraffin wax	0.1–0.2
	+Fatty acid	0.01
	+Copper soap	0.05
Ice on ice −50° C		0.5
Ice on ice at 0° to −20° C		0.05–0.1
Ski wax on snow at −10° C (14° F)		0.2
Methacrylate lacquer on snow at −10° C		0.35
Teflon on snow at −10° C		0.07
Teflon on dry sand		0.13
Teflon on Teflon or steel		0.04–0.1
Methacrylate on dry sand		0.40
Ski lacquer on dry sand		0.36
Polythene on polythene		0.8
Polythene on steel		0.3–0.5
Nylon on nylon		0.5
Wood on metals, dry and clean		0.25–0.5
Wood on wood		0.2–0.6
Brake lining on cast iron		0.4
Brake lining on cast iron and water		0.2
Brake lining on "greasy" cast iron		0.1

[a] From data in F. D. Bowden and D. Tabor, *Friction and Lubrication* (London: D. Methuen & Co., Ltd., 1956), by permission.

efficient of friction at temperatures below 900° C (1600° F). Due to the decomposition of MoS_2, the friction increases sharply above this temperature. The graphite is an effective lubricant at much higher temperatures. Oil-less bearings may be (1), sintered metal in which graphite or molybdenum sulfide fills the pores or (2) impregnated plastic washers.

A solid-film lubricating surface for space vehicle use is made from 70 per cent MoS_2 and 7 per cent graphite, bonded by 23 per cent silicates; it is unaffected by extremes of temperature, low pressure, or nuclear radiation.[1]

Low-friction solid surfaces may be formed by using a reactive gas in place of a lubricant. Hydrogen sulfide, chlorine, and hydrogen chloride have been used experimentally in high-speed cutting operations. The formation of the chemical coating of a low coefficient of friction is much faster and more effective than the chemi-sorption of an extreme pressure additive from an oil droplet. The iron chloride layer decomposes at approximately 300° C (500° F), while the sulfide surface is stable up to temperatures of 750° C (1300° F). If a molybdenum tool is used to cut aluminum, the amount of pickup on the tool is greatly decreased and the finish of the work surface much improved in the presence of hydrogen sulfide as a "gaseous lubricant." Since these gases are toxic and corrosive, special equipment would have to be evolved for industrial applications.

Reference to Table 13-3 will indicate that teflon surfaces have a very low coefficient of friction. The friction of teflon against sand is about the same as well-waxed skis against snow, or ice sliding on ice. These facts suggest the use of teflon as a solid lubricant. Since the thermal conductance of teflon is poor, the powdered material has been incorporated with sintered metal to make the bearing surface. Teflon can be applied to steel, brass, and aluminum, having a thin coating of oxide on a roughened surface; it forms a lubricating and protective coating. The film thickness should be between 0.0003 and 0.0006 in.

Teflon films have been found to give excellent protection; they can be used as a lubricant for periscopes, underwater mechanisms, gasoline gear pumps, oxygen valves, and brass cartridges. Synthetic solid lubricants are being developed for chronometers and other small mechanisms.

Review Questions

1. Define coefficient of friction.

2. How does a lubricant work?

3. Does a lubricant prevent wear?

4. What are some of the functions of a lubricating oil in a car or truck?

5. What is reduced crude?

6. What role does phenol play in the manufacture of lubricating oil?

7. What is raffinate?

---

1 "Silicate P's and Q's," **41,** No. 9 (1961), Philadelphia Quartz Co.

8. Name four solvents used to extract asphaltic or aromatic compounds.

9. List the steps in the preparation of a low-wax oil from the raffinate.

10. Write the formulas of three wax solvents.

11. What is accomplished in hydrofining?

12. Define absolute viscosity, S.U.S., centistokes, viscosity index.

13. Indicate some control tests used on lubricating oils.

14. Distinguish between boundary and fluid lubrication.

15. For what purpose would the following be added to an oil:

$C_6H_{11}(CH_2)_{21}CH_3$; $\left(R-\left\langle\bigcirc\right\rangle-SO_3\right)_2M$, where R is an alkyl group; $R_2N-\left\langle\bigcirc\right\rangle-CH_2-\left\langle\bigcirc\right\rangle-NR_2$?

16. Explain why two different types of lubricant may be named soluble oil.

17. Define thixotropic gel.

18. What type of grease would you use to lubricate (a) caterpillar tractor treads, (b) rollers in a drying kiln, (c) slow high-pressure hyploid gear?

19. Indicate the general structure of the following synthetic lubricants: a polyester, a polyglycol, a silicone fluid.

20. Name one notable quality for each of the types of lubricants mentioned in question 19.

21. What materials can be used for permanent dry lubrication?

22. A certain lubricating oil has the same viscosity as standard naphthenic- and paraffin-type oils at 210° F. The viscosities at 100° F are 320 S.U.S., 430 S.U.S., and 260 S.U.S. respectively. What is the V.I. of the oil?

Further Readings

Boner, C., *Manufacture and Application of Lubricating Greases* (New York: Reinhold, 1955).

Bowden, F., and Tabor, D., *Friction and Lubrication* (New York: Wiley, 1956).

Fitzsimmons, V., and Zisman, W., "Polytetraflouroethylene as Lubricant," *Industrial and Engineering Chemistry*, **50** (1958), 781.

Gainer, G., "Silicone Oils for Lubricating Steel as Steel," *Industrial and Engineering Chemistry*, **46** (1954), 2355.

McGregor, R., *Silicones and Their Uses* (New York: McGraw-Hill, 1962).

Moses, G., and Puddington, J., "Flow Properties of Dispersions of Calcium Soaps in Hydrocarbon Oils," *Canadian Journal of Chemistry*, **27B** (1949), 616.

Purdy, G. A., *Petroleum* (Toronto: Copp Clark, 1958).

14

The Chemistry of Electric Cells, Storage Batteries, and Fuel Cells

When we use a flashlight or start the car, we have a demonstration of electro-chemical reactions at work. These reactions have produced new substances by oxidation and reduction with a consequent flow of electrons.

This chapter presents the electrochemical principles involved in electric cells, storage batteries, and fuel cells. The subsequent chapter deals with the electrochemical processes concerned with the mechanism of corrosion and its detection, measurement, mitigation, and prevention.

14-1 Nernst's Theory

The physical chemist Nernst considered that no metal was truly insoluble. If a stick of copper is put into pure water, some copper atoms will shed their valence electrons and dive into the water as copper ions Cu^{++}. This leaves an excess negative charge on the metal electrode and thus a potential difference between the metal and the solution. An equilibrium will be established when the number of Cu^{++} ions returning to the electrode and regaining two electrons will equal the number of copper atoms going into solution as copper ions, that is,

$$Cu° - 2e \rightleftharpoons Cu^{++}$$

If the copper electrode is put into a concentrated solution of a copper salt, there will be a greater tendency for Cu^{++} to plate out than for copper to dissolve as ions. The metal therefore will have developed a positive charge. There must be some concentration of Cu^{++} in solution at which the potential between the metal and solution will be zero.

Zinc shows a much greater tendency than copper to go into solution as positive ions, and the concentration of zinc ions in solution must be much higher before equilibrium is established. Sodium metal will persist in leaving the valence electrons on the metal and getting in the swim as positive ions, even when the concentration of ions is very great.

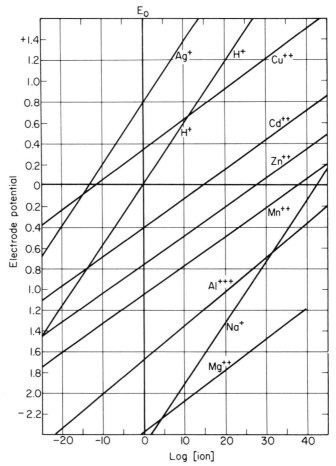

Figure 14-1 Nernst's electrode potential *vs* log ion concentration.

Nernst derived an equation which relates the electrode potential to the concentration (actually the activity) of the metal ion. It may be written

$$E = \frac{0.0591}{n} \log \frac{C}{K}$$

where C is the concentration in gram ions/liter, K is an equilibrium constant, and n is the charge or valence of the ion. Obviously, if C equals K, the potential is zero.

Hydrogen acts like a metal by forming positive ions in water. A hydrogen electrode is made by bubbling the gas at one atmosphere pressure over platinized platinum, the gas forming a thin film or "plate" over the conducting metal.

Figure 14-1 shows electrode potentials plotted against log C.

Nernst pointed out that the numerical values of K for each ion gave a quantitative estimate of the tendency of the metal to form an electrolytic solution. It was called the Electrolytic Solution-tension Constant.

14-2 Standard Electrode Potentials

A much more-convenient scale of chemical reactivity is obtained by measuring the electrode potentials at a fixed concentration of one gram ion/liter and adopting arbitrarily the standard potential of the hydrogen electrode at this concentration as 0.000 volt. (Since the conversion of a

Table 14-1. STANDARD ELECTRODE POTENTIALS
(at 25° C)

Metal-ion electrode reaction	E_0, volts	Metal-ion electrode reaction	E_0, volts
K/K^+	-2.92	Cu/Cu^{++}	$+0.345$ v
Ca/Ca^{++}	-2.84	Cu/Cu^+	0.522
Na/Na^+	-2.71	Hg/Hg^+ or $Hg_2/2\,H^+$	0.799
Mg/Mg^{++}	-2.37	Ag/Ag^+	0.800
Al/Al^{+++}	-1.67	Hg/Hg^{++}	0.854
Mn/Mn^{++}	-1.05	Pt/Pt^{++}	1.2
Zn/Zn^{++}	-0.762	Au/Au^{+++}	1.42
Cr/Cr^{+++}	-0.71		
Fe/Fe^{++}	-0.441	Ion-ion and nonmetals	
Cd/Cd^{++}	-0.402		
Co/Co^{++}	-0.277	Cr^{++}/Cr^{+++}	-0.40
Ni/Ni^{++}	-0.25	OH^-/O_2	$+0.401$
Sn/Sn^{++}	-0.136	Fe^{++}/Fe^{+++}	0.748
Pb/Pb^{++}	-0.126	$2\,Br^-/Br_2$	1.065
$H_2/2\,H^+$	0.000	$2\,Cl^-/Cl_2$	1.358

neutral metal atom to a positive ion is called oxidation, the standard electrode potentials are sometimes referred to as *standard oxidation potentials*.) When $C = 1$, the Nernst expression for the standard electrode potential is

$$E_0 = \frac{0.0591}{n} \log \frac{1}{K}$$

Table 14-1 gives the standard electrode potentials for the common metals. The table gives a quantitative aspect to the old electrochemical series. Thus sodium, with its propensity to form an electrolytic solution, has $E_0 = -2.71$ volts. The relatively inert lead gives a value of only -0.126. Copper in contact with 1 gram ion of Cu^{++} will be positive in respect to the standard hydrogen electrode, namely, $+0.345$ volts.

14-3 Electric Cell or Battery

By combining any two half-cells having different electrode potentials, a chemical battery or electric cell is obtained. Thus if a standard copper half-cell is coupled with a standard zinc half-cell by wire and a salt bridge, as shown in the diagram Fig. 14-2, the resulting cell will have a voltage of

$$E_{0_{Cu}} - E_{0_{Zn}} = 0.345 - (-0.762) = 1.017 \text{ volts}$$

For other than unit concentrations, the emf of the cell may be calculated from the Nernst equation.

$$E_C = \frac{0.059}{n} \log \frac{C}{K}$$

$$= \frac{0.059}{n} \log \frac{1}{K} + \frac{0.059}{n} \log C = E_0 + \frac{0.059}{n} \log C$$

Suppose that the concentration of the Cu^{++} is $0.001 M$ and the Zn^{++} is $0.1 M$. The voltage of this Daniell cell would be

$$E_{Cu} - E_{Zn} = \left(E_{0_{Cu}} + \frac{0.059}{2} \log [Cu^{++}] \right) - \left(E_{0_{Zn}} + \frac{0.059}{2} \log [Zn^{++}] \right)$$

$$= (0.345 + 0.0295 \log 10^{-3}) - (-0.762 + 0.0295 \log 10^{-1})$$

$$= 0.345 - 0.0885 + 0.762 + 0.0295 = 1.048 \text{ volts}$$

The Daniell cell is the result of two simple reactions:

$$Zn° \longrightarrow Zn + 2 e^-$$

$$Cu^{++} + 2 e^- \longrightarrow Cu°$$

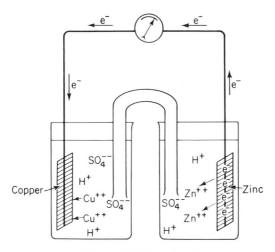

Figure 14-2 Daniell cell.

Figure 14-3 The earliest known chemical battery, from Ancient Baghdad. [From *The Laboratory*, **25**, 1957, 112. Courtesy Fisher Scientific Co.]

Electrons flow from the zinc electrode to the copper through the connecting metal, while the positive Cu^{++} ions in the solutions move toward the copper (the cathode) where they reduce the electron "pressure" as they plate out. The electron pressure is kept up by the production of a corresponding stream of zinc ions from the corrosion of the zinc electrode (the anode).

The oldest known electric cells preceded the Galvani cell by two thousand years. They were made by the Parthians who lived in Mesopotamia between 250 B.C. and 224 A.D. A cylinder of copper approximately 10 cm long and 2.5 cm in diameter formed one electrode and a central rod of iron, inserted into the contained electrolyte through a bitumen or asphalt stopper, formed the other. To keep this wet cell upright, it was cemented into a small vase (Fig. 14-3). It is thought that these cells were used in multiples to gold-plate jewelry.

14-4 Concentration Cells

While chemical batteries are normally made using two different elements or metals as electrodes, it follows from the Nernst equation that a cell can be produced from electrodes of the same material, provided the concentration of its ions in contact with each electrode is different. The emf of such a cell is

$$E_{C'} - E_{C''} = \left(E_0 + \frac{0.059}{n} \log C' \right) - \left(E_0 + \frac{0.059}{n} \log C'' \right)$$

Since E_0 is the same for each of these electrodes, the expression becomes

$$\text{emf} = \frac{0.059}{n} \log \frac{C'}{C''}$$

This is called a *concentration cell.*

Suppose $C' = 10C''$. For monovalent ions the emf $= 0.059 \log 10 = 0.059$ volt. For a divalent ion, a tenfold difference in ionic concentration would yield 0.0295 volt. While these potentials may seem small, concentration cells play a very important role in corrosion.

In any cell where changes in ionic concentration occur during use, the emf will fall. In the Daniell cell the concentration of the Cu^{++} diminishes, and the zinc ion increases, each causing the cell to "run down." The cell emf finally drops to zero. The cell is "dead." This state is reached when the ratio of the $[Zn^{++}]/[Cu^{++}]$ reaches a definite value. The ratio may be calculated from the Nernst equation:

$$\text{emf} = E_{Cu} - E_{Zn}$$

At equilibrium, emf $= 0$, so $E_{Zn} = E_{Cu}$; that is

$$(E_{0_{Zn}} + 0.0295 \log [Zn^{++}]) = (E_{0_{Cu}} + 0.0295 \log [Cu^{++}])$$

or

$$-0.762 + 0.0295 \log [Zn^{++}] = 0.345 + 0.0295 \log [Cu^{++}]$$

$$0.0295 \log \frac{[Zn^{++}]}{[Cu^{++}]} = 1.107$$

$$\log \frac{[Zn^{++}]}{[Cu^{++}]} = 37.5$$

so

$$K = \frac{[Zn^{++}]}{[Cu^{++}]} = 3 \times 10^{37}$$

This means that the concentration of copper ion in the cell has been reduced almost to zero.

For metals which are nearer together in oxidation potential, the ratio will not be as great. Lead and tin, for example, would give an equilibrium ratio such that appreciable concentrations of both ions would be present. The tin could not plate out all of the lead.

Reversing a Cell

It is possible to increase the ratio of the reducing to the oxidizing ion in a cell beyond the equilibrium value, thus causing the current to reverse. Even the Daniell cell may be made to "flow backwards." Starting with a very dilute solution of copper sulfate in the copper half-cell, the addition of sodium sulfide causes the concentration of Cu^{++} to be reduced by the precipitation of CuS, and the emf drops. The addition of KCN to the resulting *alkaline* solution lowers the concentration of the Cu^{++} still further by the formation of the very stable complex ion $Cu(CN)_4^{---}$. In the presence of excess KCN the concentration of the copper ion becomes so low that the deficiency has to be overcome by more copper ions being formed from the electrode. The copper thus has an excess of electrons, and the current reverses, the electrons flowing through the wire to the zinc, where Zn^{++} ions are now plating out.

14-5 Other Oxidation-Reduction Cells

Any pair of oxidizing and reducing substances can be used as the components of a cell. In other than metal $\rightleftharpoons$ ion reaction, the electrodes in each half-cell are usually platinum, and the vessels containing the reducing agent and oxidizing agent are connected by a porous diaphragm or salt bridge. The electrodes are connected through metal. A voltmeter or millivoltmeter may be used to compare the emf or, more properly, the cell potentials. Figure 14-4 illustrates a cell formed by connecting a solution of $KMnO_4$ with a solution of KI. It can be shown that, in a short time, oxidation and reduction have taken place, although there has been no admixing of the reagents. Free iodine can be detected in the potassium iodide solution in a few minutes, although the colored permanganate ions have only travelled a short distance in the salt bridge.

Other combinations, such as K_2CrO_4 and $FeSO_4$, $FeCl_3$ and H_2S, and even oxygen and hydrogen gas, can be readily demonstrated. A current can

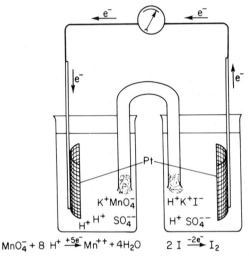

$$MnO_4^- + 8\ H^+ \xrightarrow{+5e^-} Mn^{++} + 4H_2O \qquad 2\ I \xrightarrow{-2e^-} I_2$$

Figure 14-4 A typical chemical battery formed from an oxidizing and a reducing substance.

be produced if one end of a pipe is in an oxidizing environment, and the other end is in a reducing environment.

14-6 Other Standard Electrodes or Half-cells

In order to keep the potential of a half-cell constant during use, provision must be made to prevent any changes in the concentration of the metal ion. Changes may be avoided by placing the electrode in contact with a saturated solution and by maintaining an excess of one of its slightly soluble salts. In such cases an added electrolyte such as KCl assists in the conductance. The standard hydrogen electrode is used to establish the potential of such half-cells, which then may be used as reference or standard half-cells. The most widely used standard is the calomel electrode or half-cell (Fig. 14-5). A pool of mercury forms the electrode in contact with a paste of mercurous chloride (calomel), Hg_2Cl_2, and a solution of KCl. The voltage of the standard will depend on which of three concentrations of KCl is chosen. The discordant

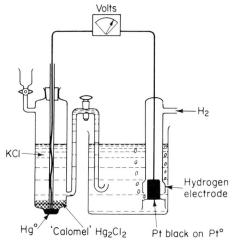

Figure 14-5 A standard cell combining calomel and hydrogen electrodes.

values for the calomel electrode in different texts are due to this fact and to differences in the experimental temperature.

Table 14-2

Potentials of standard calomel electrodes	20° C[a]	25° C[b]
With saturated KCl	0.2492 v	0.2446 v
1 molal KCl		0.2816
0.1 normal KCl	0.3379	0.3334
1 normal KCl	0.2860	0.2809

[a] J. Grant, *Hackh's Chemical Dictionary* (3 ed.; Philadelphia: The Blakiston Co., 1944).
[b] I. DeVries, *Handbook of Chemistry and Physics* (Cleveland, Ohio: Chemical Rubber Pub. Co., 1959).

Other standard electrodes, such as $Ag°$—saturated $AgCl$, and $Pb°$—$PbSO_4$ have also been used.

14-7 The Standard Weston Cell

A standard or reference cell must consist of two half-cells, both of which maintain their constant potentials. Such a cell is the *Weston* or *cadmium cell* (Fig. 14-6). The cell is shaped like a capital H. One of the vertical tubes holds a mercury electrode in contact with a paste of mercurous sulfate, Hg_2SO_4, and its saturated solution. The other vertical tube contains a

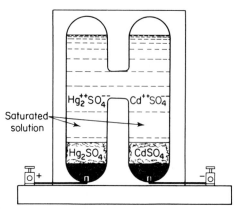

Figure 14-6 The standard Weston cell.

cadmium amalgam electrode and an excess of cadmium sulfate. The horizontal tube forms the salt bridge. The cell gives an emf of 1.0183 v at 20° C and is unaffected by moderate temperature changes. Its chief use is as a reference standard.

14-8 Accurate *p*H Measurements

When a normal calomel electrode is connected to a standard hydrogen half-cell ($H^+ = 1\,N$), the voltmeter should indicate 0.281 v at 25° C. If the hydrogen electrode is placed in a solution of unknown concentration of hydrogen ions, measurement of the emf may be used to calculate $[H^+]$ and the *p*H, since emf $= E_{calomel} - E_H = 0.281 - 0.059 \log [H^+]$; for example, if the cell gave 0.694 v, then

$$0.694 = 0.281 - 0.059 \log [H^+] \quad \text{or} \quad - \log [H^+] = \frac{0.413}{0.059} = 7.00 = p\text{H}$$

since *p*H is the negative log of the hydrogen ion concentration.

The method described above for determining *p*H is much more accurate than the use of colored indicators. Furthermore, the potentiometric method can be used on highly colored or turbid liquids, in which colored indicators would be useless, as in the case of mine waters, chemical wastes, and so on.

14-9 The Glass Electrode

The convenient *p*H meters employ a "glass electrode" instead of the hydrogen electrode. This electrode consists of a thin-walled bulb or membrane of a special high conductivity glass, containing a special buffered solution and a platinum connection. The potential of this half-cell varies directly with the pH of the external liquid or solution. Before use, the glass electrode is standardized against buffers of known pH. Strong acid or alkali will attack the glass membrane. For pH determinations above thirteen, special electrodes have to be used.

14-10 Total Acidity

While pH indicates the "active" acidity or alkalinity, *total acidity* is defined by the normality or concentration of the acid. Both are important.

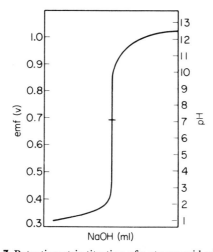

Figure 14-7 Potentiometric titration of a strong acid with NaOH.

Total acidity is determined by titration. This may be done by following the change in pH of the solution containing the glass or hydrogen electrode after each addition of standard alkali. The volume of alkali solution necessary to bring the solution to the "neutral point" or desired pH is obtained from a plot of emf versus milliliters or pH versus milliliters of alkali (Fig. 14-7).

Another electrochemical method of value in titration of opaque or dark-colored liquids is the conductance method. Two electrodes are inserted into the beaker containing the liquid and the conductance $(1/R)$ is measured. Standard alkali is added from a burette and the conductance determined after each addition. At first the addition of the alkali causes a decrease in conductance owing to the lower mobility of the sodium as compared to the replaced hydrogen ion:

$$H^+ + Cl^- + Na^+OH^- \longrightarrow HOH + Na^+ + Cl^-$$

As the equivalence point is passed the further addition of sodium hydroxide causes an increase in conductance since more ions are present. After several

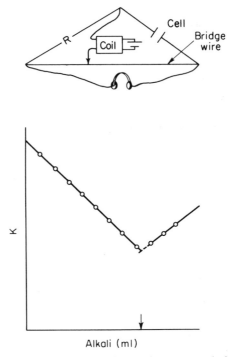

Alkali (ml)

Figure 14-8 Titration by measuring conductance *vs* ml of standard alkali solution.

increased values have been obtained, the experimental points, plotting conductance (μ) versus milliliters of standard NaOH, are joined. The intersection of the descending and ascending lines gives the end point of the titration (Fig. 14-8). The method may also be used when one of the products is insoluble, for example,

$$NaCl + AgNO_3 \longrightarrow AgCl + NaNO_3$$

Potentiometric measurements can be applied to determine the solubility of slightly soluble salts and oxides, such as corrosion products. The metal in contact with a saturated solution of its corrosion product is connected to a standard calomel cell. From the known values of the standard electrode potentials of the metal and the calomel, the concentration of metal ion can be calculated.

14-11 Polarization

When a cell is placed in use, the concentrations of ions surrounding the electrodes differ from that in the bulk of the electrolyte. The concentration gradients at the electrodes set up a back emf, and the cell potential drops. This is called *concentration polarization*. It increases with current density (amp/area) and with time (Figs. 14-9 and 14-10).

In the ordinary dry cell this polarization is diminished by the presence of ammonium chloride. Zinc ions are withdrawn by the formation of a complex $Zn(NH_3)_4^{++}$.

A second type of polarization may occur in a cell. This is caused by the formation of a resistant film of adhering atoms or molecules of gas on the electrode. Gas polarization may occur when oxygen or chlorine is liberated at anodes or when hydrogen ions are discharged at the cathode. Cathodic

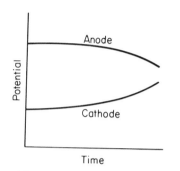

Figure 14-9 Polarization of anode and cathode *vs* time. [Courtesy International Nickel Co.]

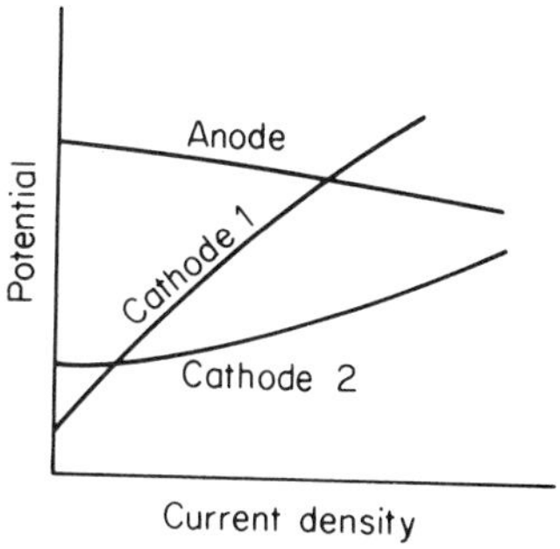

Figure 14-10 Polarization of metals *vs* current density. [Courtesy International Nickel Co.]

polarization in a dry cell occurs at the carbon electrode. The depolarizing agent used is manganese dioxide which reacts with the hydrogen to produce water and lower oxides of manganese.

14-12 Overvoltage

The emf of a standard chlorine-hydrogen cell is 1.36 v. Unless one uses platinized platinum electrodes, the decomposition voltage required to produce hydrogen and chlorine by electrolysis of the electrolyte is considerably greater. The extra voltage above the cell voltage is due to polarization and is called *overvoltage*.

Overvoltage depends primarily on the metal used for the electrode and the condition of its surface. A smooth metal exhibits a higher overvoltage than the same metal with a roughened surface, the gas being more easily evolved from projecting points or tiny grains. The overvoltage increases with increasing current density, but decreases with increasing temperature. The overvoltage may be raised by the addition of certain substances such as "corrosion inhibitors" and also by the formation of passive films on the metal surface.

The electrolysis of solutions of many electrolytes gives hydrogen and oxygen as reaction products. Everyone has seen the "decomposition of water by an electric current," but since the conductance of pure water is low, an electrolyte such as H_2SO_4, HNO_3, H_3PO_4, KOH, NaOH, or K_2SO_4 is added. When platinized platinum (black) electrodes are used, the decomposition

Table 14-3. HYDROGEN OVERVOLTAGES, 25° C

Metal	Volts (1 milliamp/cm²)	Volts (10 milliamp/cm²)
Pt, black	0.01	0.01
Pt, smooth	0.02	0.03
Au	0.24	0.39
Fe	0.40	0.56
Ag	0.48	0.76
Cu	0.48	0.58
Pb	0.52	1.09
Ni	0.56	· · ·
Al	0.57	0.83
C (graphite)	0.60	
Zn	0.72	0.75
Bi	0.78	· · ·
Sn	0.86	1.08
Hg	0.88	1.04
Cd	0.98	1.13

voltage is 1.23 v in each case, if the [H⁺] is 1 N. This is the same as the emf of the standard oxygen-hydrogen cell, as shown by the calculation

$$\text{emf} = E_{O_2} - E_{H_2} = 0.40 - 0.059 \log (\text{OH})^- - 0$$
$$= 0.40 - 0.059 \log 10^{-14} = 1.226 \text{ v or } 1.23 \text{ v}$$

With smooth platinum electrodes the decomposition voltage in each case is 1.7 v; that is, there is an overvoltage of 0.47 v.

In many electrolytic reactions and especially in electroplating and corrosion, overvoltage due to hydrogen is of major importance. Table 14-3 indicates hydrogen overvoltage on different electrodes at constant temperature and at current densities of 1 milliamp and 10 milliamp/cm². At current densities of 1 amp/cm², the overvoltage of nine of the metals in the table reach values of 1.23 to 1.29 with a mean of 1.24 v. Lower values are observed with Au, 0.80; Fe, 1.07; Ag, 1.09; and Hg, 1.12.

The importance of hydrogen overvoltage in electroplating of metals may be illustrated by the case of zinc. If platinum electrodes are placed in a solution of 1 N ZnSO$_4$ in N·H$_2$SO$_4$ and electrolyzed, hydrogen rather than zinc is plated out. Since the electrode potential of zinc is -0.76 v, while that of hydrogen is zero, the zinc shows a solution potential or tendency to stay in the form of ions of 0.76 v. If mercury is used as the cathode, the hydrogen overvoltage is so great (1.04 v) that it is now easier by 0.48 v (current density, 10 milliamp/cm^2) to plate out the zinc than to drive off hydrogen. The application of overvoltage to corrosion will be discussed later.

14-13 Reversible Cells or Storage Batteries

It has been shown that in the electric cell, oxidation-reduction reactions take place that result in a flow of electrons from the electrode where the substance is being oxidized to the electrode, where another material is being reduced. Under suitable conditions the chemical reaction which produced the initial current may be reversed and the original oxidizing and reducing substances rebuilt at the electrodes by the application of an emf. The cell is thus "recharged," and the chemical energy of the reformed anode and cathode material will again be transformed to electrical energy when the cell is put in use.

The most common storage cell or battery is made from lead plates, usually a lead alloy containing other metals such as antimony and barium. A battery ready for use consists of a negative electrode covered with gray spongy lead, and a positive plate impregnated with lead dioxide (or "peroxide"), PbO$_2$, in sulfuric acid as the electrolyte. In the fully charged cell the concentration of H$_2$SO$_4$ will be approximately 37 per cent, corresponding to a specific gravity of 1.28.

When the cell is used, the Pb $\rightarrow$ Pb^{++} + 2 e (corresponding to the Zn electrode in the Daniell cell); that is, oxidation takes place, while the lead dioxide on the other electrode is reduced:

$$PbO_2 + 2 H^+ \longrightarrow H_2O + PbO - 2 e$$

(analogous to the reaction Cu^{++} + 2 e $\rightarrow$ Cu$^\circ$). The first, then, is the reaction at the negative plate, the latter at the positive plate. Reaction with the electrolyte produces lead sulfate on both plates

$$Pb^{++} + H_2SO_4 \longrightarrow PbSO_4 + 2 H^+$$
$$PbO + H_2SO_4 \longrightarrow PbSO_4 + H_2O$$

Both of these reactions reduce the concentration of the sulfuric acid, and the specific gravity of the electrolyte therefore falls as the battery is discharged. The specific gravity should not be allowed to fall below 1.16. The cell voltage varies between 2.3 and 1.8, remaining at approximately 2.0 v until almost all of the PbO$_2$ has been reduced.

Recharging the battery reverses the electrochemical reactions. Electrons

Figure 14-11a Positive plate (left) and negative plate (right) of new "E line" nickel-iron alkaline storage battery for motive power service (electric industrial trucks). Note the absence of grid plates. Rows of perforated tubes containing nickel oxide and nickel flake are welded at ends to form the positive plate. Rows of perforated pockets containing active iron oxide interlock at sides and are welded at each extreme end to form the negative plate. Compactness of plate construction as well as cell design has resulted in 77 per cent increase in capacity in "E line" battery. [Courtesy Electric Storage Battery Co.]

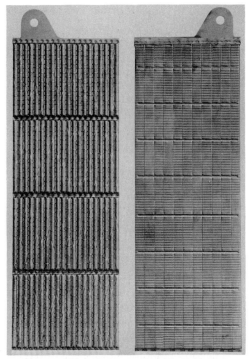

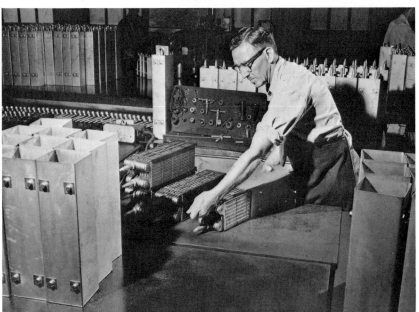

Figure 14-11b Assembling nickel-iron alkaline battery cells. The battery case is welded nickel-plated steel. [Courtesy Electric Storage Battery Co.]

Figure 14-11c Cutaway view of a nickel-iron alkaline storage battery such as utilized in railway carlighting and air conditioning service. Note space between top of plates and cell top. This permits cell to contain more electrolyte and require less frequent watering. Electrolyte consists of an aqueous solution of potassium hydroxide and a small amount of lithium hydroxide. [Courtesy Electric Storage Battery Co.]

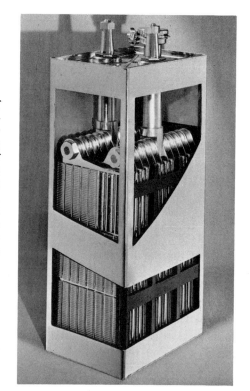

Figure 14-11d 30 MC8 nickel-iron alkaline storage battery. This 30-cell battery, utilizing standard nickel-iron cells, is used in electric industrial truck service, principally for rider-type trucks. [Courtesy Electric Storage Battery Co.]

207

are supplied by the impressed current to the negative pole and the lead ions reduced to spongy lead. Electrons are removed from the other terminal and the lead monoxide becomes oxidized to the dioxide. Thus in recharging a storage battery, the negative terminal of the power source is connected to the negative battery post, and the positive to the positive post.

14-14 The Edison Cell

Another type of storage battery is made from rechargeable Edison cells. In this cell the positive plate consists of a nickel-iron holder containing small perforated tubes filled with very thin alternate layers of nickel flake and hydrous nickel oxide. The negative plate is made up of many packets of very pure iron oxide, the containers being thin iron sheet perforated with 1900 tiny holes to the square inch. Figure 14-11a shows the structure of the positive and negative plates, Fig. 14-11b the assembling of a multiple plate cell. This will be welded into a nickel-plated steel container (Fig. 14-11c) and 20 per cent KOH solution added as the electrolyte. Figure 14-11d shows a group of these cells forming a rugged but light battery.

During charging, the iron oxide of the negative plate is reduced to pure iron, while at the positive plate the hydrous nickel oxide is oxidized to nickel dioxide:

$$FeO + HOH + 2\,e \longrightarrow 2\,(OH)^- + Fe^\circ$$
$$NiO + 2\,(OH)^- - 2\,e \longrightarrow NiO_2 + H_2O$$

When the charged battery is put into use, the reverse reactions take place. It will be seen from the equations that the concentration of KOH, the major source of $(OH)^-$, does not change during charge or discharge.

The nickel oxide-iron storage battery has several advantages over the lead battery. It is much lighter in weight and is not as susceptible to low temperatures. Even a completely discharged battery contains a high concentration of electrolyte. A sludge of ice and electrolyte will form below -17° F, but this does not solidify. The Edison cell dissipates heat generated by heavy loads or a high rate of discharge. The life of the battery is much longer because of freedom from shorts caused by displacement of active materials from the plates or from buckling of the plates themselves.

The chief disadvantage of the nickel-iron cell is its higher cost. In spite of this, it finds extensive use in mine locomotives, railway and other air-conditioning systems, and emergency lighting systems on shipboard.

14-15 The Nickel-cadmium Battery

Nickel-cadmium storage batteries are in common use in Europe. Miniature reversible cells are now available as rechargeable batteries for portable

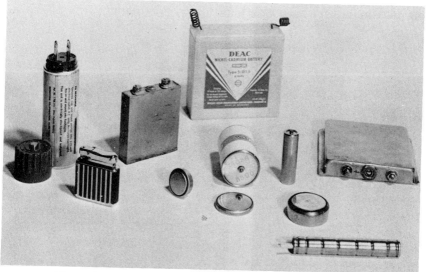

Figure 14-12 Ni-Cd rechargeable cells. The communications satellite TELSTAR is powered by Ni-Cd batteries which are recharged by solar photoelectric cells. [Courtesy E. J. Casey and DRB Labs., Ottawa.]

radios and flashlights (Fig. 14-12). A comparison of the performance of twelve-volt lead and Ni-Cd batteries is given in Table 14-4.

Table 14-4. COMPARISON OF THE PERFORMANCE AT LOW TEMPERATURES OF 12 v LEAD AND NICKEL-CADMIUM BATTERIES[a]

Temperature of charge and discharge	Amp hr output at 15 amp, down to 1.0 v/cell		Minutes cranking at 150 amp, down to 0.8 v/cell	
77° F	Nickel-cadmium	Lead-acid	Nickel-cadmium	Lead-acid
77° F	34	45	12.4	7
0	26	22	9.3	2–5
−20	20	10	7.3	1–4
−40	9	0	3.8	0
−65	2–5	0	ca 0.1	0

[a] E. J. Casey, *Chemistry of the Nickel-cadmium Battery*, Defense Research of Canada Laboratory Report 315; *Chemistry in Canada*, **12**, No. 10 (1960), 49–56.

14-16 Fuel Cells

The hydrogen-oxygen cell suggested by Davy was first demonstrated by Grove in 1839. Using platinum electrodes he found that the galvonometer placed in the metal circuit between the two gas electrodes showed a steady current. The reactions may be represented by the equations

$$2(H_2 \longrightarrow 2\,H^+ + 2\,e)\ \text{anode}$$

$$\frac{O_2 + 2\,H_2O + 4\,e \longrightarrow 4\,(OH)^-\ \text{cathode}}{2\,H_2 + O_2 \longrightarrow 2\,HOH}$$

The reaction product of this cell is water, the same as in the combustion of hydrogen. This oxidation or "flameless combustion" of a fuel gas may be carried out with other special electrodes, using oxygen or air as the cathodic material. The anodic substance may be hydrogen, methane, kerosene, methanol, or even carbon. These give up electrons, and the oxygen electrode is the electron acceptor. Such an arrangement is called a *fuel cell*. It is a means of converting conventional fuels *directly* into low-voltage current.

Within the past few years considerable research has been directed toward the production of industrial fuel cells because of their very high efficiency. Such a cell does not "run down" as long as the fuel gas and air or oxygen are supplied to the respective electrodes.

The high-pressure hydrogen fuel cell developed by F. T. Bacon uses

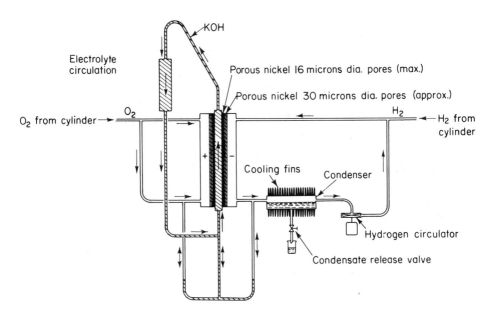

Figure 14-13 The Bacon hydrogen-oxygen fuel cell. [From G. Y. Young, ed., *Fuel Cells* (New York: Reinhold Publishing Co., 1960), by permission.]

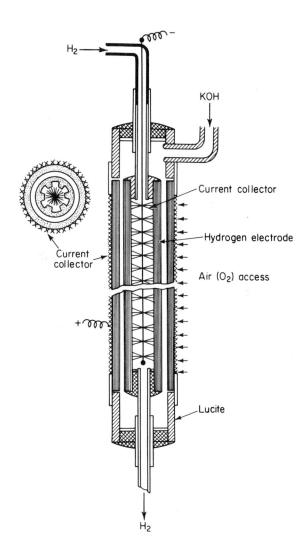

Figure 14-14 The Union Carbide fuel cell. [From G. Y. Young, ed., *Fuel Cells* (New York: Reinhold Publishing Co., 1960), by permission.]

porous-disc electrodes of sintered nickel. The pores on the gas side of the electrode are about 30 microns in diameter and 16 microns on the side in contact with the electrolyte. The electrolyte is concentrated KOH solution (37 to 50 per cent). Gas pressures of about 400 psi and an operating temperature of 200° C are normally used. A diagram of the cell is given in Fig. 14-13.

The Union Carbide fuel cell employs concentric porous carbon electrodes. The inner cylinder, which serves as the hydrogen electrode, is impregnated

Figure 14-15 Tractor powered by fuel cells. [Courtesy Allis-Chalmers Co.]

with a Pt group catalyst. Other catalysts are used in the outer porous cylinder, the oxygen (or air) electrode. The electrolyte is 30 per cent KOH (Fig. 14-14).

Several other types of fuel cells have been developed. Some use metal gauze electrodes, molten electrolyte such as eutectic alkali carbonate mixtures, and temperatures up to 800° C. There are even "bio" cells in which bacteria produce gas from organic waste matter.

The practical value of fuel cells has already been established in certain fields. The United States Army Signal Corps has used such cells for portable radar equipment. In 1959 the Allis-Chalmers Co. demonstrated an experimental electric tractor powered by fuel cells using bottled propane and

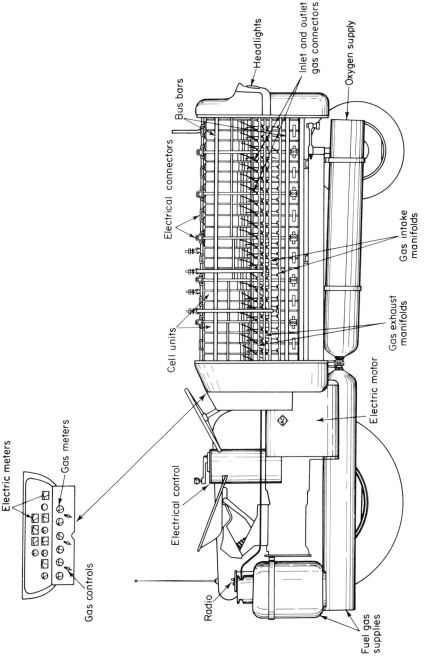

Figure 14-16 Diagram of the fuel cell power tractor. [Courtesy Allis-Chalmers Co.]

oxygen (Figs. 14-15 and 14-16). Welding operations have been performed by power supplied by a battery of Bacon fuel cells.[1]

While further research must be done on this direct and efficient method of converting the chemical energy of fuels into electric power, it is predicted that the use of fuel cells for domestic power in remote areas, and in battery driven vehicles, is not far distant.

---

1 G. J. Young, ed., *Fuel Cell Symposium* (New York: Reinhold Publishing Co., 1959); see also *Popular Mechanics* (March, 1963), p. 102.

15

Corrosion

A dictionary definition of corrosion is the gradual eating away, disintegration, or deterioration of a metal by chemical action. The term "corrosion" is not usually applied to the undesirable or destructive alteration in nonmetallic materials by weathering or other agents. This is usually referred to as "deterioration."

For centuries the causes and laws of corrosion were unknown, although certain factors which influenced corrosion had been noted. Modern studies of the cause, measurement, and prevention have amassed a very great amount of information on the subject, as indicated by several volumes, a monthly journal, and a branch of engineering devoted to this important topic.

Corrosion may be caused by the direct attack on the metal by a chemical agent. Examples of this are the reaction of chlorine with tin and magnesium, or the rapid oxidation of calcium and magnesium by oxygen at ordinary temperatures and of other metals at elevated temperatures. In the great majority of cases, however, corrosion is a manifestation of the same type of electrochemical reactions as exhibited in an electric cell.

15-1 Factors Influencing Corrosion

The rate and extent of corrosion will depend (1) on the properties of the metal and (2) on the nature of the environment. It is a common observation

215

that zinc or iron corrodes more rapidly than copper. The corrosive action of salt and slush on steel and chrome plate is all too apparent to the car owner. However, as one authority has remarked, "It seems obvious that before anyone can undertake anything but empirical methods of solving corrosion problems, he must have basic information as to the nature of corrosion and the mechanism of corrosion processes."[1]

Important corrosion factors associated with a metal are (1) its oxidation potential, (2) the presence of a cathodic metal or material, (3) overvoltage, (4) the purity of the metal, (5) its physical state, (6) the relative areas of anode and cathode, (7) the relative volume of the metal atoms and its oxide or other corrosion product, and (8) the solubility of the reaction products.

The properties of the medium or environment which greatly influence corrosion are (1) the presence of moisture, (2) the pH, (3) the oxygen and metal ion concentration, (4) the conductivity, (5) the specific nature of the cation and anion present, (6) the temperature, and (7) the presence or absence of an inhibitor.

15-2 The Oxidation Potential

The first two factors in the corrosion of a metal will be apparent from the foregoing discussion of electrochemical cells. Corrosion occurs at the anode where the positive metal ions enter the solution. The E_0 values provide an estimate of the anodic activity of the metals. Oxidation potential measurements of various alloys have been made using the saturated calomel cell as the reference electrode, the alloys being immersed in seawater. These are arranged in Table 15-1 in order of decreasing activity. The exact position in relation to corrosion tendency will however be influenced by other factors, but in general, the speed and severity of corrosion depends on the difference in potential between the anodic and cathodic metals.

Early Observations

The acceleration of the corrosion of iron when it is in contact with copper has been on record for two hundred years. This observation was made during a study of the effect of copper sheathing in protecting the bottoms of ships from the tunneling worm. Examination of the test vessel H.M.S. *Alarm*, returned from a cruise in tropical waters, showed that the copper protected the wooden planks from the worms, and also from the growth of marine plants and barnacles. The report, made to the British Admiralty in 1763, went on to state,[2]

---

1 F. L. Laque, International Nickel Co., Research and Development Department.
2 From Inco Corrosion Reporter's extract, *American Neptune*, (1941).

"We were greatly surprised to perceive the Effect the Copper had had upon Iron where the two metals touched; but it was most remarkable at the rudder iron and in the fastenings of the False Keel . . . . The Nails and Staples that fastened it were found dissolved into a rusty Paste; which was also the Case of every Nail that had been used in fastening on the thick Lead.

The same effect, but not to so great a degree was observable upon all the Bolts and Iron under water, except where the brown paper (with which the bottom was Covered) remained undecayed and thereby separated the two metals; and where this covering was perfect, the iron was preserved from Injury."

Table 15-1. RELATIVE OXIDATION POTENTIALS OF SOME ALLOYS IN SEAWATER

MORE ANODIC OR ACTIVE

Magnesium alloys
Alclad 3S
Aluminum alloys
Low carbon steel
Cast iron
Stainless steels (active)
No. 410 (12.5% Cr, 0.35% Ni, 0.5% Mo)
No. 430 (16.7% Cr, 0.31% Ni)
No. 404 (18.7% Cr, 8.8% Ni, 1.1% Mn)
No. 316 (17.8% Cr, 12.5% Ni, 1.8% Mn)
Hastelloy A (20% Fe, 60% Ni, 20% Mo)
Lead-tin alloys
Brass
Copper
Bronze
90/10 Copper-nickel
70/30 Copper-nickel
Inconel
Silver
Stainless steels (passive)
Monel
Hastelloy C (58% Ni, 11% Mo, 6% Cr, 5% Fe)
Titanium

MORE CATHODIC OR INACTIVE

Ignorance or neglect of the first principles of electrochemistry provides many instances of expensive corrosion. One classical example occurred a century and a half after the observations and recommendations of the Admiralty Board were published. This instance illustrates the old adage that a little knowledge is a dangerous thing.

The builders of the yacht *Sea Call*, in 1915, knew that monel had excellent corrosion resistance. The hull of the ship was accordingly made of monel plates, rivetted to the steel frame—with iron rivets! These rivets suffered the same (but more rapid) fate as the nails, bolts, and staples of H.M.S. *Alarm*. The sea called, the rivets sprang, the yacht sank or was scrapped.

Dissimilar metals are very often used in situations which invite corrosion. Several examples of corrosion have been mentioned in Chapter 1. Many others may be observed. In a paper on corrosion prevention, H. P. Goddard cites a case: "An aluminum electrical circuit was tied to the reinforcing steel and imbedded in the concrete floor, which was poured during cold winter weather and therefore contained calcium chloride. The chloride

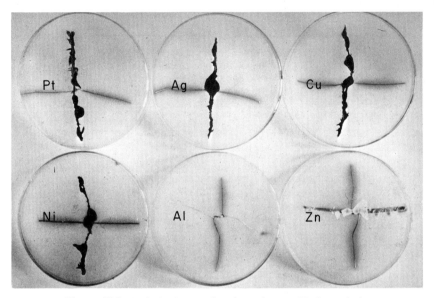

Figure 15-1 Vertical wires are iron in each case. Horizontal wires are Pt, Ag, Cu in top row; Ni, Al, Zn in lower row.

provided enough conductivity to cause galvanic corrosion of the aluminum-steel couple. This lead to a quarter of a million dollar repair job on the building."[1]

Every day some plumber inserts copper tubing to replace a section of iron water pipe, in which case the corrosion potential may exceed 0.5 v; a builder puts copper vent pipe through aluminum flashing with no insulation; and, gadgets are sold containing three or four metals or alloys differing in electrode potentials!

The degree of corrosion of different metal couples may be readily demonstrated, and the anode and cathode identified, by the use of "ferroxyl" indicator. This is a mixture of solutions of potassium ferricyanide, $K_3Fe(CN)_6$, and phenolphthalein. Wires or strips of the metals are

---

1 Presented to the Montreal Section, American Society for Metals, January, 1960.

placed crosswise in petri dishes and covered with 3 per cent agar sol containing NaCl and the corrosion indicator. When corrosion takes place, the metal ions leaving the anode react with the ferricyanide to form a precipitate which is white in the case of Mg^{++}, Zn^{++}, or Al^{+++}, a deep blue with Fe^{++}, and a dark red with Cu^{++}.

At the cathode, hydrogen ions H^+ (or OH_3^+) pick up electrons and are removed from the sol as hydrogen gas, leaving behind an excess of hydroxyl ions. In the presence of oxygen, an excess of hydroxyl ions may be produced at the cathode by the reaction $4 H^+ + O_2 + 4 e \rightarrow 2 H_2O$.[1] In both cases, the excess $(OH)^-$ causes the phenolphthalein to turn pink, thus indicating the cathodic metal.

Figure 15-1 illustrates the use of ferroxyl indicator with various metal couples.

15-3 The Effect of Overvoltage

Pure zinc placed in 1 N H_2SO_4 will corrode, forming a film and bubbles of hydrogen on the immersed surface. The initial rate of reaction is surprisingly slow, considering the high position of the metal relative to hydrogen in the electrochemical series. The corrosion or solution of the metal is slowed because of the high overvoltage, which is 0.70 v, reducing the electrode potential or the driving force for corrosion to a small fraction of a volt.

If a drop of copper sulfate solution is added, the reaction is much faster. Some copper plates on the zinc, forming minute cathodes at which the hydrogen overvoltage is only 0.33 v. If a drop of platinic chloride is added, the overvoltage on the platinized spots is still less, namely, 0.2 v.

The reduction in overvoltage is an important factor in acceleration of corrosion.

15-4 Metal Purity and Corrosion

The copper or platinum deposits on the zinc in the preceding example act as cathodic areas, forming minute galvanic cells. The same result, increased corrosion, is obtained with zinc containing impurities such as lead, iron, or carbon. Tiny electrochemical cells appear at the site of the exposed speck of impurity, and "local action" causes the corrosion of the zinc in the immediate area, the rate of corrosion increasing as more impurities are exposed. The solution of the corroding metal causes pitting.

The marked effect on corrosion rate of even small concentrations of impurities is shown in Table 15-2.

The pure metals may be classed as almost noncorroding. Cominco reports commercial production for the electronics industry of nine metals of 99.9999 per cent purity.

---

1 Or $2H^+ + O_2 + 4e \rightarrow 2(OH)^-$

The effect of impurities will depend on other factors besides relative electrode potentials. Impurities, which form a solid solution in an alloy and are therefore homogeneous, do not cause local action cells. A piece of zinc amalgamated with a film of mercury corrodes much less readily than the original sample. This is partly due to the high overvoltage of the mercury, but it is also because the chief impurity, lead, is also converted to an amalgam, which covers the other impurities.

Alloys having grain structure in which the crystals have different electrode potentials than the matrix may show marked corrosion. A common example is the dezincing of brass, especially that with 20 per cent or more zinc content.

Table 15-2. METAL PURITY AND CORROSION RATE

Metal	Purity (%)	Corrosion rate
Spectroscopic zinc	99.999	1
Zinc	99.99	2,650
Zinc	99.95	5,000
Aluminum	99.998	1
Aluminum	99.97	1,000
Aluminum	99.2	30,000

Another example of this occurs in stainless steel welds where a change in composition producing a chrome carbide and chromium-poor austentite is brought about by the localized heating. The intergranular austentite corrodes and thereby weakens the joint.

15-5 Physical State

The physical state of a metal influences its rate of corrosion. The grain size of a metal or alloy is important since the solubility of very small grains is greater than for macroscopic crystals. If the metal crystals are of colloidal dimensions their solubility may be several times greater. The orientation of the crystals at the surface of the metal may also influence corrosion. It has been found that the corrosion rate of copper metal varies on different faces of a pure copper crystal.

Metals under Stress

Even in a pure metal, stressed areas tend to become anodic. Stress causes corrosion and cracking in several alloys, particularly alpha brass, iron, and aluminum alloys in certain environments.

Recent electron microscope studies on stainless steel have detected the formation of chromium oxide platelets at the point under stress. No corrosion occurred where the stress was absent.

Cyclic applied stress, such as shaking, tapping, "stuttering," and flexing, cause *corrosion fatigue*. The repeated impacts of meshing gears set up potentials which, if the lubricant contains traces of electrolyte, may cause considerable corrosion. Zinc oxide added to the lubricant is reported to overcome this by the deposition of metallic zinc on the gear surfaces.

The effect of stress is often apparent when a freshly forged piece of metal is used in machinery along with parts made of the same metal but which have been in service for some time and in which the strains have relaxed. Such more-rapid corrosion of a new piece of metal was observed a long time

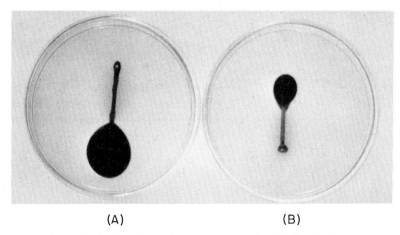

(A)   (B)

Figure 15-2 The effect of stress on corrosion. Nail (A) shows marked corrosion at the pointed end. Nail (B) has been hit on the head.

ago by the military engineers of Alexander the Great. A chain suspension bridge had been built over the Euphrates. It was noticed and recorded that new links which had to be inserted corroded faster than the old chain. A similar observation on the corrosion rate of a new section of steel pipe doesn't mean that it is not made as well now as in the past.

The effect of stress on corrosion can be demonstrated by placing a nail in ferroxyl indicator (Fig. 15-2). The head and point of the nail were placed under stress during manufacture, and the blue deposits at these areas indicate that the parts under stress become anodic. The region along the nail becomes red and thereby indicates the cathodic area. As another example, a piece of iron wire hammered in the middle will corrode at that stress point.

The susceptibility of a metal under stress to corrode helps to detect stolen car engines and identify weapons from which serial numbers have been filed or ground off. Because the steel under each line of the obliterated number remains under stress and is therefore more anodic than the rest of the metal, the corrosion of the stressed iron traces the hidden numbers when kept in contact with blotting paper saturated with electrolyte and ferroxyl indicator.

A similar procedure may be used to compare the quality of different samples of tin plate. The number of pinholes in the tin coating per unit area can be detected by the blue spots that appear on the impressed indicator paper.

Residual stress may be relieved by annealing the metal at suitable temperatures for periods of from 30 to 60 min. Annealing temperatures range from about 400° F, for certain magnesium alloys and brass, to temperatures of 1350° to 1600° F for stainless steels.

15-6 Relative Areas of Anode and Cathode

If two pieces of steel plate having the same area are connected individually, one to a copper plate of the same area and one to a copper cathode of much larger area, the latter couple will produce greater current and hence

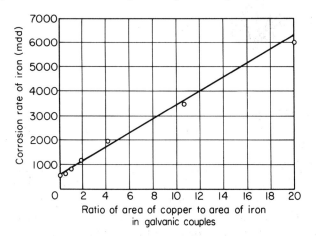

Figure 15-3 Effect of area of a copper cathode on galvanic corrosion of iron anode in aerated 3 per cent sodium chloride. [From *Corrosion Resistance*, 1941, courtesy International Nickel Co.]

greater corrosion of the steel anode. When anodic polarization is negligible and conductance remains approximately constant, corrosion of the anode is directly proportional to the cathode area (Fig. 15-3). The initial value of the corrosion rate of the iron alone in the aerated salt solution was 600 mg/sq dm/day.

The effect of relative areas is illustrated by the rapid corrosion that occurs when a small area of iron is exposed by a scratch in tin plate. The corrosion of the iron staples and nails holding the copper sheathing on

H.M.S. *Alarm*, and of the iron rivets in the case of the *Sea Call*, was greatly accelerated by the immense area of the cathodes in comparison to that of the iron anodes. The corrosion current was the same at both cathode and anode, but the current density at the small anodes was much greater. In other words, the great demand for electrons by the large area of copper or monel cathodes was met by the formation of ferrous ions, all of which had to come from the small anodes.

If steel plates are fastened with copper rivets, in an environment favorable to corrosion, the rivets will remain intact. However, the corrosion of the iron will be somewhat greater than if the copper were absent, but since the ratio of the area of the cathode to the area of anode is much less than unity, indeed a very small fraction, there will be no appreciable increase in the corrosion rate.

15-7 Relative Volume of a Metal Atom and Its Oxide

Practically all metals on exposure to the air become covered with a film of oxide a few Angstrom units thick ($\text{Å} = 10^{-8}$ cm). The film thickness will vary with the metal and the temperature and may consist of one or more oxide forms. If the space occupied by an oxidized metal atom is smaller than the space occupied by the atoms in the metal crystal or matrix, the film will be porous, allow easy access to more oxygen, and provide little or no protection against further corrosion. Magnesium, particularly, as well as other alkaline-earth and alkali metals (such as Ca, Ba, Li, Na, K) form oxides of low specific volume.

In most cases the specific volume of the oxide is greater than that of the metal. With aluminum the ratio of oxide to metal volume is 1.24. As its oxide film grows in thickness from a monomolecular layer, a tightly packed shell is formed through which either or both metal and oxygen ions must penetrate before further oxidation can occur. The film is therefore protective. However, very thick layers may develop fissures. The film can be made thicker by prolonged heating, by chemical oxidizing agents, and by anodizing. In the process of anodizing, the aluminum is made the anode in an electrolytic cell where the oxidizing environment converts metal ions to the oxide. The relative thickness of the protective film formed under different conditions is given in Table 15-3.

Nonporous, nonconducting films are formed by using borates or boric acid as electrolyte. These coatings are thinner than those obtained by use of sulfuric acid.

Several metals have a higher oxide to metal volume ratio than aluminum. The specific volume ratio is 1.6 in the case of nickel, 2.0 for chromium, and 3.6 for tungsten. One would expect that at elevated temperatures the rate of oxidation would be least for tungsten and be somewhat greater for nickel than for chromium.

The reaction of iron with oxygen is complex in that various oxides are formed, depending on temperature. Some of the oxides form solid solutions, for example, Fe_3O_4 and gamma Fe_2O_3. Alpha Fe_2O_3 and FeO are other oxides. These oxides usually contain an excess of metal ions, which makes

Table 15-3. THICKNESS OF ALUMINUM OXIDE FILMS ON ALUMINUM[a]

Method of formation	Thickness in microns (μ)
Natural (air formed)	0.01
Prolonged heating	0.2
Chemical (dichromate)	1.–3.
Anodic	4.–30.

[a] McLachlin and Godard, Aluminum Laboratories Ltd., Kingston, Ontario.

them semi-conductors, decreasing their protective value. Thick "scale," formed at temperatures around 550° C, acts as a cathode and increases corrosion of the iron exposed by cracking and displacement of some of the scale.

Passive films can be formed on iron by strong oxidizing agents such as nitric acid. Such a thin film will even prevent the deposition of a copper film when the iron is placed in copper sulfate solution. Passive films, however, are rather fragile and, when fractured, lose their protective qualities.

Passive films on stainless steel, although also very thin, are quite stable compared to the passive iron film. Being composed of oxides, this passive film will be destroyed by reduction, and the metal then will regain its activity or former potential.

Passive films on austenitic stainless steels have been studied by Rhodin, who found that the composition of the protecting film on the three types (T304, T316, and T347) was invariably richer in silicon and chromium oxides and lower in iron oxide than the theoretical oxides calculated from the composition of the alloy.

Obviously the structure of surface films on alloys is often complex. Corrosion will depend in part on the specific volume ratios of the oxides and metals involved, on the thickness and conductance of the film, as well as its reaction with the surrounding medium.

15-8 Solubility of the Corrosion Product

In the section above, we were concerned chiefly with direct oxidation and the formation of protective oxide films in air. The solubility of these and any other corrosion product is an important factor in electrolytic corrosion. Many of the oxides are insoluble in water. In other cases chemical reaction with the medium or electrolyte may form a different insoluble product, which then becomes the protective film. An example of this is the formation of insoluble lead sulfate which protects metallic lead from further corrosion by sulfuric acid. In the alloy Durichlor, which contains iron, 14.5 per cent Si, and 3 per cent Mo, the molybdenum reacts with chloride to form an inert product.

If the corrosion product is soluble, disintegration of the metal will proceed. Lactic acid is the very weak acid formed in sour milk or buttermilk. It is nevertheless decidedly corrosive due to the high solubility of its iron salts. "Pin-points" and scratches in tin-plated milk cans are thus particularly susceptible to corrosion, owing to this additional factor.

15-9 Role of the Medium or Environment

It will be apparent from the foregoing examples that the nature of the environment must be considered in any corrosion problem. Some of the corrosion factors associated with the medium are noted briefly below.

The Presence of Moisture

It is a common observation that atmospheric corrosion of iron occurs very slowly in dry air, but more rapidly in the presence of moisture. While it is true that the observed corrosion may be due to the reaction between the metal or oxide and the moisture itself (HOH), in most cases the moisture has acted as the solvent for oxygen (air) and other gases and salts to furnish the electrolyte for a corrosion cell.

Magnesium, zinc, manganese, aluminum, chromium, and iron are corroded by reaction with pure water even in the absence of oxygen. For example,

$$Mg^\circ \longrightarrow Mg^{++} + 2\,e$$

$$\underline{2\,H_2O + 2\,e \longrightarrow 2\,(OH)^- + H_2}$$

$$Mg^\circ + 2\,H_2O \longrightarrow Mg(OH)_2 + H_2$$

The potential of this cell is 1.85 v. In water saturated with air the corrosion potential is greater, namely, 3.06 v.

$$2\,Mg + 4\,(OH)^- \longrightarrow 2\,Mg(OH)_2 + 4\,e$$

$$\underline{O_2 + 2\,H_2O + 4\,e \longrightarrow 4\,(OH)^-}$$

$$2\,Mg + O_2 + 2\,H_2O \longrightarrow 2\,Mg(OH)_2$$

Gulbransen and Copan have found that when pure iron is heated to 400° C in dry oxygen, the surface becomes covered with very fine "whiskers" of Fe_2O_3, 10–15 millimicrons (10^{-6} mm) in diameter. These oxide whiskers grow to a length of 50 microns (10^{-3} mm). When iron reacts with water vapor, the oxide forms thin-bladed plates about 10×10^{-6} mm thick, 3 microns long and varying in width from 0.03 to 0.8 micron.

The corrosion of iron in dry air at ordinary temperatures is very slight. Between 60 and 80 per cent relative humidity, rusting will take place; the rust spots act as corrosion centers. The rust has a gel structure, a tangled interlocked mass of hydrated oxide strings. At high relative pressure, p/P_0, water condenses in the gel, filling capillary spaces. Any corrosive gases adsorbed and absorbed by the rust under these conditions will obviously increase the corrosion. The effect of the relative humidity on the corrosion of iron in air containing 100 ppm. of sulfur dioxide is shown in Fig. 15-4. Nickel in 1 ppm SO_2 starts to corrode at a relative humidity of 70 per cent.

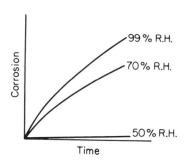

Figure 15-4 The effect of relative humidity on atmospheric corrosion of iron.

In the presence of moisture, particles of soot, flyash, charcoal, and some types of dust act as corrosion centers. Such particles have a high specific surface and adsorb gases, or they may form tiny concentration cells. The high humidity and the presence of colloidal droplets of sea spray and particles of salts, make for higher atmospheric corrosion in a maritime area.

The tendency of many metals to form basic salts, for example,

$$Pb(OH)_2 \cdot PbCO_3, \qquad Cu(OH)_2 \cdot CuCl_2, \qquad 3\ Cu(OH)_2 \cdot CuSO_4$$

among others, and hydrous oxides or so-called hydroxides, indicates the importance of moisture in corrosion.

The Effect of pH

The hydrogen ion concentration of the medium is a very important factor in corrosion. While the corrosive effect of strong acid on active metals is recognized by everyone, too little attention is often given to the actual pH of waters or fluids in contact with metal structures, pipes, or equipment.

The corrosion of iron in oxygen-free water is slow until the pH drops below 5 (Fig. 15-5). In the presence of oxygen the corrosion rate is much higher. The corrosion rate is practically constant over a range pH 4 or 5 to pH 10 or 12 depending on the oxygen concentration. At pH 4 corrosion is stimulated by the conversion of $Fe^{++} \rightarrow Fe^{+++}$ by dissolved oxygen and the subsequent reduction of the Fe^{+++} to Fe^{++} at the cathode. In less-acid solutions the excess $(OH)^-$ in the area and Fe^{++} form $Fe(OH)_2$, a gelatinous precipitate which slowly oxidizes to $FeO(OH)$ or rust. At high pH, $Fe(OH)_2$ is formed as soon as the Fe^{++} steps off the anode, blocks access to the anode, and decreases the rate.

Zinc corrodes very rapidly, even in weak acids such as carbonic acid. Fermenting organic matter will strip the zinc from the "galvanized" container. Minimum corrosion activity occurs at pH 11. In more alkaline solutions, the metal dissolves. Tin is rapidly corroded at pH values greater than 8.5. Aluminum and lead corrode in alkaline environments. Aluminum has a minimum corrosion rate at approximately pH 5.5. Aluminum ducts for venting automatic laundry dryers through basement cement walls have been found to show corrosion. Lead pipe or lead-covered cable should not be laid through ashes because of the higher pH there than in adjacent soil.

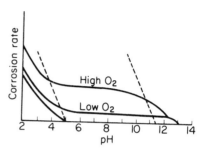

Figure 15-5 Effect of pH and oxygen concentration on the corrosion of iron.

Mine waters and many industrial wastes are acid. Drainage from worked-out and abandoned coal mines containing sulfur and sulfuric acids accelerate the corrosion of bridges, boats, dams, and intake pipes on neighboring streams. The production of acid is due to the wet oxidation of an iron sulfide, marcasite. The reaction may proceed according to the equation

$$3 FeS_2 + 11 O_2 + 4 H_2O \longrightarrow 2 Fe(OH)SO_4 + FeSO_4 + 3 H_2SO_4$$

In many mines, acid-resistant pumps and pipelines must be used.

Oxygen Concentration and Concentration Cells

The effect of oxygen concentration on the rate of corrosion of iron in solutions differing in pH is illustrated in Fig. 15-5. The rate increases with increasing oxygen supply. Because the oxide layer or film is cathodic to most metals, increasing the oxygen is akin to increasing the cathode area. Hydrogen depolarization will also be greater the higher the oxygen concentration.

It has been shown that an emf is produced when two electrodes of the same material are in contact with different concentrations of their ions. Differential aeration will promote corrosion by the formation of such concentration cells.

If the center of a steel plate is covered with a small mound of sand and exposed to the weather, it will be found that practically all the corrosion will take place under the sand. Corrosion often occurs under a metal washer, and where the wires are in contact in a metal screen. The same effect is obtained

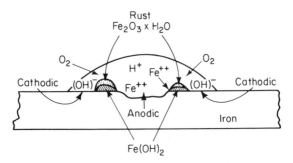

Figure 15-6 Corrosion under a drop of water or solution gives a ring of rust. This is an example of an oxygen concentration cell, the center of the covered area being poorer in oxygen than the edges.

when a small pool or large drop of saline solution is placed on an iron surface. Corrosion of the iron builds up a circle of rust at the center of the area covered by the solution.

In these cases the concentration of oxygen at the center of the covered areas soon becomes lower than the concentration at the periphery. This is due to the slow rate of diffusion of oxygen from the boundary to the center. The metal is cathodic at the edge of the drop where oxygen is plentiful and anodic in the region of low oxygen. Ferrous ions from the corroding anode meet the hydroxyl ions diffusing from the cathode areas and $Fe(OH)_2$ is precipitated. This deposit is gradually converted to rust, $FeO(OH)$ or $Fe_2O_3 \cdot xH_2O$ by absorption of oxygen. The deposit thus acts as an impediment to the movement of oxygen to the anode and corrosion is accelerated.

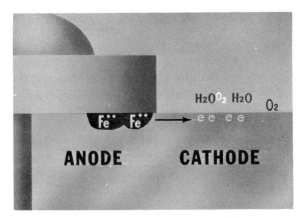

Figure 15-7 Diagram showing corrosion under an iron washer. [From a film titled *Corrosion in Action*, 1955. Courtesy International Nickel Co.]

The corrosion of iron under a drop of water is shown diagrammatically in Fig. 15-6.

Corrosion often occurs under metal washers where oxygen cannot diffuse readily (Fig. 15-7). A striking example of this type of corrosion is illustrated in Fig. 15-8. A rubber band was placed around a piece of stainless steel sheet and immersed in a dilute solution of NaCl and $FeCl_3$. Corrosion under the rubber band was so severe that the elastic has cut into the metal sheet.

Figure 15-8 An example of corrosion due to differential aeration. Oxygen depletion under the rubber band created an active anode with smaller area than the aerated cathodic portion. [From *Corrosion in Action*, 1955, Courtesy International Nickel Co.]

Buried pipelines or cables passing from one type of soil to another encounter differences in aeration with consequent corrosion. Potential differences have been measured between areas of lead pipe passing through clay and then cinders, the latter being more aerated. In this particular case differences in pH and resistance of the two types of cover, as well as the presence of unburned carbon in the cinders, are also corrosion factors.

A metal in contact with different concentrations of its ions at different points will corrode. Thus one small leak can cause extensive corrosion by the dilution and transportation of the electrolyte to an area of the pipe some distance from the original corrosion pit or leak.

Conductance of the Medium

The corrosion current will depend on the conductance of the medium, which is an important factor in the corrosion of buried structures. Dry sandy soil has a high resistance, but in moist clay and in mineralized areas, resistance is much lower. Stray currents from power leaks will be more damaging to metal structures in such soils.

Sea water has a high conductance which is a significant factor in its corrosive nature. The oil refinery in Aruba, in the Netherlands Antilles, has to use over 200 million gallons of sea water daily for cooling and other purposes. The corrosion costs are reported to exceed the cost of the crude oil and its forty different products. The case above may be cited also to illustrate the next corrosion factor.

Nature of Anion and Cation in the Medium

The chlorides of the alkali and alkaline earth metals are particularly bad for many metals and alloys; the chloride ion destroys the passive film. In contrast, some anions may form an insoluble reaction product that protects the metal; that is, it acts as an inhibitor. This is illustrated by the addition of sodium silicate to prevent "red water" or diminish rusting. The silicate forms silica gel and adsorption compounds with the corrosion product. Other examples will be found in the section on inhibitors.

The nature of the cation will also influence corrosion. Traces of copper salts or other more noble metals in mine water will accelerate the corrosion of iron pipe.

Iron and several other metals corrode more rapidly in ammonium salts than in sodium salts of the same concentration. Some types of inhibitors, which give effective protection to iron, increase the corrosion of zinc, copper, and nickel because of the formation of complex cations with these metals.

Temperature of the Medium

In general, corrosion increases with the temperature. Polarization is less, and diffusion rates are greater. The effect of temperature on the electrode potentials has been noted (page 199). The change in the corrosion rate of monel metal in sulfuric acid with a change in temperature is shown in Fig. 15-9.

Caustic embrittlement, a type of intergranular corrosion, occurs only at the temperatures associated with high-pressure boilers.

A passive metal may become "active" at a higher temperature. Blistering or hydrogen embrittlement increases with temperature. The heating process involved in refining oils causes the production of HCl from any chlorides left from the "desalting" and consequently produces greater corrosion.

Presence or Absence of Corrosion Inhibitors

An inhibitor may be considered as the opposite of a catalyst. It retards or stops the reaction. The use of corrosion inhibitors affords one method of dealing with a variety of corrosion problems.

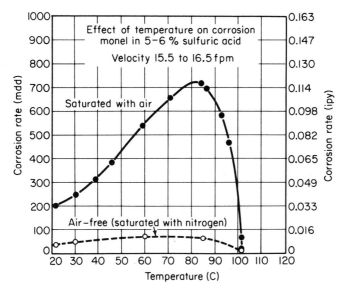

Figure 15-9 The effect of temperature on corrosion. [From *Corrosion Resistance*, 1941. Courtesy International Nickel Co.]

Corrosion inhibitors may be inorganic or organic in nature. Most inorganic inhibitors such as silicates, chromates, phosphates, and borates control the rate of corrosion by acting on the anode. The use of some of these is not advisable under all conditions. The improper use of chromate may accelerate rather than inhibit corrosion. If hydrogen polarization is present, the addition of chromate or any other oxidizer causes depolarization and increases the flow of corrosion current. Again if insufficient inhibitor is present to provide a complete film over the anode, the small areas left exposed corrode with increased rapidity, thereby causing pitting.

The use of sodium silicate provides many examples of the control of corrosion by inhibitors. One example may be cited: A ten-mile pipeline for the disposal of brine from a large oil company had developed many small leaks. Replacement appeared imminent at a cost of $80,000. However, the addition of low concentrations of sodium silicate to the brine reduced corrosion to such a degree that two and a half years afterwards the pipe was still in use and the number of leaks had been reduced.

Alkaline sodium nitrite, alone, or in conjunction with other inorganic inhibitors as phosphate, has been used to protect pipelines and tankers. Sodium benzoate,

COONa

acts as an inhibitor for mild steel. The inhibiting action of 1.5 per cent sodium benzoate with 0.1 per cent sodium nitrite in antifreeze solution is shown in Fig. 15-10. Also, hydrated lime, $Ca(OH)_2$, may act as a cathodic inhibitor by causing precipitation of $CaCO_3$ in waters containing temporary hardness, or dissolved CO_2. Colloidal particles of $CaCO_3$ are positively charged and are attracted to the cathode areas where their deposition cuts down the corrosion current.

Organic inhibitors may act in a variety of ways. Organic colloids form protective layers by adsorption. Surface-active chemicals, which contain polar

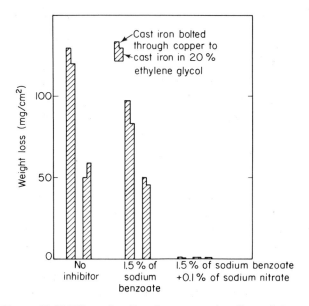

Figure 15-10 Effect of sodium benzoate and sodium nitrite on the corrosion of cast iron bolted through copper to cast iron, in 20 per cent ethylene glycol. [From Wormwell, F., Mercer, A. D., and Ison, H., *J. Applied Chem.*, (1953), pp. 133–44, by permission.]

groups that promote spreading and oriented adhesion to the surface, may be nonionic and form a film over the metal surface. Organic bases, such as the amines, pyridine, quinoline, and their derivatives, form positive ions containing hydrophobic groups or radicals. These positive cations attach themselves through the nitrogen to the cathodic areas. Their effectiveness as inhibitors depends on the number and size of hydrocarbon radicals. Primary amyl amine, $C_5H_{11}NH_2$, is much better than primary ethyl amine, $C_2H_5NH_2$, as an inhibitor. The increase in the protection obtained as the number of alkyl radicals is increased, is indicated in Fig. 15-11. A few parts per million of the tertiary amine gives almost complete protection.

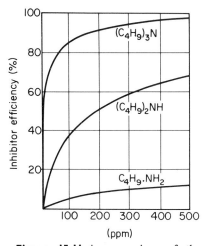

Figure 15-11 A comparison of the effectiveness of primary, secondary, and tertiary butyl amines.

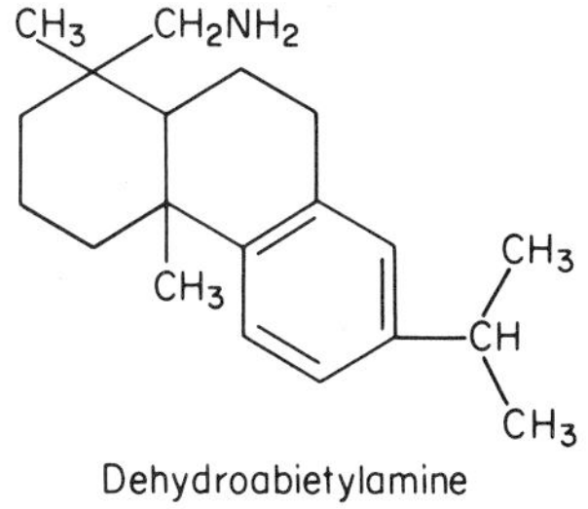

Dehydroabietylamine

Figure 15-12 An amine inhibitor derived from rosin.

High molecular weight amines derived from rosin are good corrosion inhibitors. A typical rosin amine is shown in Fig. 15-12. Its oil soluble salts, for example, the stearate, naphthenate, and other derivatives are used as inhibitors in metal cleaning or "pickling" in acid. The protective action can be seen from the data in Table 15-4. Figure 15-13 shows the effect of concentration of acid and temperature on the corrosion of steel by descaling acid with and without inhibitor.

The salt obtained by reacting rosin amine and pentachlorphenol, when incorporated in coatings for buried pipe, resists or prevents corrosion caused by soil bacteria.

Other amine derivatives may have specific uses. The compound 2-hydroxy-propylamine nitrite is a nonionic compound recommended for preventing the corrosion of tinned containers by such products as liquid soaps, phenolic and pine oil disinfectants, and concentrated solutions of quaternary ammonium wetting agents.

Table 15-4. Effect of Rosin Amine Derivative as a Corrosion Inhibitor For Mild Steel in 15% HCl

Concentration of inhibitor (%)	Corrosion (in./yr)
0.00	16.34
0.02	0.585
0.04	0.243
0.10	0.122
0.20	0.132

Some organic inhibitors are anionic surface-active agents containing such polar groups as sulfide, hydrosulfide, alcohol, and some acids. They may act in some cases as antioxidants, inhibiting the formation of peroxides and corrosive peracids.

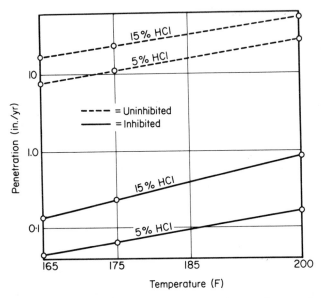

Figure 15-13 The effect of 0.2 per cent inhibitor on the corrosion of mild steel by HCl at different temperatures. [Courtesy Hercules Powder Co.; c.f. Bried, E. A., and Winn, H. M., *Corrosion*, **7**, (1951) 180–85.]

Vapor Phase Inhibitors (VPI)

Vapor phase inhibitors are materials which vaporize readily and form an inhibiting or protective layer. These inhibitors are used to protect steam lines in the presence of CO_2 or the corrosion of steel and iron in the presence of moisture and SO_2. Small metal parts may be protected from atmospheric corrosion by placing them in envelopes made from paper impregnated with the VPI. Instead of using a layer of grease or oil as a rust preventative, large metal parts may be wrapped in impregnated covering. In storing spare aircraft engines, some crystals of VPI are blown into each cylinder through the spark plug hole (Fig. 15-14). The outside of the engine is then wrapped in low-porosity, plastic-coated paper containing some of the inhibitor. Two very successful volatile inhibitors are dicyclohexyl ammonium nitrite and cyclohexyl amine carbonate. Under severe moisture conditions, they should not be used for copper and the other metals which form ammonia-complex ions. Figure 15-15 shows the effectiveness of vapor phase inhibitors.

Figure 15-14 Pistons, rings, and other critical parts of aircraft engines in storage can be kept rust-free by injecting small quantities of VPI-250. [Courtesy Shell Oil Co.]

A   B

Figure 15-15 Watch parts (1.00 per cent carbon steel) after one year's exposure in a moist atmosphere: (A) Protected by VPI, (B) Without VPI.

Octadecyl amine, hexadecyl amine, and dioctadecyl amine are not vapor phase inhibitors, but form an impervious nonwettable film. They are added to boiler water (see Chapter 21) and in radiator compounds (Chapter 16). They are cheaper than the vapor-phase type. These long-chain amines are also detergent in behavior. The desired protective level is achieved with 15 to 30 ppm.

15-10 Corrosion Testing

There are a number of methods for testing the corrosion of a metal. Various "accelerated" tests, such as the salt-spray test, do not always serve to predict the behavior of the metals when exposed to other corrosive environments. Laboratory corrosion experiments, when properly correlated with field tests, may be interpreted to provide the approximate evaluation of materials and the selection of protective measures.

Corrosion rates are often determined by the loss in weight from clean metal "coupons" or standard test pieces during the selected period. The results are expressed $mg/dm^2/day$, (MDD), or $oz/ft^2/day$ or month. Assuming that the surface corrosion was uniform and proceeded at a uniform rate, these units may be converted to depth of corrosion or penetration, millimeters, or inches per year (IPY).

$$MDD \times \frac{1.437 \times 10^{-3}}{S.G. \text{ of metal}} = IPY$$

The comparison of the numerical results described above should be reinforced by microscopic examination of the test specimens to check the nature of the corroded surface, the number and depth of pits, and the presence of intergranular corrosion. In the dezincification of brass the copper is redeposited in a rather spongy form. Here loss in weight does not assess the damage.

Measurements of corrosion potentials by coupling the test plate to a standard half-cell, supplemented by determinations of the corrosion current, are of value in determining the corrosion tendency of the material.

Electrical instruments, such as the corrosometer, measure the change in resistance of a standard probe as corrosion converts the metal to corrosion product. A second reference probe covered with a highly corrosion-resistant coating is connected to a bridge arrangement, and the ratio of the resistance of the corroding test piece to the resistance of its noncorroding twin is directly related to the extent of corrosion. From the slope of the penetration versus time curve, the results can be converted to mils or microinches per

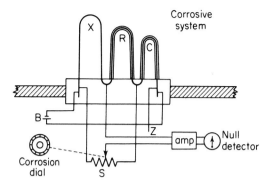

Figure 15-16 Diagram of an instrument for determining corrosion by change in resistance. *X*—exposed element or alloy; *R*—protected reference electrode; *C*—a standard covered element for checking stability of *R*. The change in resistance as indicated by the position of the slider *S* (dial reading) is related to corrosion units such as mils or inches per year. [Courtesy Crest Instrument Research Division.]

year (IPY $\times$ 10^{-3} or 10^{-6}). A simplified diagram of the circuit through the probe and meter is given in Fig. 15-16.

The exposed element is shown as loop *X*, and the covered reference element as the loop *R*. An added covered element, *C*, is used to check the resistance of the reference element *R*. The *R/C* ratio should be constant during the life of *X* or duration of the test.

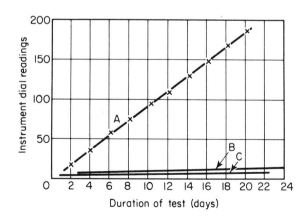

Figure 15-17 Corrosion rates of three alloys in a pulp and water slurry, *p*H 3.4-4.1 as determined by a Corrosometer. *A*—mild steel; *B*—phosphor bronze (W40 $\times$ 10); *C*—Type 347 s.s. (S4 $\times$ 1). The corrosion rates were found to be *A*, 56.4 mils/yr.; *B*, 0.8 mils/yr.; *C*, 0.008 mils/yr. [Data from Crest Instrument Research Division.]

The test probe X and reference element R are connected across the slidewire S when making a corrosion measurement. The position of S at bridge balance is indicated by a dial on the control panel. High sensitivity is obtained by an amplified null-point detector. Connections of C to slidewire via Z are not shown on the diagram.

Features of the resistance method are (1) corrosion rates can be determined without removal of the test pieces; (2) the sensitivity is high (0.1 to 0.4 microinch for flat test strips 1 to 4 mils thick); (3) a series of probes at different locations allow checks to be made at different stages of a process, for example, refining; (4) changes in corrosion rates can be detected early and remedial action evaluated; (5) tests are made without interruption of the process.

Figure 15-17 shows the corrosion rates of three different alloys in a pulp and water slurry, with a pH of 3.4 to 4.1 as determined by this method.

15-11 Corrosion Control

Some general principles for the mitigation or control of corrosion derived from the preceding discussion are summarized below:

(1) The choice of metal should depend not only on its cost and structure, but also on its chemical properties and its environment in use. To reduce corrosion to a minimum, the metal should be annealed, or if an active metal, insulated from more cathodic metals. When two metals are to be in contact, the values for the oxidation potentials should be as nearly the same as possible. The area of the more noble or inactive metal should be smaller than that of the anodic or active metal. A protective coating over *both* metals will reduce the chance of pitting.

(2) Moisture should be excluded. Stored metal parts sealed in a low-permeability plastic, enclosing activated silica or alumina gel will be protected for years. If moisture or electrolyte solution is present, an inhibitor should be used.

(3) The acidity or alkalinity of the environment must be controlled since each metal shows minimum corrosion at a specific pH. Total acidity can be reduced most cheaply by the addition of limestone, $(CaCO_3)$, or slaked lime, $Ca(OH)_2$, but in acid waters containing sulfuric acid, the relatively low solubility of the resulting $CaSO_4$ makes neutralization a slow process. The more expensive soda ash, (Na_2CO_3), is widely used. If pH control is not feasible, corrosion can be reduced by inert coatings and inactive metals.

(4) Equipment design should avoid sharp crimps or bends, lap joints, or baffles which might produce stagnant areas with accumulation of sediment or scale. Such areas are more affected by corrosion caused by the formation of concentration cells.

Sacrificial Anodes and Cathodic Protection

When it is impractical or impossible to alter the nature of the corrosion medium, two other methods of corrosion control may be employed. One is to use sacrificial anodes, and the second is to impose a countercurrent on the corrosion cell or system.

Sacrificial anodes are made from active metals. Magnesium bars are bolted along the sides of ships near the bilge keel to protect the hull. Magnesium rods are inserted into domestic water boilers or tanks to prevent rusty water. Calcium metal slugs used to cut down engine corrosion are now marketed.[1] The calcium metal is attached to the drainage plug of the oil pan of the car or truck. Tests conducted at the National Research Council Laboratories and by trucking and taxi companies have indicated that the oil will remain clean from three and one-half to ten times longer. In addition to the protective action against corrosion, it has been found that the calcium compounds formed by reaction with the decomposition or oxidation products of the oil act as added detergent.

Cathodic protection is the name given the application of an impressed current which converts the corroding metal from an anode to a cathode. Direct current is applied to an anode, usually graphite or high silicon iron, buried in the soil or immersed in the corrosion medium, and connected to the protected structure. This type of protection is of particular value with buried structures such as pipelines and tanks, transmission line towers, marine piers, and laid-up ships.

Cathodic protection is often used in conjunction with protective coatings, since no coating gives permanent protection. In spite of the use of various types of coatings, the annual replacement cost of buried pipe in Great Britain has been estimated as over £5,000,000. Current requirements for a 3 in. pipe coated with hot enamel was found to be between 0.021 to 0.113 amps per mile. Even lead-sheathed cable requires cathodic protection. In one experiment, a difference of 0.20 v was found between the "bright" and oxide-coated or "filmed" lead surface in one type of soil.

In a recent report on the cathodic protection of ships' hulls, complete protection is said to be provided when the potential difference between the steel and sea water and the saturated calomel electrode is −0.78 v.

The committee compares the advantages and disadvantages of cathodic protection versus sacrificial electrodes. The advantages cited for the impressed current are: it is adjustable to suit changing needs, installations are lighter in weight, and once installed, the cost of protection is less.

The advantages attributed to sacrificial anodes are: they are easier to

---

1 Developed by Puddington and Sirianni, National Research Council, Ottawa.

install and are self-contained, they require no supervision, and they are not as vulnerable to electrical or mechanical damage.

Spencer points out that soil bacteria, which can reduce sulfate in the soil, may create corrosive conditions which require a higher metal/electrolyte potential than can be supplied by magnesium anodes.

Applied current in the cathodic protection of one structure may adversely affect a neighboring pipeline or other buried metal by leakage or stray currents.

Trailing platinum-clad silver or copper anodes are in use for the cathodic protection of submarines.

Review Questions

1. Give the Nernst equation for the half-cell potential.

2. Show how the emf of a battery can be calculated.

3. Show that a current can be obtained when the same metal is in contact with two different concentrations of its ion.

4. The E_0 for Zn $= -0.76$ v and for Cu $= +0.34$ v. What is the emf of a Daniell cell in which $Cu^{++} = 0.001$ M and $Zn^{++} = 0.1$ M?

5. A piece of Cu cable is in contact with 0.001 M Cu^{++} at one end and 0.01 M Cu ion at the other end. What emf will be produced? Show the direction of electron flow.

6. The calomel half-cell has a potential $+0.280$ v at $20°$ C. What will be the potential of a calomel-H_2 cell if the pH of the solution in the hydrogen half-cell equals 5?

7. Silver chloride has a solubility of 1.5×10^{-3} g/liter. What would be the half-cell potential for $Ag°$ in this solution? (E_0 for $Ag° = 0.80$)

8. The emf of a H^- Cd cell is $+0.865$ v. The $H^+ = 1$ N and the $Cd°$ is in contact with a saturated solution of cadmium sulfide. E_0 for Cd is -0.40 v. What is the solubility of CdS?

9. Define overvoltage.

10. From the tables for electrode potential given in the text, will Ni or Cd corrode more readily when these two metals are in contact in a corroding medium?

11. Enumerate five factors of importance in the corroding action of a medium.

12. Discuss the effect of oxygen and CO_2 in the corrosion of iron.

13. Is a neutral solution less corrosive than a solution of pH 8 in the case of zinc? Iron?

14. What is meant by local action?

15. What chemicals can be used as an indicator for corrosion of iron?

16. Describe three types of corrosion.

17. Indicate the effect of water vapor, gases, soot, and salts on atmospheric corrosion.

18. Show how the protective action of a corrosion inhibitor depends on molecular structure.

19. Give the formula for dimethyl amine; methyl aniline; tertiary ethyl amine; cyclohexylammonium nitrite.

20. Name three inorganic inhibitors and state their mode of action.

21. Indicate the principles of cathodic protection.

22. How can a metal be made "passive"?

23. Corrosion of steel, SG 7.86, was 300 MDD. Express as IPY.

24. Explain the difference in the nature of the protection of iron by galvanizing and tin plating.

25. Give the characteristic properties of chromium, cadmium, and nickel as applied to protective coatings.

26. The use of limestone or chalk to control total acidity and pH is illustrated by the following rhyme (author unknown):

> Johnny, finding life a bore,
> Drank some H_2SO_4.
> Johnny's father, an M.D.,
> Fed him $CaCO_3$.
> John is neutralized, it's true,
> But he's full of CO_2!

Write the equation for the reaction.

Further Readings

Clark, W., "Design from the Viewpoint of Corrosion," *Metallurgical Review*, 3 (1958), 11.

Evans, U., *Corrosion* (New York: Macmillan, 1960).

Fontana, M., "Corrosion Column," *Industrial and Engineering Chemistry*, 1949–1959 issues.

Greathouse G., and Wessel, C., *Deterioration of Materials* (New York: Reinhold, 1954).

Serada, P., "Atmospheric Factors Affecting the Corrosion of Steel," *Industrial and Engineering Chemistry*, **52** (1960), 157–60.

Spencer, K., "Cathode Protection," *Chemistry and Industry* (1953), pp. 2–10.

Uhlig, U., ed., *Corrosion Handbook* (New York: Wiley, 1948).

Corrosion in Action (The International Nickel Co., 1955). Text of film on corrosion.

16

Antifreeze; Radiator
Compounds; Brake Fluids

16-1 Antifreeze

Antifreeze is a substance which is added to a solvent, usually water, to lower its freezing point to some chosen temperature. The most common use for antifreeze is to protect the cooling system of automotive engines in winter. It is also used to prevent the freezing of gas pipelines and, added to gasoline, to prevent "icing" of the carburettor or a frozen fuel line if there happens to be some water in the gas tank.

There must be an attraction between solute and solvent molecules in order for the solute to dissolve. It would therefore be expected that the vapor pressure of the solvent would be lowered if these attractive solute molecules were present. The temperature-vapor pressure curve for the solution will then be below the curve for the pure solvent, cutting the vapor-solid curve at a temperature below the normal freezing point (Fig. 16-1). The extent of the lowering (ΔF) depends on the concentration of the solution. For aqueous solutions of nonelectrolytes, such as alcohols, one gram molecular weight of solute per 1000 grams of water[1] freezes at $-1.86°$ C.

---

1 This is a *molal* solution and must not be confused with *molar* concentrations, which are expressed as moles per 1000 milliliters of solution.

The two substances most widely used as antifreeze in the United States and Canada are ethylene glycol and methanol. Ethanol, once the largest selling antifreeze, has been displaced to a great extent. Other alcohols such as *iso*-propyl alcohol, propylene glycol, and glycerol may also be used. During World War II many strange concoctions were put into the cooling system of the car or truck: honey, corn syrup, sugar, and sometimes calcium chloride brine. Even kerosene was used as the coolant!

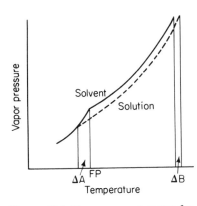

Figure 16-1 Vapor pressure curves for a solution and solvent.

There are several important considerations in formulating a good antifreeze solution. The properties which the ideal antifreeze should possess are:

1. Low molecular weight.
2. Low cost.
3. Low volatility.
4. Good heat conductance.
5. High specific heat.
6. Chemical stability.
7. Complete miscibility with water.
8. Low viscosity at low temperatures.

9. It should be noncorrosive to metals.
10. Inert towards rubber connections.
11. Nonfoaming.
12. Harmless to the car finish.
13. Have no tendency to leak or "creep."
14. The liquid or vapors should be nontoxic.
15. The vapor should not form explosive mixtures with air.

The molecular weight of methanol, CH_3OH, is 32, which is the lowest of any of the compounds used; therefore, methanol gives the greatest degree of protection per gram or per quart (sp gr 0.7924). Its cost per gallon is low. Its poor qualities are its high volatility (bp 64.5° C) and consequent loss by evaporation, its tendency to give corrosive products if not properly inhibited, the toxic nature of its fumes, and its effect on certain car finishes.

Ethylene glycol, bp 197.2° C, sp gr 1.116, is the base of most of the "permanent" types of antifreeze. Its molecular weight of 62 indicates that more of it is required to achieve the required protection than of either methanol or ethanol. It has a greater tendency to foam and to leak through hose or gaskets than the other two. The viscosity of a 40 per cent glycol solution at −30° C is 30 times the viscosity of water. The chief advantage of glycol is its very low vapor pressure. Any evaporation of the antifreeze solution will be due to loss of water, and since the glycol lowers the vapor pressure of the water, even the evaporation of the water will be less than if no antifreeze were present.

Three antifreeze solutions made from methanol, ethanol, and ethylene glycol bases, each giving a freezing point of −20° F, were found to boil

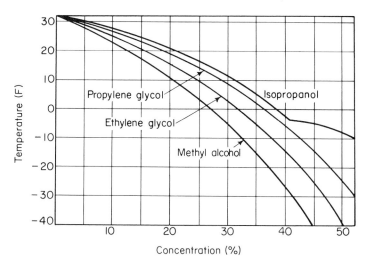

Figure 16-2 The relation between volume concentration of common types of antifreeze to the freezing point of the solution.

at 179° F, 180° F, and 223° F, respectively. The boiling point of the solution is of particular importance in "after boil." This may occur after the engine is turned off and is due to the increase in temperature of the solution caused by the residual heat of the engine. Or, large bubbles of vapor formed at the hot surface may so increase the volume in the cooling system that some of the solution is lost through the overflow. As one garage attendant expressed it, "The engine lost its alcohol by *blurping*." Overflow losses may be large when methanol is used.

The freezing points (initial crystallization) of the four most common antifreeze solutions at different concentrations are plotted in Fig. 16-2. Since the

Table 16-1. EFFECT OF INHIBITORS ON CORROSION OF DIFFERENT METALS WHEN PLACED IN DIFFERENT ANTIFREEZE SOLUTIONS AND IN WATER

| Medium | Loss of metal, in mg | | | | |
	Fe	Al	Cu	Brass	Solder
1. Methanol solution	1995	49	29	43	24
2. Methanol with inhibitor	1	1	10	2	10
3. Ethanol solution	1390	21	42	4	18
4. Ethanol with inhibitor	0	3	23	8	23
5. Ethylene glycol solution	793	45	101	101	267
6. Ethylene glycol with inhibitor	0	0	1	1	40
7. Distilled water	1524	5	93	93	234
8. Distilled water with inhibitor	0	4	32	20	32

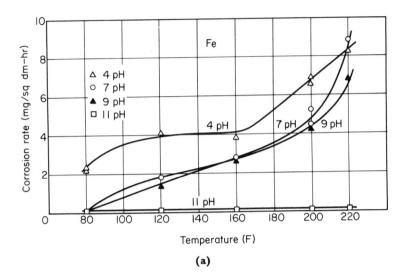

(a)

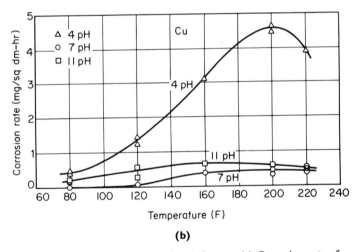

(b)

Figure 16-3 Metal corrosion in antifreezes: (a) Corrosion rate of steel in 40 per cent ethylene glycol—water solution as a function of temperature in an open system; (b) Corrosion rate of copper in 40 per cent ethylene glycol—water solution as a function of temperature in an open system. [From Agnew, R. J., Truitt, J. K., and Robertson, W. D., *Industrial and Engineering Chemistry*, **50**, (1958), 649, by permission.]

amount of the inhibitors and additives may vary in different brands, the freezing point may deviate slightly from the curves in the figure.

In the normal cooling system, air is continuously introduced by solution and entrainment. Air or exhaust gases may also get into the system through poor gaskets or water pump seals. At operating temperatures, such conditions tend to promote corrosion, even when the coolant is distilled water. When antifreeze is added, the alcohols may be oxidized to corrosive acids. Inhibitors are therefore added to prevent this. Table 16-1 shows the corrosion of different metals and alloys when immersed for 200 hours in different types of antifreeze solutions and in water at 170° F. Corrosion was measured by the loss in weight of the 12 sq in. sheet.

The effect of pH on corrosion in 40 per cent glycol-water without inhibitor is shown in Fig. 16-3a and 3b.

It is apparent from the table that inhibitor should always be present, even in summer when water is the usual coolant. It will also be noted that the corrosion of solder could not be prevented but that the production of rust was eliminated with all three types of antifreeze.

Various inhibitors are used. Among them are the amines such as tributyl amine and rosin amine, paraldehyde, emulsified oils, and tetraborates. At high antifreeze concentrations, the borates are effective buffers against acids and are satisfactory inhibitors. At low antifreeze concentrations they are ineffective, particularly against the corrosion of iron, steel, and aluminum. This is illustrated by the data in Table 16-2.

Electrolytes should in general be avoided as they promote corrosion. However, research on possible antifreeze materials during the last war, showed that a satisfactory antifreeze could be made from sodium benzoate with sodium nitrite as inhibitor (Fig. 15-9). Molybdates are reported to be effective in preventing corrosion of aluminum engine blocks.

Manufacturers of glycol for permanent type antifreeze are now advocating replacement of antifreeze each winter; this is not solely to promote sales. The inhibitor may be exhausted at the end of the season and reuse would give

Table 16-2. CORROSION OF DIFFERENT METALS WHEN IMMERSED IN CONTACT WITH EACH OTHER AT 160° F

Medium	Antifreeze concentration % volume	Corrosion loss, in mg, in 14 days					
		Steel	Cast iron	Al	Cu	Brass	Solder
Tap water	0	828	824	95	7	8	38
Permanent-type antifreeze with inhibitors	20	1	1	26	9	5	28
	40	1	1	7	4	4	19
Permanent-type antifreeze with borax inhibitor	20	230	330	174	5	7	20
	40	73	78	18	5	6	26

increased corrosion. Even if inhibitor is added, the result may not be satisfactory, because the antifreeze may have become too acid or the added inhibitor may not be compatible with any of the former inhibitor that may be present.

Table 16-3.

Property #	1	2	3	4	5	6	7	8	9	10	11	12	13	14	15
	E, Excellent.				G, Good.				F, Fair.			P, Poor.			
Methanol	E	E	P	G	G	P	E	E	P	E	E	P	G	P	P
Ethanol	E	G	F	G	G	F	E	E	F	E	E	F	G	G	G
Iso-propyl alcohol	G	G	G	G	G	G	E	G	F	G	G	G	G	G	G
Ethylene Glycol	G	F	F	G	G	F	E	F	F	G	F	E	P	G	E
Propylene Glycol	F	F	E	G	G	F	E	F	F	G	F	E	P	G	E
Honey	P	P	F	G	G	F	P	P	G	E	G	G	G	E	E

It has been found that mixed inhibitors may permit more corrosion than occurs when each is used alone. Table 16-3 compares various antifreeze compounds according to the properties mentioned above.

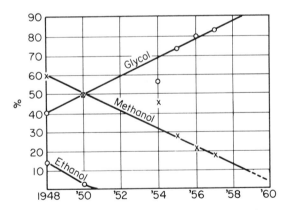

Figure 16-4 The change in the proportional use of glycol and methanol for the years 1948–58. The curve for ethanol represents the decline in use of this substance in terms of per cent of all antifreeze materials.

The addition of chemical inhibitors to antifreeze compounds has already been mentioned. Other properties may be improved by additional additives.

These include foam inhibitors and substances like diacetone alcohol,

$$OH$$
$$|$$
$$(CH_3)_2CCH_2COCH_3$$

to reduce the viscosity of permanent type antifreeze at low temperatures.

Since the last war, the two antifreeze materials used the most have been methanol and glycol, with the latter gaining increasing preference in spite of higher cost. Figure 16-4 shows the proportional usage of these two materials during the period 1948 to 1958. The subsequent five years show an irregular decrease in the use of methanol. In 1948 industrial ethanol accounted for 15 per cent of the antifreeze used; and in 1950, 3 per cent; and in 1960, almost zero per cent. Methanol and ethanol added to gasoline will prevent frozen fuel lines due to condensed or adventitious water in the tank.

16-2 Carburettor Deicing Compounds

Carburettor icing may occur in cool damp weather. The absorption of heat by the evaporating gasoline causes frost or ice formation. This may also be prevented by methanol vapor in the gasoline. Another type of additive is effective in concentrations of only 50 to 100 ppm. It acts by lowering the surface tension, thus permitting the fog droplets to spread over the metal surface instead of building a network of ice crystals to impede the mixed gases. These surface-active agents are ether derivatives of ethanol containing

phenoxy, ⬡ O—, and ethoxy groups, C_2H_5O—.

16-3 Radiator Compounds

The proper maintenance of the cooling system of a car or truck requires other chemical products. In the United States approximately 5,000,000 packages of radiator cleaning agents are sold annually. This represents a small percentage of the water-cooled vehicles which accumulate scale, rust, and other deposits from the water, clogging the narrow channels in the radiator core.

The most-common type of radiator "compound" employs a two-fold treatment. One part of the package contains oxalic acid. This acts first. The organic acid attacks and dissolves rust. It also reacts with the "lime" or calcium carbonate deposited from water containing carbonate hardness. The carbon dioxide liberated in the process helps to loosen the scale and suspend the resulting sludge. Sometimes the acid is accompanied with a wetting agent which promotes the penetration of the acid into the smallest crevices. After the solution has circulated for several minutes, it is drained off.

The second part of the treatment is an acid neutralizer and metathesizing agent such as sodium carbonate or phosphate. *Metathesis* is the conversion of one precipitate to another by double decomposition. Here the calcium sulfate scale is converted to a suspension of calcium carbonate by reaction with sodium carbonate,

$$CaSO_4 + Na_2CO_3 \rightleftharpoons CaCO_3 + Na_2SO_4$$

The extent of the conversion depends on the ratio of the solubility products of the two precipitates.

Metathesis may be illustrated by a simple experiment. If a suspension of lead chromate (chrome yellow pigment) in hot water is filtered, the filtrate is observed to be colorless, indicating that not more than a trace of chromate has dissolved. If, however, a warm solution of sodium carbonate is added to a portion of the pigment and the suspension filtered, the filtrate immediately shows the color of the chromate ion. The reaction is represented by the equation

$$PbCrO_4 + 2Na^+ + CO_3'' \longrightarrow PbCO_3 + 2Na^+ + CrO_4''$$

The success of the metathesis is determined by the concentration of CO_3'' available and the ratio of the solubility products of the chromate and carbonate. The solubility product of

$$PbCrO_4 = [Pb^{++}] \times [CrO_4''] = 2 \times 10^{-16};$$

K_{sp} for
$$PbCO_3 = [Pb^{++}] \times [CO_3''] = 1.5 \times 10^{-13}$$

Since the lead ion is common to both equations $[CrO_4'']/[CO_3''] =$ approximately $\frac{1}{750}$. This means that when equilibrium is reached in the competition of chromate and carbonate ions for the lead, one chromate ion is present for 750 carbonate ions. The experiment shows that in spite of the relatively high concentration of carbonate required by the ratio, conversion did take place. The K_{sp} for $CaSO_4$ is approximately 10^{-5} and for $CaCO_3$, 10^{-8}. In this case the equilibrium will be $[SO_4'']/[CO_3''] = \frac{1000}{1}$; that is, the conversion of the sulfate scale to carbonate will take place very much more easily than the metathesis of the lead chromate to lead carbonate in the experiment above.

The suspension produced by the second step in the treatment is flushed out of the cooling system, and replaced by clean—preferably "softened" water—with some corrosion inhibitor or antifreeze, depending on the season.

Sodium silicate in low concentrations in the coolant acts as an inhibitor. In higher concentrations it is used as a sealer for a cracked engine block.

Various "dopes" designed to plug or diminish radiator leaks often contain organic materials which form gels. These tend to reduce the efficiency of the cooling system.

16-4 Brake Fluids

The discussion of hydraulic brake fluids is related to that of antifreeze since many of the criteria for a good antifreeze also apply to brake fluids. Several components are common to both. A brake fluid must be noncorrosive, nonvolatile, not injurious to the rubber piston cups, must be chemically stable, miscible with other brake fluids, inexpensive, and have a surface tension such that the fluid will not leak past the piston. In addition to these qualities, it must be a lubricant for the piston; furthermore, the viscosity must not be too high at −40° F or too low at summer temperatures.

The hydraulic brake, now standard equipment on most automobiles, was first adopted on Dusenberg cars in 1922. Chrysler followed in 1924 with a brake developed by Loughead. This used a hydraulic fluid consisting of castor oil diluted with ethyl alcohol. Castor oil has remained the basic component of brake fluids because of its consistency or "body" and because it is almost the only oil which does not attack the rubber piston cups. It is a nondrying oil. It remains liquid down to zero F. The solidification point is lowered by admixture with solvents.

Present-day brake fluids may contain castor oil and one or more of several thinners or pour-point depressants. Some of these are chosen for their low vapor pressure. For example, amyl alcohol has a vapor pressure of 2.5 mm at 20° C. Cellosolve has a vapor pressure of 3.0 mm, n-butyl alcohol, 5.0, and diacetone, 9.0 mm. Inhibitors to prevent corrosion and others to resist gum formation are also added.

Many patented brake fluids have appeared during the past years. An examination of the solvents listed in the patents disclosed that only one-quarter were suitable and that all had some objectionable features.

Synthetic rubber, resistant to softening and swelling by solvents, has replaced natural rubber in the piston cups. This has extended the list of usable liquids.

Hydraulic fluids for other than brake assemblies include water emulsions, phosphate esters, chlorinated biphenyl, and silicones.

Review Questions

1. Define molal and molar solutions.
2. Discuss the properties of glycerol, $CH_2OHCHOHCH_2OH$, as an antifreeze.

3. Classify kerosene according to Table 16-3 as to antifreeze rating.

4. The specific gravity of isopropyl alcohol is 0.785. What would be the freezing point of a solution made by mixing equal volumes of the alcohol with water?

5. Calculate the freezing point of an antifreeze solution made by combining two quarts of methanol (sp gr 0.7960) with a pint of glycerol (sp gr 1.260) and three quarts of water.

6. What concentration of ethylene glycol is necessary to give an aqueous solution freezing at $-30°$ C?

7. Cite the qualities of an ideal brake fluid.

8. Define after-boil. What factors are responsible for it?

9. Sodium silicate is sometimes used in antifreeze. Why? How does it act?

10. What type of antifreeze should be used in mountainous country? Why?

11. Neither methanol nor glycol antifreeze is as effective a coolant as water. On what properties does the cooling action depend?

12. Name three types of additives used in commercial antifreeze.

13. A windshield deicing liquid containing 80 per cent isopropyl alcohol and 20 per cent glycol by weight is sprayed on until the film of ice (3 mm in thickness) is melted. What would be the maximum area of ice removed by 100 g of the spray, if the temperature is 27.5° F and the density of the ice is 0.92?

Further Reading

Howard, F. L., Brooks, D. B., and Streets, R. E., *A Review on Antifreeze* (National Bureau of Standards, Circular 576, Washington, D.C., (1956)).

17

Plastics

Plastics are synthetic resins which can be molded or formed into stable shapes by the application of heat and pressure. They are synthesized by a process called polymerization. This produces very large molecules by joining together hundreds of small molecules. The motto of the polymer chemist might well be the same as that of the United States, *E Pluribus Unum* (One from Many). The prefix "poly" means many. It often appears in the name of the plastic, for example, polyethylene. This name indicates that the material is formed by the combination of many molecules of ethylene gas, obtained from the cracking of oil.

The word "plastic" is used very loosely by the uninformed. One sometimes sees advertisements for "plastic" containers and "plastic" varnish. This is no more precise than to describe a particular garment as a "cloth" dress, or stainless steel cutlery as "metal" knives. There are now scores of different plastics and hundreds of combinations and modifications of the different types, all of which differ in properties. Unfortunately, in the past, not all manufacturers who used these chemical materials selected the plastic best suited for the product they marketed. Some suppliers are now licensing the manufacturer to prevent the incorrect use of their product. Others effect this by technical services and advertising directed at the consumer. The engineer should know the types of plastics available, and their individual characteristics in order to make intelligent use of these new materials.

There are two main groups of plastics: thermoplastic resins and thermosetting resins. The first group retain their ability to be remolded if they are reheated. The thermosetting resins, in contrast, lose their ability to change their shape under pressure when the heating is carried above that necessary to give the initial plastic flow in the mold. The rigid setting or "curing" is produced by three-dimensional chemical bonding induced by the high temperature. Examples of thermoplastics are cellulose derivatives, polystyrene, the vinyl polymers, polyethylene, nylon, and methacrylates. The thermosetting resins are represented by the phenolics or bakelites, casein plastics, urea-formaldehyde, melamine, various polyesters, and alkyd resins. The thermoplastic materials are composed of linear polymers, whereas the thermosetting types consist of giant molecules which have grown in all directions and have become entangled and combined with each other.

It will be shown that whether or not the polymer forms a thermoplastic or thermosetting resin depends on the chemical structure of the molecule and the type of chemical reaction that takes place.

Plastics are usually supplied to the manufacturer in the form of powder, flakes, or granules. The article may be made by pressure molding or by forcing the softened plastic through a die to form tubes, sheets, rods, or almost any shape. The substance may be applied in liquid form to impregnate paper, cloth, wood, glass matté, or glass cloth for conversion to laminates. The impregnated sheets, cut to the desired shape, are bonded by the application of heat and pressure. Plastic boats, car bodies, luggage, table tops, chairs, insulation panels, and even football helmets may be made from laminated plastics.

Several types of plastics are now produced as solid foam. These lightweight materials are used for insulation, cushions, packaging, or to produce buoyancy—as little as twelve pounds of "expanded" plastic may support 150 pounds in water. One of the expanded plastics is so light, tough, stable and elastic that it may be used as an inner lining for outdoor clothing and even for "solid" tires.

17-1 Cellulose Derivatives

Cellulose Nitrate

The first commercial plastic was made by chemically modifying cellulose, one of nature's polymers. Cellulose consists of thousands of glucose-like rings each of which contains three alcohol groups (—OH). By reacting these groups with nitric acid, cellulose nitrate is formed.

The partially nitrated cellulose mixed with camphor gives a plastic easily softened and molded. This plastic is called *celluloid*. The function of the camphor is to act as a plasticizer to enhance the molding properties. Many

$$
\begin{bmatrix}
\end{bmatrix}_{2000-3000}
$$

Cellulose

other substances may be used for this purpose. Nitrocellulose containing 10.5 to 11.5 per cent nitrogen is used for molded and extruded articles. Since 11.1 per cent nitrogen corresponds to the nitration of two of the three OH groups, in lacquers with 11.5 to 12.1 per cent nitrogen, between two and three of the hydroxide groups in the glucosan ring must have been nitrated. Full nitration would give 14.1 per cent nitrogen. The explosive guncotton contains from 12.1 to 13.8 per cent nitrogen.

The properties depend on the degree of nitration; for example, the solubility of the plastic in organic solvents increases to a maximum at approximately 11.5 per cent N. Cellulose nitrate plastics are tough, transparent, and easily molded. Tool handles, drawing instruments, spectacle frames, and many other objects are made from this material. The first "artificial leather" was made by coating fabric with nitrocellulose suitably colored and embossed. It still finds use in coverings for upholstery, books, and luggage.

A disadvantage of the material for some purposes lies in its low ignition temperature. The colorless plastic tends to yellow with age. It becomes brittle at low temperatures.

Cellulose Acetate

If concentrated acetic acid or acetic anhydride is used instead of nitric acid, the resulting product is cellulose acetate. This material is not only used for transparent sheet and anything that can be made therefrom, but also as celanese and fortisan textiles. Since cellulose acetate is much less inflammable than cellulose nitrate, it has displaced the latter in the manufacture of photographic film. Cellulose acetate-butyrate is a copolymer having lower water absorption than the acetate alone.

Ethyl Cellulose

The toughest of the cellulose plastics is ethyl cellulose. Chisel handles, mallet heads, and other objects which have to withstand impact, for example, the U.S. Army canteen and the ends of containers for supplies dropped by parachute, were made from this material.

Ethyl cellulose is made by first treating cellulose with caustic soda to produce soda cellulose, and then making this product react with ethyl chloride to give an average of 2.5 ethoxyl groups per $\frac{1}{2}$ ethyl cellulose monomer.

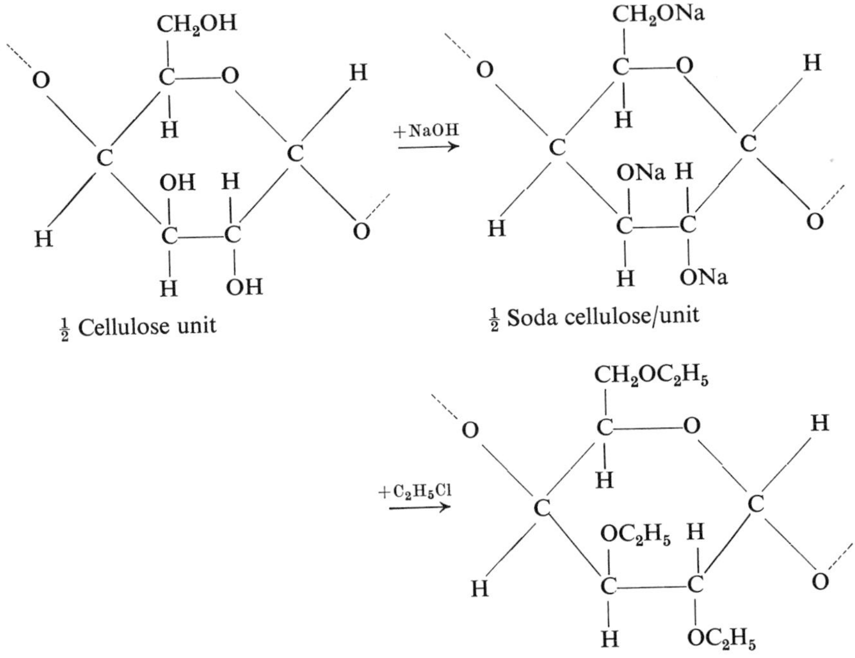

$\frac{1}{2}$ Cellulose unit

$\frac{1}{2}$ Soda cellulose/unit

17-2 Synthetic Addition Polymers

Polyethylene

While the cellulose plastics are prepared by chemical treatment of a ready-made polymer, most plastics and synthetic resins are synthesized by polymerizing small molecules. The simplest example of such a synthesis is in the production of polyethylene or polythene. The raw material for this versatile plastic is ethylene gas, $CH_2{=}CH_2$. The ethylene may be obtained in three ways: as a by-product from the cracking of hydrocarbons in oil refining, by the dehydrogenation of ethane, and by the dehydration of the molecule of ethyl alcohol.

During polymerization the ethylene molecules are activated by the breaking of one of the coordinate double bonds, leaving an active electron on each of the two carbon atoms. Under suitable conditions these activated molecules join together to form a very long hydrocarbon molecule.

$$n(CH_2{=}CH_2) \longrightarrow n(-CH_2{-}CH_2{-}) \xrightarrow{+2H} H(CH_2{-}CH_2)_nH$$

The original high-pressure process gave some branched polymers; polyethylene formed at low pressure has a higher melting point, density, and tensile strength. It is a linear crystalline polymer.

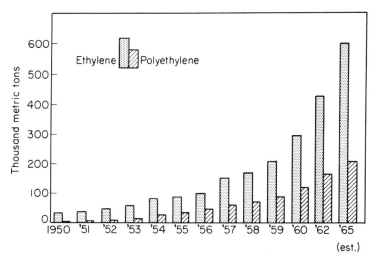

Figure 17-1 The annual production of ethylene and polyethylene in Great Britain. [Courtesy *Chemical Age*, London, **85**, (1961), 360.]

In 1962 polyethylene production in the United States, approximately $1\frac{1}{2}$ billion pounds, exceeded that of any other plastic and its production curve is still rising. The increasing use of this plastic is not confined to North America. Figure 17-1 is a plot of production trends in Great Britain. The tremendous growth in sales of this material is due to its many desirable properties. Polyethylene is a very light plastic which is chemically inert and therefore can be used to make containers for hydrofluoric and sulfuric acid. It has very low water absorption, is an excellent insulator, and is flexible even at low temperatures. Polythene sheets can be easily joined by a hot iron. Some of its uses are for light flexible pipes, vapor barriers, waterproof floors for water storage ponds, electrical conduits, protective covering for football fields, for "curing" concrete, as a translucent covering for winter construction, for high-frequency insulation, for squeeze bottles and many other types of containers. Figures 17-2 and -3 illustrate two uses in engineering.

Figure 17-2 Polythene pipe to form radiant heating in the cement floor of a large garage. [Courtesy Canadian Industries Ltd.]

Figure 17-3 Polythene used for underlay in road paving. This prevents loss of cement and produces a concrete less permeable to ground water and frost break-up. [Courtesy Canadian Industries Ltd.]

Polypropylene

Polypropylene resembles polyethylene in many of its properties. Both polymers have low water absorption and are resistant to acids and alkalies. Both have excellent electrical properties, with dielectric constants 2.0 to 2.3 and volume resistivities 10^{15} to 10^{16} ohm/cm. Polypropylene is the lightest polymeric material in use. Its specific gravity is only 0.91; a rope made from

Figure 17-4 [From *Hercules Chemist*, **36**, (1959) 22, courtesy Hercules Powder Co.]

this polymer will float. Figure 17-4 shows a ship's hawser made from polypropylene fiber.

A Manila rope, of 10 in. circumference (approximately 3 in. diameter) with a breaking strength of 77,000 lb, has an average weight of 299 lb/100 ft. A polypropylene rope with a breaking strength of 79,000 pounds has a circumference of $7\frac{1}{2}$ in. (2.5 in. diameter) and weighs only 125 lb/100 ft. Furthermore, when a Manila rope is wet, it increases in bulk and weight. Propylene rope does not do so because the material has very low water absorption.

The flexibility, resilience, and resistance to staining of polypropylene make it suitable for carpet fibers. Its high softening temperature permits its use for hot water pipes and for articles and wrappings which can be sterilized by heat. Thin films of the material shrink on being heated, however, and this property is made use of in packaging to produce a tight, form-fitting, transparent wrapper. Disposable drinking cups, bottles, and containers of all sizes are made from this polymer.

Polythene Derivatives

The polymer made from tetrafluoroethylene, $CF_2{=}CF_2$, called *Teflon*, has many remarkable properties. It has less water absorption than even ethylene, namely, 0.00 per cent, as compared with polyethylene's 0.01 per cent. The melting point of the polymer is so high that techniques similar to those employed in powder metallurgy have to be used in forming sheets and molding articles. The material is chemically inert, attacked by almost nothing except molten alkali metals. A sample kept at 570° F for a month had loss of tensile strength of only 10 per cent. Two Teflon surfaces have a coefficient of friction comparable to that of ice on ice. Polytetrafluoroethylene has very low friction on other surfaces. This plastic is used as a solid lubricant film on ammunition, gun mechanisms, and as a bearing surface for light loads (see Chapter 13). It does not stick to other materials and is therefore called an *abhesive*; it is accordingly used to make nonsticking stopcocks for burettes and as a thin tape for covering pipe threads, so that no matter how tight the pipes may be coupled, they can be unscrewed. Teflon costs $5.50 to $8.00 per pound. It can be machined, punched, and drilled. Its specific gravity is 2.2.

Polymerized monochlortrifluoroethylene has many of the properties of the tetrafluorine polymer, but to a lesser degree. It is easier to mold, but decomposes at a lower temperature (390° as compared with over 750° for teflon). It is plastic from −320° F to 390° F. A common trade name is Kel F.

Other Ethylene Derivatives

POLYVINYL PLASTICS

Ethylene may be taken as a prototype for many common plastics. The unsaturated radical derived by the removal of one hydrogen of the ethylene molecule was long ago given the name "vinyl." Thus in the compounds

$$CH_2{=}CH, \quad CH_2{=}CH, \quad CH_2{=}CH, \quad CH_2{=}CH$$
$$\quad | \qquad\qquad | \qquad\qquad\quad | \qquad\qquad\quad |$$
$$\quad OH \qquad\quad Cl \qquad\qquad\qquad\qquad\quad (C_2H_3O_2)$$

one of the hydrogens of ethylene has been replaced by a substituent group or atom. These are vinyl alcohol, vinyl chloride, vinyl benzene, commonly called "styrene," and vinyl acetate, respectively. They give long polymers which have the same type of skeleton, but differ in the nature of the appended groups. If two of these substances are mixed, the resulting copolymer will have properties depending on the proportion of the monomers used. Most of the vinyl monomers are made from acetylene. Thus vinyl acetate can be formed by the reaction of a molecule of the gas and a molecule of acetic acid in the presence of mercuric sulfate as a catalyst

$$CH{\equiv}CH + H{-}(C_2H_3O_2) \longrightarrow CH_2{=}CH(C_2H_3O_2)$$

Also $\qquad CH{\equiv}CH + HCl \longrightarrow CH_2{=}CHCl$

Polyvinyl alcohol may be obtained by hydrolyzing the acetate. Polyvinyl alcohol forms elastic films, and it is usually copolymerized with vinyl acetate or reacted with aldehydes to give flexible sheets such as are used in the manufacture of safety glass.

POLYVINYL ACETATE (VYA)[1]

This plastic, of low molecular weight, is a good adhesive. The higher polymers form clear thermoplastic resins which have excellent molding qualities because it expands slightly on solidifying, and thus fills every nook and cranny in the mold. In emulsion form, it is used in water latex paints.

POLYVINYL CHLORIDE

This can be polymerized to a rubber-like polymer. It is copolymerized with 5 to 20 per cent of VYA to give a series of plastics known as *vinylites*. The outstanding qualities of this class of synthetic resin are scuff resistance, low water absorption, low inflammability, and stability at low temperatures. The polymer has to be mixed with a plasticizer before extrusion or molding. One of the recent uses of vinylite was for expansion joints between concrete blocks in the St. Lawrence Seaway. Garden hose, sheeting, raincoats, shower curtains, grinding wheel bonding, ground sheets, artificial leather, electrical insulation and insulating tape, phonograph records, and many other articles are formed from these vinyl compounds. Figure 17-5 shows a fume duct and exhaust fan made from rigid polyvinylchloride. Until 1959 the vinyl plastics led all other plastics in quantity production. They are now in second place.

VINYLIDENE CHLORIDE

If both the hydrogens on one of the carbons of ethylene are replaced by chlorine, the compound called vinylidene chloride is obtained. When this is polymerized, a very useful inert plastic is produced.

---

1 AYAA, AYAB, etc., designate vinyl acetate resins of different mol. wts.

$$\begin{matrix} H & Cl \\ | & | \\ C = C \\ | & | \\ H & Cl \end{matrix} \longrightarrow \left(\begin{matrix} H & Cl \\ | & | \\ -C-C- \\ | & | \\ H & Cl \end{matrix} \right)_n$$

The material is known as *Saran*. Tygon is a copolymer with vinyl chloride. Saran tubing is not attacked by strong acids. It can be machined and welded

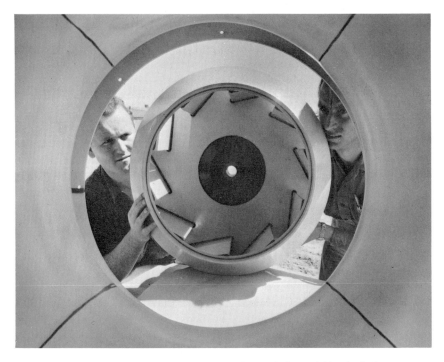

Figure 17-5 Fume duct and exhaust fan made from rigid polyvinyl chloride. [From *Plastics Sphere* **8**, No. 3, (1959) 13, courtesy Canadian Industries Ltd.]

by warming the ends of the tube with a hot iron and pressing them together. Vinylidene chloride polymers are water resistant. Textiles made from extruded fibers are used for weatherproof awnings, outdoor upholstery, screening, and so on. Saran tubing and sheet have excellent flexibility. A tube of the material with a wall thickness of $\frac{1}{16}$ in. was flexed through a $15°$ arc 2.5 million times without cracking. A copper tube of the same dimensions failed after 500 cycles.

POLYSTYRENE

This is the cheapest transparent plastic material. Styrene or vinyl benzene can be made by dehydrogenating ethyl benzene. Styrene looks and smells a lot like toluene. If an unopened bottle of the liquid is allowed to stand for a long period, it will gradually solidify by polymerization. In the presence of a catalyst, polymerization takes place rapidly. The resin has very low water absorption and is insoluble in most acids and alkalies, alcohols, acetone, or

Figure 17-6 Methacrylate lenses. [Courtesy American Optical Co.]

gasoline. It is soluble in benzene or aromatic hydrocarbons and in chlorinated solvents and esters. As it has good dimensional stability, it is used to make rulers. Light transmission through 0.1 in. sheet is 92 per cent It is a good dielectric, the breakdown voltage being 550 to 700 v per mil. Styrofoam was one of the first expanded plastics used for buoyancy, packaging, insulating, and decoration. Styrene is an important copolymer in the manufacture of Buna S rubber (page 281).

17-3 Acrylates

Probably the best known of this group of thermoplastic materials is *Lucite* (or polymethyl methacrylate) because of its outstanding optical properties (Fig. 17-6). The relation of the acrylates to the vinyls, and hence to ethylene, will be seen from the formulas.

$$CH_2{=}CH$$
$$|$$
$$COOH$$
Acrylic
acid

$$CH_2{=}\overset{\displaystyle CH_3}{\underset{\displaystyle COOH}{C}}$$
Methyl
acrylic acid

$$CH_2{=}CH$$
$$|$$
$$COOCH_3$$
Methyl
acrylate

$$CH_2{=}\overset{\displaystyle CH_3}{\underset{\displaystyle COOCH_3}{C}}$$
Methyl
methacrylate

Polymerization again produces a straight chain.

Methyl methacrylate transmits 98 per cent of the sunlight, including the ultraviolet. Owing to internal reflection, light entering one end of a spiral or bent rod of methacrylate will emerge from the opposite end with almost un-diminished intensity. For this reason it is used to pipe light behind opaque objects or to transmit pictures through a bundle of the fibers and appropriate lenses.

ACRYLIC NITRILE

This can be made by adding HCN to acetylene or by a less-direct route, from ethylene. The chief use of the polymer is as a textile fiber, for example, Orlon. The monomer is copolymerized with butadiene to form an elastomer known as Buna N or Perbunan.

17-4 Linear Condensation Polymers

All the thermoplastic resins mentioned above consist of linear molecules formed by true polymerization without the loss of any portion of the reacting monomers. Other linear thermoplastics can be prepared by what is known as condensation reactions during which water or some other molecule is evolved. When an alcohol and an organic acid react, the acidic hydrogen and the OH of the alcohol are eliminated as water, and the ester is formed by the union of the free radicals. If the alcohol is a glycol, that is, it has two OH groups, and the acid is a dibasic acid, condensation can proceed at each end of the molecules to produce a long chain; for example,

$$HOCH_2CH_2OH + HOOC{-}\langle\bigcirc\rangle{-}COOH \longrightarrow$$

Glycol   Terephthalic acid

$$H\left[{-}CH_2CH_2{-}O\overset{\displaystyle O}{\overset{\displaystyle \|}{C}}{-}\langle\bigcirc\rangle{-}\overset{\displaystyle O}{\overset{\displaystyle \|}{C}}{-}O{-}\right]_n H$$

to give the linear polyester "Terylene" or "Dacron." This polymer forms fibers having high tensile strength and many other desirable properties. "Mylar" is a tough, transparent film made by extruding the polyester in the form of a thin sheet.

Another well-known fiber formed by a condensation reaction is *nylon*. The components are a diamine, $H_2H(CH_2)_6NH_2$, called *hexamethylene diamine*, and a dibasic acid $HOOC(CH_2)_4COOH$, adipic acid. Again water is eliminated, and the methylene or $—CH_2—$ links are joined together through nitrogen and carbon of an amide group $(RNHCO—)$.

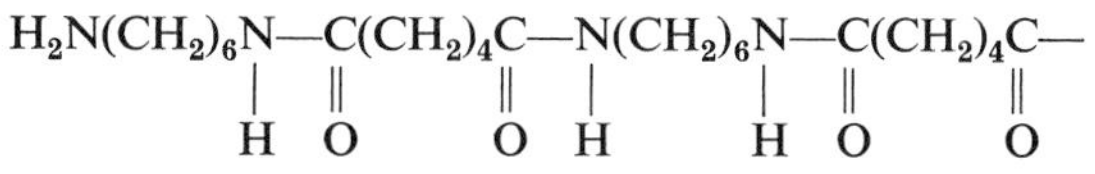

$$H_2N(CH_2)_6N—C(CH_2)_4C—N(CH_2)_6N—C(CH_2)_4C—$$
$$\overset{|}{H}\ \overset{\|}{O}\qquad\overset{\|}{O}\ \overset{|}{H}\qquad\overset{|}{H}\ \overset{\|}{O}\qquad\overset{\|}{O}$$

Nylon is not only used for the production of fibers, but is also molded and extruded to make rollers, bristles, and castings. Water may be used as a lubricant for nylon bearings.

17-5 Thermosetting Resins:

Three-dimensional Polymerization

The earliest thermosetting plastic was called *Bakelite*, after the Belgian-American chemist Bakeland who patented it in 1909. It was prepared by the condensation of phenol and formaldehyde. There are today a great number of different phenol-formaldehyde resins which find a variety of uses as water-soluble adhesives, laminating adhesives, varnish and lacquer resins, and thermosetting molding powders.

The nature of the product depends on several factors, the principal ones being the proportion of the reactants and whether the catalyst is acidic or basic. If the mole ratio of phenol to formaldehyde (P/F) is greater than 1, that is, phenol is in excess, the reaction proceeds in an almost linear fashion.

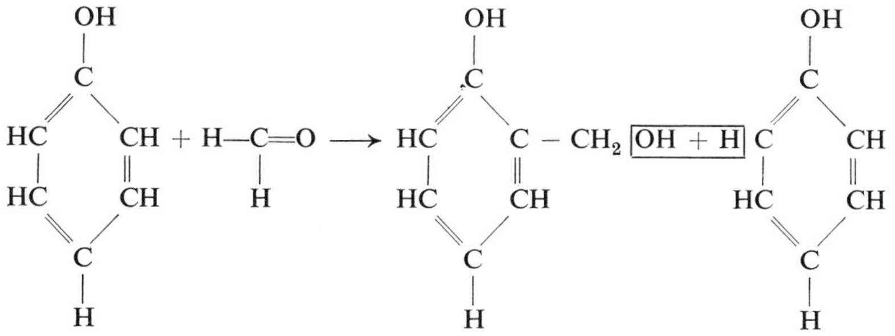

The first reaction produces an addition compound. The formaldehyde captures a hydrogen from the ortho or para carbon of the benzene, becoming

$$\begin{array}{c} H \\ | \\ -C-OH \\ | \\ H \end{array}$$

This group takes the place of the captured hydrogen on the benzene ring. The new compound then condenses with another molecule of phenol, a molecule of water being given off with the result that two phenols are now joined by

$$\begin{array}{c} H \\ -C- \\ H \end{array}$$

called a *methylene bridge*. These reactions are repeated many times as illustrated below.

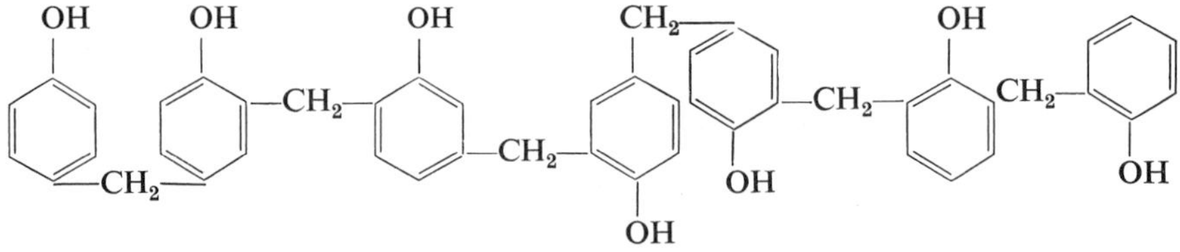

This is more or less linear and is fusible and soluble in organic solvents. It is called a *novolac*.

With the addition of more formaldehyde to a novolac, so that the ratio of phenol/formaldehyde becomes 1 or less, more —CH_2OH (methylol) groups are formed, and consequently adjacent chains may be cross-linked or "set" when the resin is heated. This is then a casting resin.

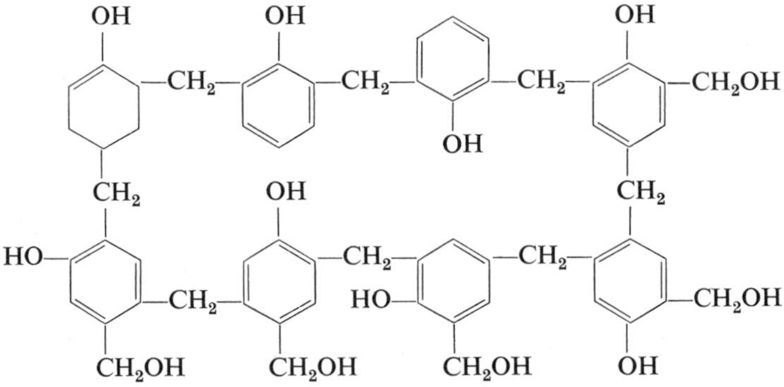

When the ratio phenol/formaldehyde is small, the excess formaldehyde gives an abundance of methylol groups on the initial product in both ortho and para positions; and these, in the presence of an alkaline catalyst, may react at once with phenol to produce three-directional linking. Some may react together to form an ether-type bridge

$$-CH_2OH \quad OHCH_2- \longrightarrow -CH_2OCH_2-$$

These resins make good adhesives. Because of excess alcohol groups, they can be combined with drying oils for varnishes and enamels.

Formaldehyde also forms condensation polymers with phenol derivatives such as the cresols.

Urea Plastics

Urea,

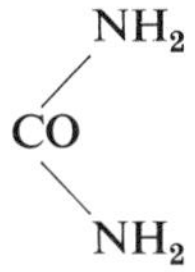

$$\begin{array}{c} NH_2 \\ / \\ CO \\ \backslash \\ NH_2 \end{array}$$

reacts with formaldehyde to give a condensation product used for molding and as a laminating adhesive. It is also used to impregnate wood to prevent cracking. Thin sections or sheets of impregnated wood can be permanently shaped by heat and pressure. The condensation reaction may be represented by:

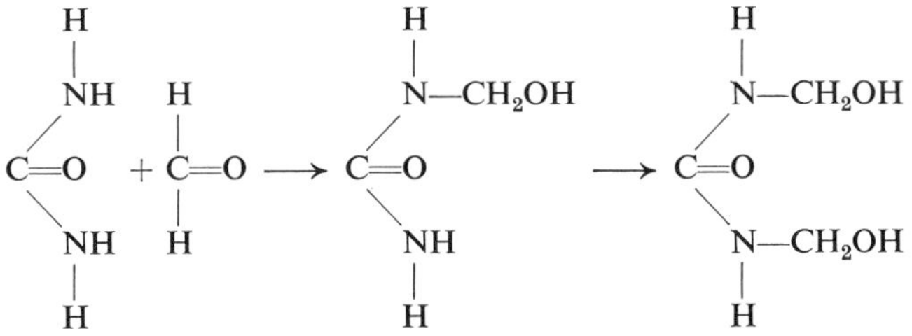

$$\begin{array}{ccccc} H & & H & & H \\ | & & | & & | \\ NH \quad H & & N-CH_2OH & & N-CH_2OH \\ / & | & / & & / \\ C=O & + C=O \longrightarrow C=O & \longrightarrow C=O \\ \backslash & | & \backslash & & \backslash \\ NH \quad H & & NH & & N-CH_2OH \\ | & & | & & | \\ H & & H & & H \end{array}$$

Monomethylol urea   Dimethylol urea

These may then react with more urea with the elimination of water

HOCH$_2$NHCONHCH$_2$OH + N$_2$HCONH$_2$ ⟶ HOCH$_2$NHCONHCH$_2$OH
Dimethylol urea   Urea   A tri-mer

etc. Or, if formaldehyde is in excess, both the hydrogens on some amine groups may react, forming linkages to give a thermosetting resin.

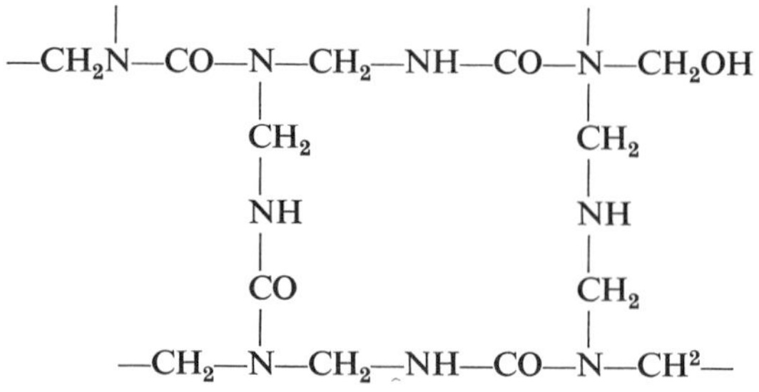

$$-CH_2N-CO-N-CH_2-NH-CO-N-CH_2OH$$

$$\begin{array}{cc} CH_2 & CH_2 \\ | & | \\ NH & NH \\ | & | \\ CO & CH_2 \end{array}$$

$$-CH_2-N-CH_2-NH-CO-N-CH^2-$$

Melamine

Melamine, which has the formula

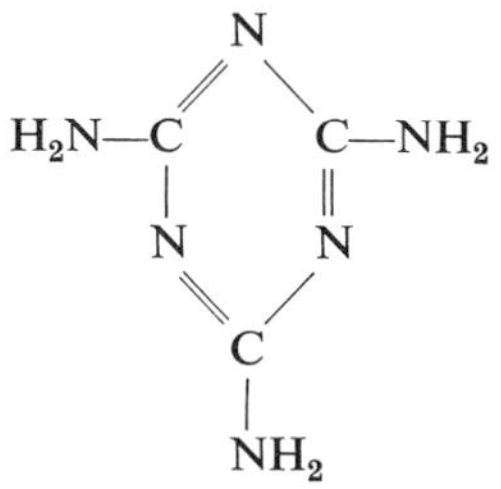

can play the same game with formaldehyde, forming bonded networks of melamine rings. The plastic known as Melamac is used for dishes, for increasing the wet strength of paper, for shrink-proofing wool, and for adhesives.

Formaldehyde also forms resins with other materials containing amino groups, such as the proteins.

Glyptals and Alkyd Resins

The glyptals are polyesters formed by the condensation or esterification of glycerol ($CH_2OH-CHOH-CH_2OH$) with a dibasic acid, phthalic acid

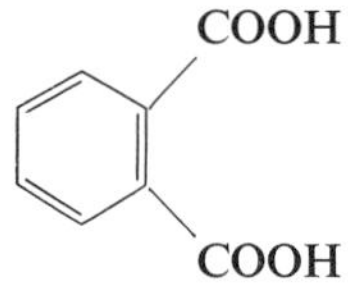

The name is derived from the names of the reactants. Since glycerol has more than two active OH groups, cross-linked polymers will result. These resins are very valuable for varnishes and other protective coatings.

Other polyfunctional alcohols such as pentaerythritol,

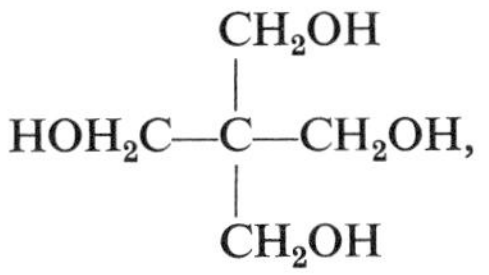

$$CH_2OH$$
$$|$$
$$HOH_2C—C—CH_2OH,$$
$$|$$
$$CH_2OH$$

inositol,

$$CHOH$$
$$/ \quad \backslash$$
$$HOHC \qquad CHOH$$
$$| \qquad |$$
$$HOHC \qquad CHOH$$
$$\backslash \quad /$$
$$CHOH$$

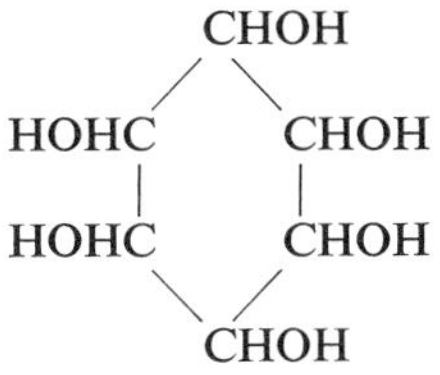

and other dibasic or polybasic acids form similar resins. These are called *alkyd resins*. They are playing an increasing part in the paint industry (see Chapter 19).

Epoxy resins are special three-component polyesters that set at room temperature, and give tough weatherproof, hard and firm adhesives, and bonding agents that are used to produce glass-fiber boats, and other structures.

Polyurethane is another type of polyester having the general structure represented by the formula

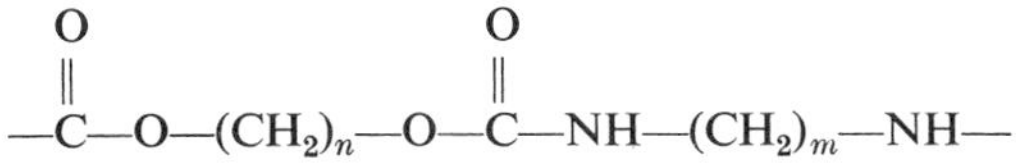

$$
\overset{\displaystyle O}{\overset{\displaystyle \|}{—C}}—O—(CH_2)_n—O—\overset{\displaystyle O}{\overset{\displaystyle \|}{C}}—NH—(CH_2)_m—NH—
$$

Polyurethane is of particular interest as foamed or expanded plastics and as adhesives.

Cumarone resins are derived from coal tar fractions. They are widely used in the manufacture of asphalt tile; in fact, practically all light colored tile contains this resin. They are also used in aluminum paints and bronzing liquids. Their resistance to water and alkali imparts or improves these properties in a varnish.

17-6 The Silicones

A very interesting and important family of polymers arise from the condensation of compounds of the element silicon. This element, which is so plentifully distributed in the rocks and minerals, has its position in the periodic table in Group IV, immediately below carbon. It should then exhibit a covalence of four and show some of the chemical behavior of carbon. The gas SiF_4 is produced when hydrofluoric acid acts on glass.

Silicon tetrachloride, $SiCl_4$, has a structure similar to carbon tetrachloride. The English chemist Kipping found that three of the chlorines of the $SiCl_4$ could be exchanged for phenyl radicals (C_6H_5—), by treating it with chlorobenzene, C_6H_5Cl, in the presence of sodium metal.

$$SiCl_4 + 6\,Na + 3\,C_6H_5Cl \longrightarrow (C_6H_5)_3SiCl + 6\,NaCl$$

Magnesium metal has the ability to combine readily with both parts of an alkyl halide like methyl chloride, forming a compound

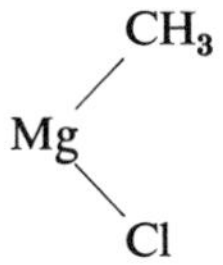

$$Mg \underset{\displaystyle Cl}{\overset{\displaystyle CH_3}{<}}$$

The magnesium would really prefer another chloride to the organic radical, and so when this reagent, called a *Grignard reagent*, meets $SiCl_4$ in the proper environment, namely, in dry ether, the exchange is effected. By increasing the proportion of the Grignard reagent to $SiCl_4$, all four of the chlorides may be replaced by the alkyl radicals.

The chloride in the resulting organic silicon compounds can be replaced by hydrolysis, OH groups being substituted.

$$(CH_3)_3SiCl + HOH \longrightarrow HCl + (CH_3)_3SiOH$$

This is called *trimethyl silanol.* On hydrolysis the disubstituted compound

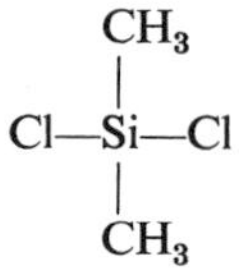

$$\begin{array}{c} CH_3 \\ | \\ Cl-Si-Cl \\ | \\ CH_3 \end{array}$$

gives

$$\begin{array}{c} CH_3 \\ | \\ HO-Si-OH \\ | \\ CH_3 \end{array}$$

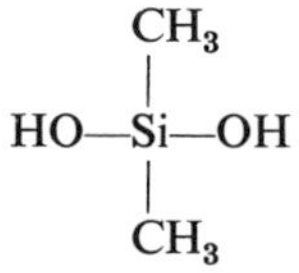

dimethyl silanol. This compound can undergo condensation reactions and give linear polymers.

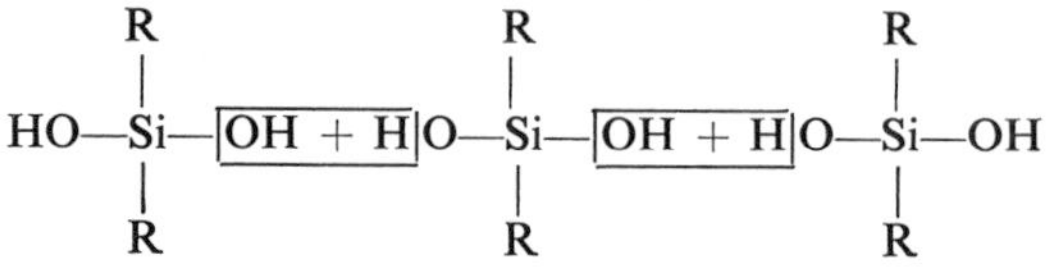

$$\begin{array}{ccccccc} R & & R & & R \\ | & & | & & | \\ HO-Si-\boxed{OH+H}O-Si-\boxed{OH+H}O-Si-OH \\ | & & | & & | \\ R & & R & & R \end{array}$$

This results in a chain of alternate silicon and oxygen atoms with organic groups on the silicon. The —(Si—O)— skeleton is the same as that of asbestos and mica. It is apparent that the heat-resistant qualities of this combination will be manifest in the properties of the silicone. The long linear polymers vary in properties from liquids to elastic solids (see Silastic Rubber, Chapter 18). The silicone oils are used for heat-resistant lubricants, mold release compounds, and as waterproofing and water-repellent agents, (Fig. 17-7), anti-foaming compounds, in heat-resistant and fire-retardant

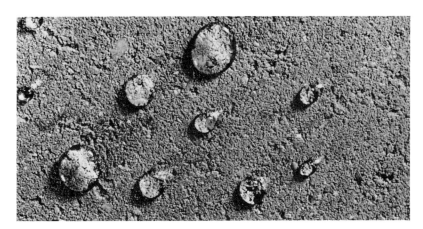

Figure 17-7 Water repellency of a concrete surface treated with silicone. [Courtesy Dow-Corning Corp.]

paints, high-temperature greases, liquid dielectrics, and liquid springs (at 50,000 psi silicone fluids have 17 per cent compression).

Only two monosilanols, R_3SiOH, can unite by condensation.

$$R_3SiOH + HOSiR_3 \longrightarrow R_3SiOSiR_3$$

Since each of the six radicals may be different, or present in any combination, a large number of different silicones can result. These give water-repellent vapors and heat-transfer liquids.

The trisilanols

$$R—\underset{\underset{\displaystyle OH}{|}}{\overset{\overset{\displaystyle OH}{|}}{Si}}—OH$$

can grow in three directions. They give hard, dense, heat-resistant thermosets used in electrical insulation, and with glass cloth in heat-stable laminates for "heat dams." One such application is found in the "F-100" in which a metallized 0.0626 in. sheet is exposed to 1200°F. The opposite side reaches a temperature of 490° F maximum, with the air temperature $\frac{3}{8}$ in. from the sheet only 260° F. Other data on specific applications will be found in the discussion of the appropriate topics; for example "Lubrication," Chapter 13, and "Special Paints," Chapter 19.

Plastics can be tailor-made for specific uses by selecting the monomer, by combining several materials, and by the introduction of halogens or other substituents. Figure 17-8 pictures valves made with gates which are not

Figure 17-8 Valves made with a dichlorinated polyether. This is not attacked by chlorinated solvents such as CCl_4. [Courtesy Canadian Industries Ltd. and Hercules Powder Co.]

attacked by chlorinated solvents. The plastic used is a dichlorinated polyether,

$$\left[CH_2-\underset{\underset{CH_2Cl}{|}}{\overset{\overset{CH_2Cl}{|}}{C}}-CH_2O- \right]_n$$

Plastics or synthetic resins are playing an important role in rocketry and space research. Printed electric circuits, antenna housings, light-weight instrument enclosures, heat shields, re-entry cones, and, combined with glass cord, even rocket motors are made with plastics. Indeed, an almost completely plastic space rocket is an actuality.[1]

---

1 W. C. Howit, "Plastics as Heat Insulators in Rocket Motors," *Industrial and Chemical Engineering*, **52** (1960), 761.

Name	Source	Monomer or segmer	Outstanding properties	Typical uses
Cellulose Cellophane Rayon Viscose	Wood Cotton Straw NaOH + CS₂	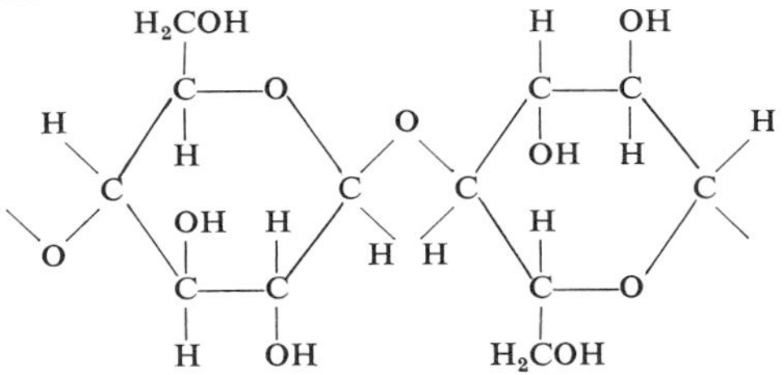 (cellulose ring structure: H₂COH, OH, H₂COH groups)	Regenerated cellulose of lower mol. wt.	Textiles, tire cord, transparent film
Pyralin Pyroxylin, etc. Nitrocellulose	Cellulose HNO₃ + H₂SO₄	—OH replaced by —O—NO₂ groups	Tough, transparent, soluble in esters, ketones; ignites easily	Tool handles, lacquers
Cellulose acetate, Celanese Lumarith Plasticele	Cellulose Acetic acid Acetic anhydride	—OH groups in cellulose replaced by acetate groups	Better flame resistance and molding qualities; rather high water absorption	Safety film, transparent sheets, enclosures, textiles
Ethylcellulose Ethocel	Soda cellulose Ethyl chloride	—OH groups changed to —OC₂H₅ groups	Toughest of cellulose derivatives	Mallet heads, handles, trim, fabric coating
Polyethylene Polythene	Ethylene	—CH₂CH₂—	Inert, stable, flexible at low temperatures, low water absorption, lightest	Vapor barrier insulation, flexible piping, rope, carpets, film, coating, containers
Polypropylene		CH₃ | —CH₂CH₂—		
Tetrafluoethylene Teflon, TFE. Kel F, TFCE.	F₂ + C₂H₄	—CF₂—CF₂— —CClF—CF₂—	Extremely inert, adhesive, molded by powder technique, high temperature softening point	Radar parts, nose cones, gaskets for high temperatures Solid lubricant
Polyvinylacetate, Gelva, AYA—, polyvinylacetate	CH≡CH + HO·C—CH₃ ‖ O	—CH₂—CH— | OOC·CH₃	Expands on solidification	Adhesive, sharp molding, emulsion paints
Vinyl alcohol Resistoflex PVA	—CH₂—CH— | OOC·CH₃ + H₂O Hydrolysis of polyvinylacetate	—CH₂CH— | OH	Low polymer soluble in water, high polymers insoluble; good tensile strength, flexibility	Tough film, soluble or insoluble in water for metal coatings, paper, textiles

Table 17-1. SUMMARY OF PLASTICS AND SYNTHETIC RESINS (CONT.)

Name	Source	Monomer or segmer	Outstanding properties	Typical uses
Polyvinylchloride Koroseal, Geon	$CH{\equiv}CH + HCl$	$-CH_2CH-$ $\quad\;\; Cl$	Requires plasticizer, low solubility, not attacked by acid chlorine, oils, or water; rubber-like elasticity	Gaskets, tank linings, expansion joints
Vinylite	Polyvinylacetate Vinyl chloride	$-CH_2-CH-CH_2-CH-$ $\quad\;\; OOCCH_3 \quad\;\; Cl$	Properties depend on proportion of polyvinylacetate and chloride; from clear plastics to rubber like polymers; scuff resistant	Instruments, tiles, phonograph records, waterproof films and coatings
Vinylidene chloride Saran Tygon	$CH_2{=}CH_2 + Cl_2$ copolymer	H Cl —C—C— H Cl	Inert to strong acids and alkali; can be machined; low water absorption	Textiles, film, pipes for acids and alkalies
Polystyrene	$C_6H_5C_2H_5$	$-CH_2CH-$ (phenyl)	Light, transparent, cheap, stable	Molded cases, rulers, foamed insulation
Methylmethacrylate Lucite Paraplex Plexiglas	CH_3COCH_3 + HCN + CH_3OH	CH_3 $-CH_2-C-$ $COOCH_3$	Excellent optical properties, good molding	Reflecting signs, lenses, transparent enclosures, car tail lights, ornaments, emulsion paints
Acrylic Nitrile Acrylan Orlon	$CH{\equiv}CH + H{-}CN$	$-CH_2-CH-$ $\quad\;\; CN$		Fiber and resin

LINEAR CONDENSATION POLYMERS

Name	Source	Monomer or segmer	Outstanding properties	Typical uses
Terylene Mylar Dacron	$HOCH_2-CH_2OH$ Glycol + HOOC(phenyl)COOH Terephthalic acid	H H O O —C—C—O—C—(phenyl)—C—O— H H	Temperature resistant, strong fiber, tough film, water-resistant	Strong films, textiles, and cords
Nylon	$H_2N{(}(CH_2)_6NH_2 + $	$HOOC(CH_2)_4COOH$ Nylon salt	Low water absorption; tough	Textiles, rope, bristles,

274

Name	Source	Monomer or segmer	Outstanding properties	Typical uses
Silicone	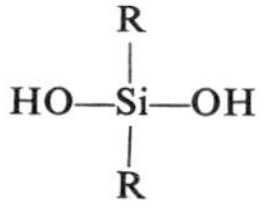 R—Si—OH with R groups (Silanediol)	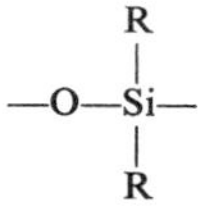 —O—Si— with R groups	Heat resistant, water repellent, liquids or solids, abhesive	Special lubricants, heat-resistant vehicles, greases, silastic rubber

TWO AND THREE DIMENSIONAL POLYMERS

Name	Source	Monomer or segmer	Outstanding properties	Typical uses
Glyptals	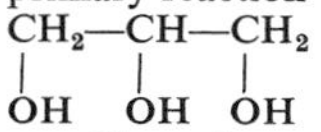 primary reaction CH$_2$—CH—CH$_2$ / OH OH OH (Glycerol) + Phthalic acid	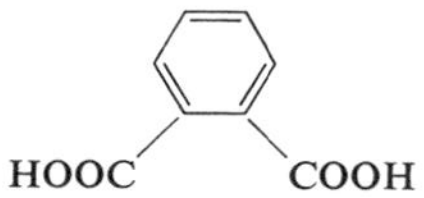 HOOC— / —COOH Phthalic acid	Cross-linked resin	Varnish and enamels
Silicone resins	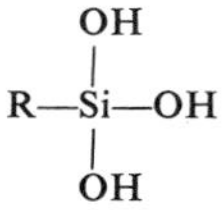 OH / R—Si—OH / OH	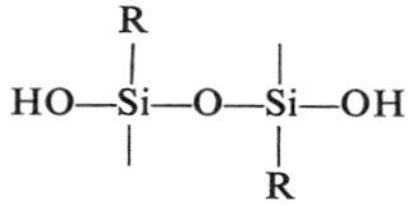 R / HO—Si—O—Si—OH / R	Heat-resistant resin; properties depending on nature of the radical R and degree of polymerization	Heat-resistant coatings and insulators
Phenol formaldehyde	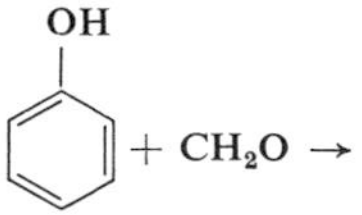 OH (phenol) + CH$_2$O →	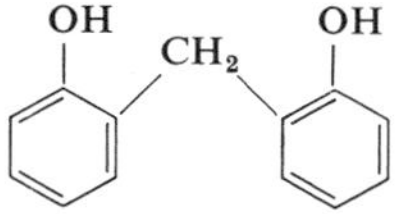 OH / CH$_2$ / OH	Thermoset, solubility, hardness, etc., depends on ratio P/F and extent of cure	Adhesive for laminates, varnish, lacquers, molded parts, insulators
Urea formaldehyde / Uformite / Beetle	H$_2$N·CO·NH$_2$ + HCHO	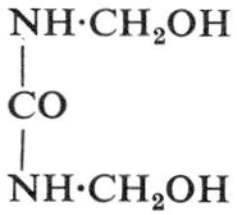 NH·CH$_2$OH / CO / NH·CH$_2$OH	Translucent molding resin	Low temperature and pressure impregnating, adhesive, bonding agent, molding resin
Melamine formaldehyde	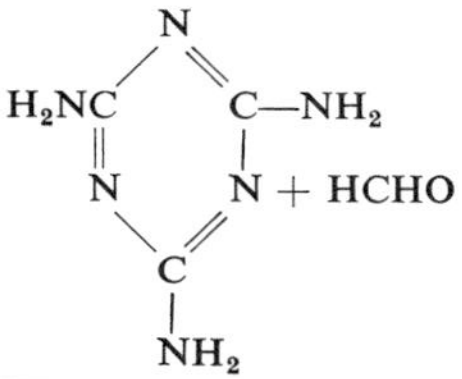 H$_2$NC—C—NH$_2$ ... N + HCHO ... NH$_2$	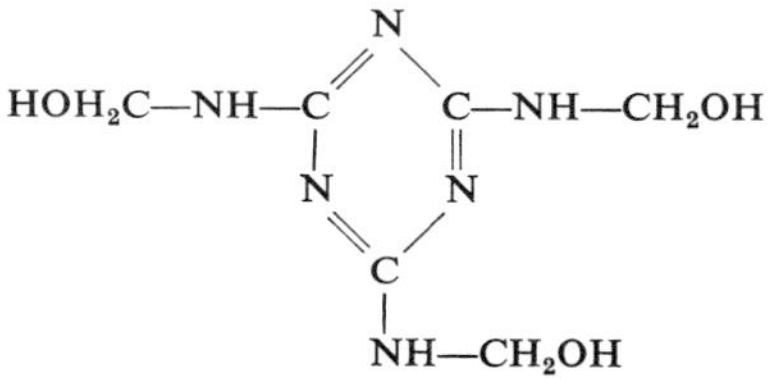 HOH$_2$C—NH—C—C—NH—CH$_2$OH ... NH—CH$_2$OH	Heat resistant resin	Dishes, lampshades, coating resin; used for nonshrinkage of textiles and high wet strength for paper

275

Table 17-2. PROPERTIES DETERMINING USES OF PLASTICS[a]

(1. Properties of primary importance; 2. Other important qualities)

Material	Tensile strength + rigidity	Toughness	High dielectric	Water absorption	Chemicals	Weathering	Heat	Flexibility	Optical properties	Colorability	Maximum continuous service, Temp., °F.	Approximate price range, $/lb
Thermoplastics:												
ABS material[b]	1	1	2	–	2	2	–	–	–	1	225	0.50–0.60
Acetal	1	2	2	–	2	–	1	–	–	1	225	0.95
Acrylics	1	–	–	–	2	1	–	–	1	–	190–200	0.51–0.59
Cellulose acetate	1	1	2	–	–	–	–	–	1	1	180–200	0.36–0.65
Cellulose acetate buryrate	1	1	2	1	–	1	–	–	1	1	180–200	0.40–0.72
Cellulose propionate	1	1	2	1	–	–	–	–	1	1	180–200	0.40–0.72
Chlorinated polyether	–	–	–	1	1	–	1	–	–	–	300	6.00
Ethyl cellulose	2	1	–	–	–	–	–	1	–	1	180–200	0.67–0.80
TFE-flurocarbon	–	2	1	1	1	1	1	–	–	–	500	4.50–7.45
CFE-flurocarbon	2	–	1	1	1	1	1	–	–	–	390	7.00–8.00
Nylon	1	1	2	–	2	–	1	–	2	2	250	1.18–2.00
Polyethylene	1	1	1	1	1	–	–	1	1	2	175–212	0.33–0.43
Polypropylene	1	1	1	1	1	–	1	–	1	2	230	0.47
Polystyrene	1	–	1	–	2	–	–	–	1	1	140–160	0.25–0.44
Polystyrene modified	1	1	2	–	1	–	1	–	–	1	212	0.25–0.44
Vinyl	1	1	1	2	1	–	–	1	1	1	175	0.27–0.43
Thermosets:												
Epoxy	1	–	1	1	1	1	–	–	–	1	300–350	0.65
Melamine	–	–	1	1	2	–	–	–	–	–	210–250	0.42–0.45
Phenolic	1	2	2	–	2	–	1	–	–	–	350–400	0.17–0.40
Polyester (other than molding compounds)	1	2	2	–	2	–	–	–	1	1	300–400	0.32–0.50
Polyester (alkyd, DAP)	2	2	1	1	–	–	1	–	–	–	450–500	0.34–0.53
Silicone	–	–	1	1	–	–	1	–	–	–	550	1.68–5.40
Urea	–	–	–	–	2	–	–	–	–	1	170	0.19–0.33

[a] Adapted from M. W. Riley, "Engineers Guide to Plastics," *Materials in Design Engineering*, **49**, No. 156 (February 1959), 107.

[b] Materials containing Acrylonitrile, Butadiene, and Styrene.

18

Elastomers

18-1 Natural Rubber

An elastomer is a linear polymer which exhibits elasticity and other rubber-like properties.

Columbus recorded in his journal that the natives of Central America rendered garments and footwear waterproof by smearing them with the sap of a tree. The chief source of natural rubber is the species of tree named *Hevea Brasiliensis*. Nature's elastomer, rubber, is also found in several other plants, shrubs, and vines. The white milky sap of the common milkweed contains some rubber.

In the early development of the rubber industry, the sole source of the material was the wild rubber tree. Brazilian natives collected the latex from the jungle. They would dip flat wooden sticks or paddles repeatedly into the latex and then held and turned them in the warm smoke of a wood fire. The tars and formaldehyde in the smoke served to coagulate the latex and prevented putrefaction of the small amount of protein present. When the accretion of smoked rubber on the dipstick reached a sufficient size, usually 20 to 50 pounds, it was shipped down river. Natural rubber is now obtained almost entirely from rubber plantations which had their origin from seeds smuggled out of Brazil.

Natural rubber is polymerized *isoprene* or 2-methyl-1,3-butadiene

$$CH_2 \!\!=\!\! C \!\!-\!\! CH \!\!=\!\! CH_2$$
$$|$$
$$CH_3$$

277

The monomer is

$$(—CH_2—C=CH—CH_2—)_n$$
$$\underset{CH_3}{|}$$

There are from 2000 to 3000 monomer links in the polyhydrocarbon chain. The latex of the rubber is an emulsion containing 35 per cent rubber, stabilized by proteins amounting to 2 per cent. The rubber droplets are quite small, having diameters of 0.5 to 3.0 microns. The emulsion may be broken by the action of enzymes on the protective colloid of the natural latex, or by the addition of coagulating chemicals.

Natural rubber is now prepared by coagulating latex with acid. After being washed, the coagulated curd is passed through rollers or "milled." The pale crepe may be treated with smoke to give the product "smoke sheet."

Table 18-1. THE EFFECT OF VULCANIZATION ON SWELLING

Grams of sulfur per gram of rubber sample	0	1.2	6.0	39.0	47.0
Volume after 24 hr in benzene (cc)	30	13.0	6.0	1.4	1.1
Original volume 1.0 cc					

In 1884 Charles Goodyear patented his discovery that heating the rubber with sulfur increased the tensile strength, elasticity, and resistance of the product to swelling. This process he called *vulcanization*.

In vulcanization, the sulfur attacks the unsaturated bonds in the rubber polymer, forming cross-links with adjacent molecules. The increase in resistance to solvents is indicated by the reduction in swelling with increase in vulcanization, as given in Table 18-1.

The unvulcanized sample increased in volume 3000 per cent while the highly vulcanized sample increased only 10 per cent.

Rubber, like several synthetic polymers, displays a tendency to have the polymers line up or become orientated when stretched. The X-ray diffraction pattern changes from the diffused ring denoting the random or amorphous state to a regular pattern such as shown by ordered arrangement of atoms or molecules in crystals. The ability to be stretched, or extensibility, decreases rapidly when the coefficient of vulcanization (grams of sulfur per gram of rubber) exceeds 8.

Figure 18-1 shows the effect of different catalysts or "accelerators" on the strength developed at different curing periods. Catalysts 1 and 2 have a very short curing time, but overcuring causes a sharp reduction in tensile strength. Accelerator #5 would be best for the vulcanization of a thick article which would heat up rather slowly. With this catalyst, 40 min overcure would not seriously reduce the tensile strength.

In manufacturing rubber articles, the rubber is first put through a milling or kneading process during which the rubber is stretched and masticated;

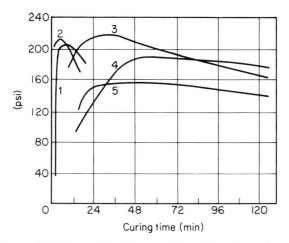

Figure 18-1 The relation between time of curing and tensile strength of natural rubber vulcanized with different accelerators. #1 and #2 give very rapid vulcanization, but even a few minutes overcure causes a rapid decrease in tensile strength. #3 requires 25 min to reach maximum strength. If curing is continued past 35 min, the strength drops off. #4 and #5 are not sensitive to prolonged cure.

the long polymers are oriented and are degraded in length. The material becomes more plastic. Chemical plasticizers or internal lubricants are added, along with resins and tacifying agents, fillers such as carbon black and clay, antioxidants, sulfur, and accelerators for vulcanization. These are thoroughly worked into the rubber in the mill or Banbury mixer (Fig. 18-2).

The outstanding properties of natural rubber are its elasticity, its tensile strength, and its ability to undergo repeated flexing without becoming overheated. This latter property is very important as the side walls of a tire are flexed with every revolution of the wheel.

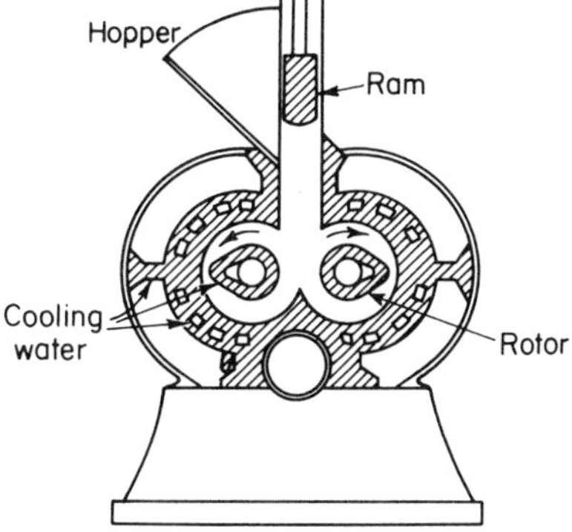

Figure 18-2 Banbury mixer.

18-2 Synthetic Rubber

Some rather poor synthetic rubber was produced in Germany during World War I, but it was not until World War II that world production of synthetic rubber exceeded that of natural rubber. In 1939 the world's

Table 18-2. GROWTH IN PRODUCTION CAPACITY FOR
SYNTHETIC RUBBER IN THE UNITED STATES

Type	1942	1943	1944	1962[a]	1963[a]
	\multicolumn{5}{c}{Thousands of Long Tons}				
Buna S	60	400	850	1193	1220
Buna N	18	20	25	46	47
Butyl	7	62	132	90	92
Neoprene	19	30	69	124	125
Thiokol	3	24	60		
Stereoregulated[b] rubber				93	160

[a] Actual or predicted production.
[b] Rubber in which the side chains or substituent groups next to the unsaturated or olefin bonds may be arranged on the same side or on the opposite side of the polymer chain, thus regulating the properties.

production of natural rubber was approximately one million tons, of which the United States used between 60 and 70 per cent. In early 1942, after the capture of Singapore and Malaya by the Japanese, this was suddenly reduced to less than 5 per cent of peacetime requirements. In 1941 the amount of synthetic rubber being produced in North America was in the neighborhood of 16,000 tons, and this was largely speciality rubber not suitable for tires. The tremendous achievement of chemists and chemical engineers and of industry in making good the staggering loss of one of the sinews of war will be obvious from the figures in Table 18-2. Starting from scratch, processes

Figure 18-3 Part of a synthetic-rubber plant. [Courtesy Polymer Corp., Sarnia, Canada.]

were developed, plants designed and built, raw materials secured; after three years, rubber was made available in quantities four times greater than all the rubber used in a peace-time year. Further, some of the elastomers produced had properties which are superior for specific uses. The consumption of synthetic rubber in the United States is now over a million long tons per year. Canadian production in 1961 was approximately 150,000 long tons. Production in the United Kingdom increased from 10,000 metric tons in 1958 to approximately 120,000 metric tons in 1962. Figure 18-3 shows a portion of a synthetic rubber plant.

Table 18-3. Swelling of Some Vulcanized Elastomers[a]

Liquid	Natural Rubber	Buna S	Buna N	Butyl	Neoprene	Thiokol
		Percentage increase in volume				
Gasoline	230	125	25	275	20	2
Kerosene	200	105	10	375	50	1
Diesel oil	120	175	8	500	75	7
Benzene	285	200	165	300	155	75
Carbon tetrachloride	670	300	150	350	160	35
Acetone	25	25	105	5	20	20

[a] Average values compiled from several sources. Since the properties of a rubber are influenced by the conditions of cure, the amount of fillers, resins and other materials, these values are not exact but do indicate that natural and butyl rubbers are very easily swollen by several organic liquids, while Thiokol is only slightly affected.

Synthetic rubber may be divided into six types: (1) buna S or GR—S; (2) buna N, NBR, or perbunan; (3) neoprene, CR, or polychloroprene; (4) polyisobutylene, Vistanex, butyl rubber; (5) Thiokol; and (6) silicone rubber or Silastic. Several variations of each type exist. The source of raw materials and outstanding properties of these are summarized in Tables 18-3 and 18-4.

Buna S, GR—S, Ameripol, SBR

Buna rubber was the name of an elastomer manufactured in Germany from polybutadiene. Polymerization was catalyzed by metallic sodium; hence the name of the rubber was coined from the prefix Bu and the symbol for sodium.

The most important synthetic rubber is buna S, or SBR, a copolymer of approximately 75 per cent butadiene and 25 per cent styrene. The former is an easily condensed gas (bp $-4.5°$ C) which is stored under pressure in spherical tanks (Fig. 18-3). Styrene is a liquid (see page 263). The two components are brought together into a mixing vessel containing an aqueous solution of emulsifying agent. A polymerization catalyst is added along with

Table 18-4. ELASTOMERS

Name	Source	Monomer or segment	Outstanding properties
Rubber Polyisoprene	$CH_2=C-CH=CH_2$ 　　$\|$ 　　CH_3 Isoprene	$-CH_2-C=CH-CH_2-$ 　　　$\|$ 　　　CH_3	High elasticity, tensile strength, and flex; easily attacked by oils and chlorinated solvents; poor gas retention
Buna S GR–S SBR	$CH_2=CH-CH=CH_2$ Butadiene $+ C_6H_5CH=CH_2$ Styrene	$-CH_2-CH=CH-CH_2-CH-CH_2-$ 　　　　　　　　　　$\|$ 　　　　　　　　　(phenyl)	Good resistance to wear, sunlight, ozone
Buna N NBR Hycar OR Chemigum	Butadiene $+ CH_2=CH$ 　　　$\|$ 　　　CN Acrylonitrile	$-CH_2-CH=CH-CH_2-CH-CH_2-$ 　　　　　　　　　　$\|$ 　　　　　　　　　CN	Similar to buna S, but better resistance to oil
Neoprene CR	$CH_2=C-CH=CH_2$ 　　$\|$ 　　Cl Chloroprene	$-CH_2-C=CH-CH_2-$ 　　　$\|$ 　　　Cl	Good resistance to HC solvents, sunlight

Table 18-4. Elastomers (cont.)

Name	Source	Monomer or segment	Outstanding properties
Vistanex PIB	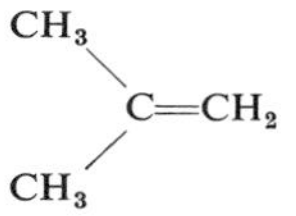 CH_3 $C{=}CH_2$ CH_3	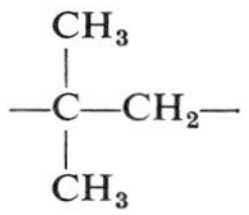 CH_3 $-C-CH_2-$ CH_3	Very elastic, best for gas retention, poorer tensile strength than natural rubber, chemically inert, sticky, soluble in hydrocarbons, resistant to ozone, low resilience. (N.B: Properties of both IIR and PIB)
Butyl rubber IIR	Isobutene or Isobutene + isoprene	(+ 2% butadiene) 97 to 99.7% isobutene	
Thiokol A	$Cl{-}CH_2{-}CH_2{-}Cl + Na_2S_4$	$-CH_2{-}CH_2{-}S{-}S{-}S{-}CH_2{-}CH_2{-}$ $\overset{\|}{S}\overset{\|}{S}$	Most resistant to solvents, low tensile strength
EPR Ethylene-propylene	$CH_2{=}CH_2 + CH_3CH{=}CH_2$	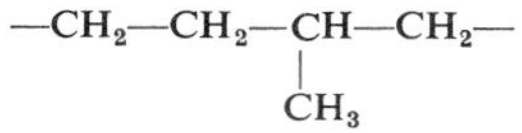 $-CH_2{-}CH_2{-}CH{-}CH_2-$ CH_3	Ozone and weather resistant
Koroseal	$CH_2{=}CHCl$ Vinyl chloride	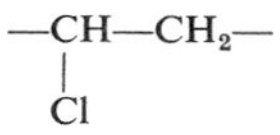 $-CH{-}CH_2-$ Cl	Acid and water resistant; elastic
Silastic	CH_3 $HO{-}Si{-}OH$ CH_3	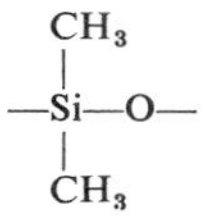 CH_3 $-Si{-}O-$ CH_3	High heat stability, flexible at low and high temperatures

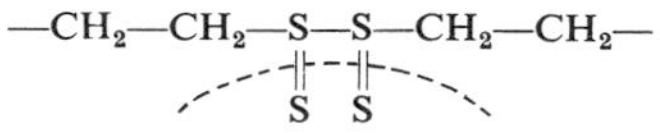

283

modifying agents which control the size and shape of the polymer. When polymerization has reached the required point, a stopper and inhibitor are

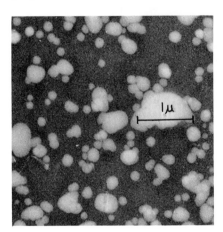

added. An electron photomicrograph of a buna S latex is given in Fig. 18-4. The latex is coagulated, as in the production of natural rubber. The curd is washed, squeezed through rollers (Fig. 18-5) and dried in an oven (Fig. 18-6). It is then milled and emerges as crepe or thin sheets which may be piled and cut into "cakes" of 65 to 85 pounds (Fig. 18-7). The various steps are illustrated in Fig. 18-8.

Buna S requires more carbon black to achieve full strength than does natural rubber. It is more resistant to ozone and weathering and somewhat more resistant to oils than the natural product. The so-called "cold rubber" is buna S formed at a lower temperature than that used in the original manufacture. It has better tensile

Figure 18-4 Electron photomicrograph of a synthetic rubber latex. The scale indicates 1 micron (10^{-3}) mm. [Courtesy Imperial Oil Ltd. and Esso Research Center, Linden, N.J.]

strength and less tendency to slip on a wet surface than the first buna S.

Buna N, NBR, Perbunan

Buna N is a copolymer of butadiene,

$$CH_2{=}CH{-}CH{=}CH_2$$

and acrylic nitrile,

$$\begin{array}{c} (CH_2{=}CH) \\ | \\ CN \end{array}$$

The source materials of acrylic nitrile are HCN and acetylene or ethylene oxide.

Buna N (perbunan) is superior to natural rubber in resistance to swelling in mineral and vegetable oils, gasoline, and many common solvents. The nitrile rubber also shows less tendency to "creep" under impressed loads than natural rubber. The tensile strength of the synthetic is not as high as the natural product. The effect of the addition of carbon black on increasing tensile strength and elongation is more pronounced for the butadiene-nitrile polymer than for natural rubber. Less sulfur is required for the vulcanization of buna S and buna N.

Figure 18-5 On its way to the drying operation, copolymer rubber in water slurry is passed through a squeeze-roll vacuum filter to remove most of the water. [Courtesy Polymer Corp.]

Figure 18-6 A gas-fired drier. The drier in the copolymer plant can handle up to 200,000 lb of rubber per day. Each drier is 65 ft long and 25 ft high. [Courtesy Polymer Corp.]

Figure 18-7 Some grades of rubber are talc-coated before packaging in jute bags. [Courtesy Polymer Corp.]

Neoprene, CR, or Polychloroprene

While polyisoprene

$$\left(\begin{array}{c} -CH-C=CH-CH_2- \\ | \\ CH_3 \end{array}\right)_n$$

was not produced synthetically until a few years ago, the polychloroprene

$$\left(\begin{array}{c} CH_2-C=CH-CH_2- \\ | \\ Cl \end{array}\right)$$

was marketed in 1932. Polymerization of 2-chloro-1,3-butadiene proceeds readily at room temperature. It was the only synthetic rubber being produced in North America in 1941, except for a few tons of Thiokol.

Emulsion polymerization is used in the manufacture of polychloroprene. The latex particle is very much smaller than that in *Hevea*, having droplets only 0.05 to 0.07 micron in diameter. After coagulation by acetone or other organic coagulants, followed by drying, the material called the alpha polymer can be milled. Heating the alpha polymer converts it to another cross-linked

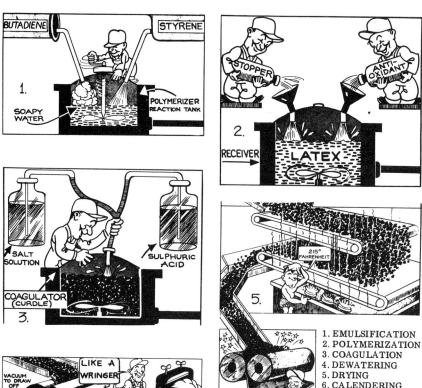

Figure 18-8 The manufacture of buna S rubber. [Reproduced by permission of Deco Trefoil, Denver, Colo. and Mr. Jas. Shepherd.]

polymer, that is, the material is "self-vulcanizing." Cross-linking is accelerated by zinc oxide, sulfur, litharge, and some other materials. Added carbon stiffens the neoprene, but does not increase the tensile strength.

The converted "vulcanized" polymer, called neoprene, has much greater resistance to heat, oxidation, sunlight, solvents, acids, and other chemicals than does natural rubber. It is therefore used for flexible hose or tubing, insulation, washers, rubber soles, gloves, and protective clothing, where oils or acids may be encountered. The effects of fats and oils on the tensile strength of neoprene and natural rubber are compared in Fig. 18-9.

Fluoroprene from the corresponding fluorine derivative finds use as an elastomer under higher temperature conditions. Unlike chloroprene, it copolymerizes easily with styrene, giving elastomers of excellent tensile strength.

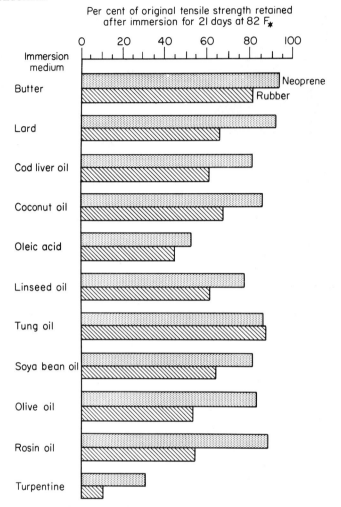

Figure 18-9 A comparison of the effects of fats and oils on the tensile strength of neoprene and natural rubber.

Polybutylenes: Vistanex and Butyl Rubber

The first patent for the production of polyisobutylene

$$\left(\begin{array}{c} CH_3 \\ | \\ -C-CH_2- \\ | \\ CH_3 \end{array}\right)_n$$

appeared in 1937. The elastomer is produced at very low temperatures. The effect of temperature on the size or molecular weight of the polymer is shown in Table 18-5. Polymers of molecular weight 400,000 have been obtained at temperatures around $-250°$ C.

Polyisobutylene has the structure represented by the formula

$$
\begin{array}{cccc}
CH_3 & CH_3 & CH_3 & CH_3 \\
| & | & | & | \\
-C-CH_2- & C-CH_2- & C-CH_2- & C-CH_2- \\
| & | & | & | \\
CH_2 & CH_3 & CH_3 & CH_3
\end{array}
$$

but more exactly by a three-dimensional model which shows a long elastic skeleton with a spiral arrangement of methyl groups. The polymer is obviously a saturated hydrocarbon and may therefore be expected to have

Table 18-5. Effect of Temperature on the Polymerization of Isobutylene, PIB

Temperature, ° C	$-10°$	$-25°$	$-45°$	$-80°$	$-90°$	$-95°$
Molecular weight of polymer	10,000	13,000	25,000	80,000	120,000	225,000

chemical properties resembling the high-molecular-weight paraffins. Since there are no residual double bonds, this rubber does not vulcanize. It will not be attacked by acids and alkali. The absence of unsaturated bonds will make for high stability and resistance to ozone, ultraviolet, and "ageing." This elastomer, which has been marketed for years under the name Vistanex, has good electrical properties and low water absorption. Among its outstanding qualities are (1) high stretch, and (2) very low permeability to gases. Polyisobutylene is soluble in gasoline and other paraffin oils, in hydrocarbons and in chlorinated solvents.

Butyl Rubber, IIR

Butyl rubber is a copolymer of isobutylene and butadiene, in the proportions of 98 and 2 per cent respectively or isobutylene and 0.3 to 3 per cent isoprene (2-methylbutadiene). Polymerization is carried out at very low temperatures ($-140°$ F). The addition of a diene to the isobutylene produces not more than 3 per cent of the unsaturation of natural rubber. Some cross-linking can therefore be effected between the chains by heating with lead dioxide or sulfur in the presence of suitable accelerators. Unlike most elastomers, butyl rubber is not improved in tensile strength by the incorporation of carbon black, although it does raise the elasticity and resistance to abrasion.

The chief use for butyl rubber is for inner tubes and tires or coated fabrics for gas retention. The resistance to weathering and ageing and to diffusion of gases and water vapor is superior to that of natural rubber. Vulcanized butyl rubber may have an elongation at the break point of 1000 per cent, as compared with 710 per cent for natural rubber. Vistanex has also a high stretch, but its tensile strength is considerably lower than that of vulcanized butyl.

Thiokols

As the name suggests, Thiokols are elastomers in which sulfur forms part of the polymer chain. Like the discovery of synthetic dyes by the English chemist Perkins, this so-called "inorganic rubber" was also found "by accident." It is more correct to say that both these discoveries were the unexpected results of research.

The American chemist, J. C. Patrick, observed the formation of a yellowish elastic solid when an aqueous solution of an inorganic substance, sodium polysulfide, was heated with ethylene dichloride (CH_2Cl—CH_2Cl). Further investigation of the reaction led to a patent in 1932 covering the manufacture of the first type of Thiokol. Since then, several additional varieties have been marketed.

The formation of a Thiokol may be represented by the general equation

$$n\,(Cl—R—Cl) + Na_2S_4 \longrightarrow 2\,NaCl + \left(\begin{array}{c} S \\ \| \\ —R—S—S— \\ \| \\ S \end{array}\right)_n \text{or } H\left(\begin{array}{c} S \\ \| \\ —S—R—S— \\ \| \\ S \end{array}\right)_n H$$

R may be such groups as ($—CH_2—CH_2—$) to give Thiokol A,

$$(—CH_2—CH_2—O—CH_2CH_2—)$$

giving Thiokol D, or

$$(—CH_2—CH_2—O—CH_2—O—CH_2—CH_2—)$$

to give Thiokol F.

If the tetrasulfide elastomers are treated with NaOH, the side-chain sulfurs are stripped off, converting the polymer to a polydisulfide, for example,

$$—S—CH_2—CH_2—S—S—CH_2—CH_2—S—S—CH_2—CH_2—S \cdots$$

Thiokols are outstanding in their resistance to swelling and disintegration by organic solvents. Kerosene, gasoline, fuel oils, and lubricating oils have practically no effect. Benzene and its derivatives cause some swelling. Thiokols are by far the most effective of the synthetic rubbers against halogenated solvents which attack neoprene and other less-resistant elastomers. A comparison of the swelling of several different elastomers by various organic liquids is given in Table 18-3.

Thiokol films have low permeability to gases. Relative diffusion rates of hydrogen through similar films of Thiokol, Vistanex, neoprene, buna N, and natural rubber have been reported as 1, 1.3, 2.7, 7.2, and 11.4 respectively. Thiokol rubber has certain deficiencies. It tends to flow or lose shape under continuous pressure. Its tensile strength is also much below that of natural rubber. Recent work has diminished these shortcomings.

The chief engineering applications of the Thiokols depend on the superior qualities mentioned above. Fabrics coated with Thiokol are used for barrage balloons, life rafts and jackets, the latter inflated by compressed carbon dioxide. Thiokols are used for lining hose for conveying gasoline and oil, in paints, for printing rolls, for diaphragms, gaskets, and seals in contact with solvents.

An interesting development took place during the World War II. When submarine activity off the East Coast became so great that a high proportion of the oil tankers were sunk, attempts were made to compensate for this loss by transporting oil from the Gulf by tank cars. Shortage of tank cars and priority demands for steel for other purposes greatly hampered the program. Steel box cars were converted to tank cars by cutting a hole in the roof and making an oil resistant Thiokol bag to fit the inside of the car.

Collapsible, leak-proof, gas tanks are made by making use of specific properties of different elastomers. The walls of these tanks consist of three layers. The inside layer is made from Thiokol. The outside layer is buna S which has a higher tensile strength than the Thiokol. The middle layer is either a natural rubber or butyl rubber (Fig. 18-10). If the walls of the tank

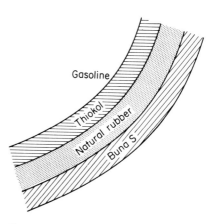

Figure 18-10 Section through collapsible "puncture proof" gasoline tank.

are pierced, gasoline comes into contact with the middle layer, which being made of an active polymer swells rapidly and plugs the hole. Trucks carrying collapsible tanks are in use in Australia for delivering gasoline or oil. This saves dead weight (Fig. 18-11). Oil is also transported by sea in Thiokol-lined nylon "sausages" pulled by a tug.

Vinyl Rubber

Plasticized vinylite, containing 13 to 15 per cent vinyl acetate, has many rubber-like properties. It is flexible and elastic, scuff resistant, and possesses low water absorption. Some vinylites can be stretched to three times their

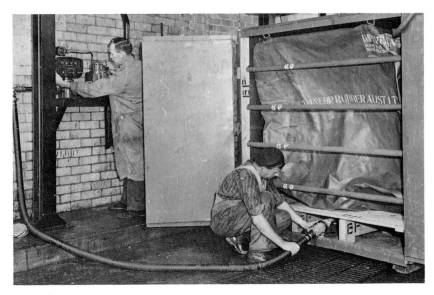

Figure 18-11 Fitting a 600 gal collapsible oil-tank into a box which can be shipped as deck cargo. [Courtesy B. P. Australia Ltd.]

original length. "Rubber" ground sheets, rain coats, and rainproof coverings for equipment were some of the first materials fabricated with a substitute for natural rubber, and these vinylite films or impregnates and other polymers have permanently displaced natural rubber for such purposes.

Silicone Rubber or Silastic

Careful condensation of pure silicon diols, for example, dimethyl silicon diol

$$\begin{array}{c} CH_3 \\ | \\ HO-Si-OH \\ | \\ CH_3 \end{array}$$

produces long elastic chains up to a molecular weight of 500,000. The properties of the elastomer are modified by the selection of the radicals attached to the silicon, by regulating chain length, and by the choice of fillers in compounding.

The outstanding property of this type of elastomer is its resistance to extremes of temperature. Silastic rubber retains its resiliency at temperatures of $-50°$ C ($-70°$ F). Silastic also maintains its elasticity at elevated temperatures. A special silastic remains flexible over a range of $-130°$ F to $600°$ F. Thermal stability is indicated by a loss of only 3 to 10 per cent of its

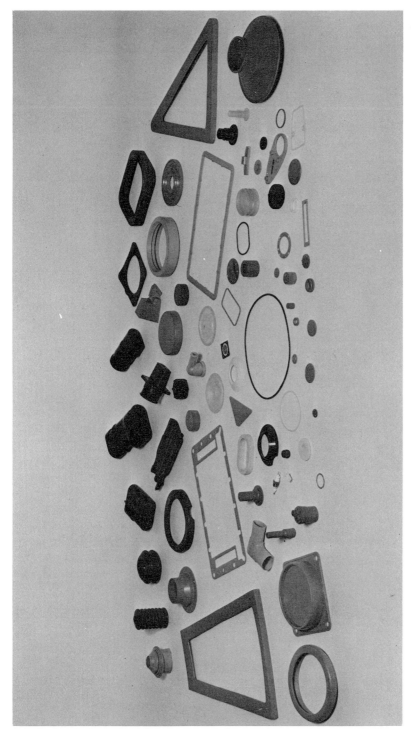

Figure 18-12 Silastic gaskets, diaphragms, and other articles for use at high and low temperatures. [Courtesy Dow-Corning and Armet Industries Ltd.]

tensile strength after 1000 hours at 200° C (390° F). The material is not suitable for use in contact with an open flame. Silastic has a higher thermal conductivity than most other elastomers. Its tensile strength is about 900 psi, considerably lower than that of natural rubber. The dielectric properties are good. Water absorption after seven day immersion is approximately 1 per cent. Silastic is used for insulation of flexible leads. At very high temperatures the insulation will ignite and burn, leaving a fine white silica ash. Since this ash is a nonconductor, cables insulated with silicone rubber have often remained serviceable even when the original elastomer was destroyed by fire.

Most types of Silastic will swell in organic solvents. Recently, a Silastic product was marketed which is resistant to several organic solvents.

Silastic rubbers find use as gaskets, seals, and rollers, wherever resilience is required at very low or moderately high temperatures, such as in aircraft or domestic oven doors. Figure 18-12 shows a variety of Silastic articles for engineering uses.

Many modifications of the six types of elastomers above have been developed chiefly by copolymerization with various synthetic resins. These modified elastomers furnish the engineer with a wide selection of materials suitable for special uses. An example of a relatively new hydrocarbon rubber is a copolymer of ethylene and propylene, EPR. This rubber has outstanding resistance to ozone and weathering. It has lower tear resistance and higher air permeability than buna S (SBR), but can be lined with butyl to correct the latter property.

Review Questions

1. What natural products may be modified to make plastic materials?

2. Name the outstanding properties of nitrocellulose, cellulose acetate, and ethyl cellulose.

3. What is the difference in the polymerization which produces thermoplastic and thermosetting resins?

4. Show by chemical formulas the reaction which produces glyptal, polystyrene, polyethylene, bakelite, buna S, silicone resin, and Silastic rubber.

5. What plastic would you choose for high insulating properties, high temperature resistance, transparency to ultraviolet light, chemical resistance, low water absorption?

6. Give the formula for the monomer and an engineering use based on an outstanding property of the polymer vinylchloride-acetate, vinylidene chloride, and methyl methacrylate.

7. Name three types of synthetic rubber.

8. What type of rubber would you use (a) for a flexible connection to a steam line, (b) as a gasket for a pipe containing a chlorinated solvent, (c) in a solvent to form a "cement" or "adhesive"?

9. Name the following giving an important use of the material,

$$CH_2=CH-CH=CH_2, \qquad -CF_2-CFCl-, \qquad (CH_3)_2C=CH_2$$

10. Give an example of a polyester textile, a latex for a water paint, a nonbakelite varnish resin, an adhesive for metals, and an *ab*hesive.

11. Why is carbon black added to rubber?

12. What takes place during vulcanization of rubber?

13. Which of the following plastic foams will have greatest strength for equal bulk density: polystyrene, bakelite, polyurethane?

14. Describe the structure of a leakproof collapsible oil or gas tank.

15. *o*-Cresol, gives a resin when treated with formaldehyde. List some of the properties and uses of the resin.

Further Reading

Winding, C., and Hiatt, G., *Polymeric Materials* (New York: McGraw-Hill, 1961).

19

Protective Coatings

The most common way to prevent the deterioration of many different materials is to protect the surface. This is done by applying a resistant film which excludes the corrosive or destructive agent. Paint, which is the product most widely used for this purpose, is essentially a suspension of fine opaque particles in a fluid vehicle. The chief function of the suspended particles is to cover, hide, and decorate the applied surface. The vehicle usually provides a bonding and protective film. Modern paints contain more than these two components, however.

The past twenty years has seen greater advances in paint technology than in the previous 200 years. Except for some new organic pigments, most of the development has been made by altering the vehicle. This may be done by rearrangement of the unsaturated bonds, by combining oil with a variety of synthetic resins, by the addition of synthetic oils, new thickening and suspending agents, and new synthetic thinners.

Emulsion paints first appeared on the market in 1949. In these paints the vehicle is water, or more exactly an aqueous solution, and the dispersed phase droplets of drying oil and pigment, enamel, or a latex of rubber or resin. Special paints are now available for acid or alkaline environment. There are luminous paints and paints which discourage the attack of plant and animal organisms. New materials can make a paint heat-resistant or fire-retardant or both. A paint can be formulated which will even tell the approximate temperature.

19-1 Drying Oil Paint

This type of paint, the principal protective coating for exterior use, consists of (1) a vehicle which is unsaturated fatty oil, (2) the pigments, and (3) "extenders." The vehicle contains (4) dissolved "dryers" and (5) a thinner or solvent such as turpentine or mineral spirits.

Chemical Nature of Drying Oils

All of these are fatty oils, that is, they are glyceryl esters of fatty acids and may be represented by the general formula

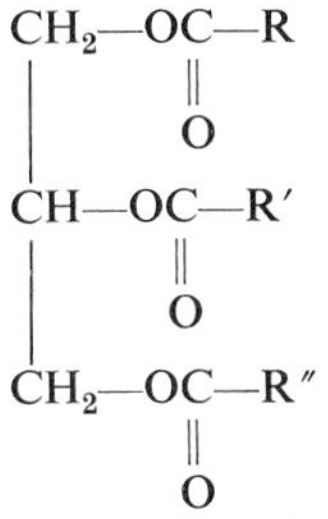

$$CH_2-OC-R$$
$$\parallel$$
$$O$$
$$CH-OC-R'$$
$$\parallel$$
$$O$$
$$CH_2-OC-R''$$
$$\parallel$$
$$O$$

Glyceryl   Fatty acid
radical   radicals

The long unsaturated radicals R, R', and R'' are attached by the carboxyl groups to the bonds of the glyceryl radical. These unsaturated acid radicals are from oleic acid, $C_{17}H_{33}COOH$; linoleic acid, $C_{17}H_{31}COOH$; linolenic acid, $C_{17}H_{29}COOH$; and ricinoleic acid, $C_{17}H_{32}(OH)COOH$, a hydroxy acid. Stearic acid, $C_{17}H_{35}COOH$, is the corresponding saturated fatty acid. The properties of the oil depend on the proportion of these different long chain fatty acids in the molecule. The structure of the acids is indicated below.

$$CH_3-(CH_2)_7-CH=CH-(CH_2)_7-COOH$$
Oleic

$$CH_3-(CH_2)_7-CH_2-CH_2-(CH_2)_7-COOH$$
Stearic

$$CH_3-(CH_2)_4-CH=CH-CH_2-CH=CH-(CH_2)_7-COOH$$
Linoleic

$$CH_3-CH_2-CH=CH-CH_2-CH=CH-CH_2-CH=CH-(CH_2)_7-COOH$$
Linolenic

$$OH$$
$$\vert$$
$$CH_3-(CH_2)_5-CH-CH_2-CH=CH-(CH_2)_7-COOH.$$
Ricinoleic

On dehydration, ricinoleic acid gives linoleic acid.

When an oil which contains such unsaturated bonds is exposed to the air, oxygen is absorbed with the formation of an organic peroxide, for example,

$$CH_3—(CH_2)_4—CH—CH—CH_2CH—CH—(CH_2)_7—COOH$$
$$\underset{O—O}{|\quad|}\qquad\underset{O—O}{|\quad|}$$

"Blown" and "boiled" linseed oil contains these peroxides which act as catalysts and accelerate the "drying" or formation of the hard, stable film. The diperoxide undergoes rearrangement or isomerization, giving a keto and a hydroxyl group with the evolution of heat. It is this heat of oxidation which has caused the "spontaneous combustion" so common when oily paint rags are left in a pile.

$$CH_3(CH_2)_4—CH—CH—CH_2C—CH(CH_2)_7—COOH$$
$$\underset{O—O}{|\quad|}\qquad\underset{O\ \ OH}{\|\quad|}$$

This keto-hydroxy form can polymerize or condense with other similar molecules to form the cross-linked film. This film is plastic. It is only slightly soluble in acetone or cold alcohol but does dissolve readily in ether, carbon tetrachloride, carbon bisulfide, benzene, and hydrocarbons of the paraffin family. In solubility it thus resembles a hydrocarbon. The porosity of the film will depend on the nature and concentration of the drying oil. Tung oil films are less porous than those formed by linseed oil.

Iodine Number

The degree of unsaturation, and hence the tendency of a fatty oil to absorb oxygen and "dry" may be estimated by a chemical test known as the *iodine number*. This represents the number of milligrams of iodine absorbed per gram of oil. Linolenic acid would be expected to absorb three times as much iodine as oleic acid. A mineral oil, such as paraffin oil, would have a very low iodine number.

Saponification Number

Another test which serves to check the nature of the paint vehicle, is the *saponification number*. This is obtained by heating the sample of oil with a measured amount of potassium hydroxide dissolved in alcohol. The alkali converts any fatty oil to soap, and the excess KOH is determined by titration with standard acid from which the milligrams of KOH used per gram of oil can then be calculated. This is the saponification number. Mineral oil, being a hydrocarbon, will not combine with the KOH and will give a saponification number of zero. A fatty oil will have a number between 150 to 195. A low number would thus indicate the presence of a large amount of thinner or adulteration with mineral oil. The *acid number* indicates the amount of free fatty acid present. One gram of oil is warmed with 50 cc of alcohol and titrated with $N/5$ KOH. The mg of KOH equivalent to the free acid is the acid number.

The Vehicle

LINSEED OIL

Linseed oil has been used for a protective coating, with and without pigments, for centuries. When Canada was still New France, it was recorded, in 1720, that the annual crop of flaxseed or linseed amounted to 55,000 lb. Production is now many millions of bushels, largely from the Midwest. World supplies come chiefly from the Argentine and Eastern Europe. Flaxseed contains 32 to 43 per cent oil. Most of the oil is extracted by hot pressing along with some gelatinous material. The latter may be removed by filtration of the warm oil with Fuller's earth and the filter press; or, simply by allowing the "raw" linseed oil to stand for a long time, during which this gelatinous material settles out.

Blown linseed oil is prepared by blowing air through oil heated to 265° F. Boiled oil is heated to 500° F in the presence of litharge, PbO, which reacts with the oil to form a drier, lead soap. Other driers may be added. These treated oils give faster drying, glossy films. About two-thirds of linseed oil production goes into paints and represents 68 to 70 per cent of all paint oils used. Large quantities are also used in the manufacture of linoleum, printers' inks, plastics, and soap.

Linseed oil has an iodine number of 170 to 187. Its saponification number is 190 to 195. It solidifies (freezes) at −28° C.

TUNG OIL

Also called *Chinawood oil*, it is an excellent drying oil. Tung oil is obtained from the nut of the tung tree. It was first used for paints in 1852. One of its characteristics is rapid drying, a stable film being formed in 30 to 50 min. The raw oil forms an opaque film, so it is first heated at 180° C with lead or manganese. The film formed from the treated oil is less porous than the linoxyn film from linseed oil. Its hardness also makes it suitable for porch and floor paints, marine paints and varnishes. It is an unsaturated fatty oil as indicated by its high saponification number of 160 to 190 and iodine number value of 156 to 165. Its acid number is 1.0 to 3.5.

SOYA OR SOYBEAN OIL

This vegetable oil ranks second in the volume used for paints. It is obtained from a bean used for many years in Manchuria as a food. Selective breeding of the plant has produced varieties in which the beans contain 20 per cent oil. The oil has a saponification number of 192 and an iodine number of 130. It is therefore slower drying than linseed oil and is not as good for exterior paints. It is often mixed with more rapid drying oils such as tung oil or perilla oil to modify the drying rate and to make the paint film more flexible. The acid number is low (1.0). Soybean oil is also used in the preparation of alkyd modified paint vehicles (page 301).

PERILLA OIL

This is a rapid drying oil made from the oily seeds (35 to 45 per cent oil) of a plant cultivated in China, Japan, Korea, and India. Attempts have been made to cultivate it in the United States. This oil has the highest iodine number of all the drying oils, namely, 185 to 205, and an acid number of 1 to 5. The oil is better when heated before application. A mixture of perilla and soybean oils resembles linseed oil.

Another rapid drying and hard finish oil is obtained from Oiticia nuts (*Licania rigida*) from Brazil. This oil contains a fatty acid called licanic acid having three unsaturated bonds and also a keto group, forming about 78 per cent of the oil. The oil is used primarily for enamels and varnishes but is also substituted for tung oil in high gloss and marine paints.

CASTOR OIL

Castor oil is used principally in paints and plasticizers. Its chief drying acid radical is ricinoleate. The dehydration of the ricinoleate produces conjugated double bonds.[1] These neighboring unsaturated linkages are much more active than more widely separated ones in bringing about polymerization of the film. Dehydrated castor oil is notable for water resistance and flexibility, which it imparts to the paint film. Another feature of this oil is its ability to wet and bind more pigment than other vehicle oils. It has an iodine number between 112 and 120, a saponification number of 188 to 194, and an acid number between 3.5 and 6.0.

MENHADEN OIL

This oil is derived from a type of herring found in large quantities along the Atlantic Coast. It was from this fish that "Lower Manhattan" of New York City got its name. The menhaden fish, like the candle fish of the Pacific, is very oily. The oil is extracted by steam and pressure, the residues being used for fertilizer, poultry, and pet foods. The processed oil has an iodine number of 150 to 178. It is therefore a good drying oil. Its saponification number is 190; the acid number is high, 3 to 11.

---

[1] These are double bonds separated by a single bond as in $CH_2{=}CH{-}CH{=}CH_2$, for example.

The oil makes a good binding film that is resistant to heat and weather. It does not blister nor peel and has found special uses, such as in paints for smoke stacks, boiler fronts, firedoors, and so on. Although cheaper, it is now being supplanted by silicone paints and lacquers which have higher resistance to elevated temperatures (see Special Paints).

Other fatty oils, chiefly from plant seeds—even wild mustard seed—are sometimes used in cheap paints.

MODIFIED OILS

The excellent qualities of today's oil paints may be attributed in part to "modified" vehicle oils. Natural drying oils may be isomerized so as to give

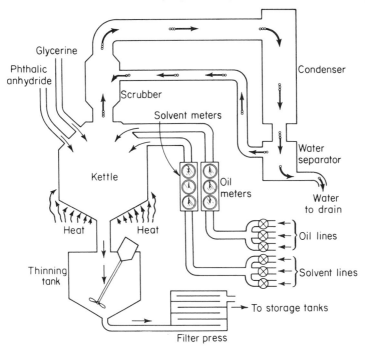

Figure 19-1 The preparation of alkyd modified vehicles. [From *CIL Oval*, Courtesy Canadian Industries Ltd.]

the double bonds in the conjugate position. This makes for more rapid film formation. Thus conjugated linseed oil fatty acids gel in 34 min, while the unmodified sample requires 5 hr at the same temperature.

The modern paint vehicle may contain an alkyd resin in which drying oils have been incorporated chemically. One of the bonds of the polyhydric alcohol, such as glycerol or pentaerythritol, is attached to the unsaturated fatty acid. This acts as a built-in plasticizer and also imparts drying properties to the resin compound. As was shown earlier (Chapter 17), the number of alkyd resins is legion. The properties of the oleoresin will depend on the type of oil used and on the components of the resin ester. Advantages claimed for the oil-modified resins are better adhesion of the resulting film, better flexibility, and greater solubility in less expensive thinners. These compounds are of special importance in enamels and varnishes. Figure 19-1 illustrates the preparation of such paint and varnish resins.

Special vehicles are sometimes required for special purpose paints. These will be discussed in the appropriate section.

Thinners

Thinners are largely used to reduce the viscosity of the drying oils, to increase penetration of the vehicle, and to increase the solubility of certain desirable additives in the vehicle. The oldest and most widely used thinner for oil paints is turpentine. This is said to have been distilled from the exuded gums of conifer trees since the first century A.D. It is also obtained by steam distillation of twigs, sawdust, chips, and tree stumps. Weathered pine

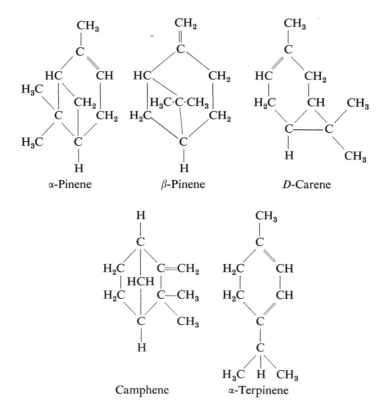

Figure 19-2 Some terpenes found in turpentine.

stumps may contain as much as 20 per cent oleoresins, of which turpentine and pine oil represent 5 to 25 per cent. The remainder consists of resin acids or rosin. These substances are chiefly cyclic olefins and belong to a class of compounds called *terpenes*, widely distributed in nature, that have the general formula $(C_5H_8)_n$. In the case of turpentine, the terpenes present have the general formula $C_{10}H_{16}$, that is, $n = 2$. (See Figure 19-2.)

The major components of turpentine are α-pinene, β-pinene, and camphene. There are of course several others which are characteristic of the species of conifer from which the turpentine is obtained. Being unsaturated compounds, the terpenes tend to absorb oxygen, polymerize, and "thicken,"

Table 19-1. THE COMPOSITION OF TURPENTINES

Terpene	Source of the Turpentine		
	Gum (%)	Wood (%)	Sulfate (%)
α-pinene	60–65	75–80	60–70
β-pinene	25–35	...	20–25
Camphene	...	4–8	...
Others	5–8	15–20	6–12

forming a film. The three different sources of terpenes, exuded gums, waste wood, and the by-product of sulfate pulp made from southern pine, are given in Table 19-1.

While United States production of turpentine has remained fairly constant, around 600,000 bbl per year over the past ten years, and the proportion of the solvent extracted from wood refuse has increased 50 to 75 per cent, the major source is now sulfate pulp.

ROSIN OIL

Made by destructive distillation of rosin, this oil is used in paints and contains a number of acid derivatives of tricyclic and other terpenes. Typical of these is abietic acid, having two unsaturated bonds. Since they contain a carboxyl group, they can form salts with basic pigments. Rosin oil has a relatively low saponification number in comparison with a fatty drying oil.

Abietic acid

This is a low-viscosity paraffin fraction, boiling between 150° and 200° C. When the paint film dries, this type of thinner is lost by evaporation. Special "odorless" thinners are synthesized from refinery gases in the same manner as gasolines (Chapter 8).

The thinner may contain solvents such as ketones or esters to prevent precipitation of resins incorporated in many modern paints. The aromatic hydrocarbons such as toluene have less tendency to cause precipitation of the resins than paraffin spirits.

Driers

Driers are catalysts of the drying process, that is, the absorption of oxygen. They are usually metal soaps, resinates, or naphthenates of zinc, lead, cobalt, manganese, and vanadium. "Japan" driers are solutions of these compounds in naphtha or benzene. Vanadium driers are 2.5 times faster than manganese driers, and five times faster than corresponding lead compounds. Amounts used vary from 0.2 per cent for lead to 0.01 to 0.05 per cent for vanadium and cobalt. Too much drier tends to produce hard, brittle paint films. Lead oxide pigment reacts with paint oil to produce lead soaps which catalyze the drying of the film.

Pigments

The chief function of the pigment is to provide color and opacity in the dried film. The chemical composition of the pigments, their size distribution, particle shape, refractive index, and the proportion of pigment to vehicle, all affect the properties of the paint. Even the color of the pigment representing the wavelengths absorbed and reflected influences the stability of the paint film.

The pigments used in oil paints were at first almost entirely colored earths and minerals. A few pigments were manufactured by the Ancients. White lead was described by Pliny the Elder. The pigment was also used as "face powder" by the Roman maids and matrons. About the year 15 B.C. a jar of this cosmetic was found in the ruins of a dwelling which had been burned, but the white powder had been changed to a brilliant red. For centuries afterward red lead was made by the calcination of white lead. The Egyptians prepared a form of antimony sulfide. In addition to the older natural pigments, modern paints may contain a number of synthetic inorganic pigments and a few organic ones.

The important properties of pigments in paints are color, hiding power, oil absorption, flow characteristics or rheology, and chemical behavior.

COLOR

Color is affected by light absorption and reflection. A blue pigment reflects principally the blue part of the spectrum while absorbing green, yellow, and red. The absorption and reflection bands may be broad. Thus Prussian blue reflects some green. So does chrome yellow, although it absorbs some green and red and all of the blue wavelengths. It reflects yellow to give its predominating shade. There are different qualities of white because of slight absorption by different white pigments of specific wavelengths; for example rutile, TiO_2, reflects only 20 per cent of light having a wavelength of 4000 Å. The reflected light is therefore slightly yellow. Anatase, TiO_2, however, reflects 95 per cent of light of this as well as the other wavelengths in the visible spectrum.

Reflectance and absorption in the infrared and ultraviolet are of importance in camouflage paints. In World War I, a captured German plane, marked with the black Teutonic cross, was sent on reconnaissance behind the German lines. Two concentric circles of white zinc oxide paint, invisible to the naked eye, had been painted on the white background of the wing. When viewed through field glasses equipped with filters which transmitted only violet and ultraviolet, the carbon-black cross faded and the zinc oxide rings appeared, thus identifying the aircraft. Carbon black reflected a high proportion of the ultraviolet and so the cross appeared white. Zinc oxide absorbed the ultraviolet and thus appeared black in ultraviolet light. Special paints must be formulated to simulate the high reflectance of foliage for infrared as well as the visible green. Pigments having the same chemical composition may differ markedly in shade and color due to differences in particle size, or to aggregation of the fine particles. The finer the particles, the greater is the proportion of scattering of the light. Hence the color is paler and contains more blue than the light reflected from the larger particles.

White Pigments. The principal white pigments in use today are listed in Table 19-2. White lead, which was the favorite white pigment for many years, has been displaced to a considerable extent by titania and titanox mixtures with different extenders. Production of titanium dioxide in the United States amounts to over 490,000 tons annually, of which approximately 60 per cent represents paint pigments. In Canada, production has increased from 16,500 tons in 1953 to 36,400 tons in 1961. Between 70 to 75 per cent of production was used in the paint industry.

Titanium dioxide occurs in two forms, anatase and rutile. The latter has the more condensed and stable crystal structure, and hence a higher refractive index, dielectric constant, and greater hardness. Both pigments show a very high reflection for all the wavelengths of the visible spectrum (98 per cent) and are therefore the whitest of the white pigments. This property finds application in paints designed to prevent evaporation losses from solvent and gasoline storage tanks and to reduce the heating effect of the sun on buildings, particularly in the tropics. Such paints are somewhat better than aluminum paint (90 to 95 per cent reflection).

The whiteness of a paint also depends on the vehicle. A drying oil gives a yellowish tint, which is "corrected" by the addition of blue or violet pigment or color. For white paints the whiteness may be evaluated by the color index. This is given by the expression

$$\text{color index} = \frac{\% \text{ reflection with amber filter} - \% \text{ with blue filter}}{\% \text{ reflection with green filter}}$$

The smaller the color index, the whiter the paint.

Table 19-2. HIDING POWER, REFRACTIVE INDEX, AND OIL ABSORPTION OF WHITE PIGMENTS

Pigment	Hiding power sq ft/lb	Refractive index	Oil absorption
TiO_2, Rutile	147	2.70	18–20
TiO_2, Anatase 98%	115	2.55	26–27
Zinc sulfide	58	2.37	10–18
30% Rutile, 70% $CaSO_4$	57	1.98	21
30% Anatase, 70% $CaSO_4$	48	1.87	23
30% Anatase, 70% $BaSO_4$	46	1.91	15
Titanated Lithopone	44	1.90	22
High-strength Lithopone, 50% ZnS	44		20
Lithopone, 30% ZnS, 70% $BaSO_4$	27	1.84	13
Zinc oxide	20	1.99	15–22
ZnO, 35% white lead	20		
Antimony oxide	20	2.09–2.29	
White lead ($Pb(OH)_2PbCO_3$)	15	1.94–2.09	7–13
Blanc fixe ($Pb(OH)_2PbSO_4$)	13	1.93	26–30
Extenders			
Barytes, $BaSO_4$		1.64	6–12
$BaCO_3$ (witherite)		1.60	
$CaSO_4$ (anhydrite)		1.59	
$CaCO_3$ (calcite)	Very low	1.57	
Silica (quartz)		1.55	20–50
Diatomaceous earth		1.45	
Average vehicle		1.50	

A paint or enamel yellows with age. This depends on both pigment and vehicle. The effect of composition of some Titanox pigments is shown in Table 19-3.

White lead is basic lead carbonate with a composition approximating $Pb(OH)_2$—2 $PbCO_3$. The pigment acts as a mild drier, giving an elastic, but tough dried film. It should not be used in paints or enamels for kitchens or

Table 19-3. Effect of Ageing on Whiteness of Alkyd-type Enamel

Pigment	Initial Values		Values After 8 Months	
	Brightness[a]	Color index	Brightness	Color index
TiO₂, Anatase 30%, CaSO₄ 70%	86.0	3.6		
Titanox A-168, Anatase 97%	89.0	3.7	87.0	11.0
Titanox A, Anatase 97%	89.0	4.2	86.0	16.0
Titanox RA, Rutile 97%	90.0	5.5	87.5	13.0
Titanox RA10, Rutile 98.5%	90.0	5.9	87.5	16.0

[a] The figure for brightness represents the percentage of light reflected by a cake of dry pigment, using the standard green filter in a Hunter multipurpose reflectometer.

bathrooms, owing to the reaction of the lead with sulfide gases to produce black lead sulfide. When used on exterior surfaces, any sulfide usually becomes converted to white sulfate. Under abnormal conditions this atmospheric oxidation may not be fast enough. The following news dispatch cites a case in point.

FIND CAUSE OF HOMES' COLOR CHANGE

LYNDHURST, N.J. (AP)—A senior state engineer gave discouraging news Wednesday to home owners who awoke Tuesday to find their houses mysteriously changed in color.

A hydrogen sulfide in the atmosphere discolored the paint by creating lead sulfide from the lead base paint.

Lester Barrer explained the mystery this way, after two of his chemists examined the houses.

This was bad news to 200 home owners who had their houses discolored. Residents reported an extensive fog settled over the area Monday night.

A hopeful solution was suggested by an Arlington, Va., chemical engineer, who said the residents can restore the color to their homes "at practically no cost at all" with a supply of hydrogen peroxide often used to bleach hair.

Sublimed white lead is essentially basic lead sulfate, $Pb(OH)_2$—$PbCO_3$. Some zinc oxide is usually present.

Zinc white is a very fine pigment, manufactured by oxidizing or burning vaporized zinc metal. As previously mentioned, this pigment has high absorption for the ultraviolet and hence reduces chalking of other pigments when mixed with them in a paint.

Zinc sulfide is a creamy white powder. It is prepared by treating the metal or oxide with hydrochloric acid and then reacting the zinc chloride with barium sulfide. It has good hiding power and is not affected by hydrogen sulfide. It is used alone or as one of the components of Lithopone.

Lithopone is made by mixing solutions of barium sulfide and zinc sulfate. As a result of an ordinary "double decomposition," two insoluble products, barium sulfate and zinc sulfide, are formed and precipitate together. The barium sulfide used in the manufacture of both zinc sulfide and Lithopone is derived from the mineral barytes, $BaSO_4$, by roasting it with coke:

$$BaSO_4 + 2\,C = BaS + 2\,CO_2$$

"High strength" Lithopone has 50 per cent ZnS added. It has better hiding properties than ordinary Lithopones, (28 to 30 per cent ZnS).

Red Pigments. The most important red pigments are natural and prepared iron oxides, red lead, chrome reds, cadmium, and cadmium-selenium. Some ochres when heated or calcined, become dark red, and some umbers are red-brown.

Venetian red is made by reacting ferrous sulfate and lime. In the furnace this gives ferric oxide and anhydrite

$$2\,FeSO_4 + 2\,CaO \longrightarrow Fe_2O_3 + 2\,CaSO_4$$

The shade of red varies with the temperature of preparation. It is a good permanent color, excellent for wood surfaces, but not recommended for metals, since the $CaSO_4$, being slightly soluble, gives ions which act as an electrolyte in a corrosion cell. It may also contain some SO_3 not neutralized by the lime.

Indian red is a natural ferric oxide pigment, that is, a hematite iron ore, ground finer. The ore usually contains from 88 to 95 per cent Fe_2O_3, with some clay or siliceous matter. This pigment is excellent for ironwork.

Red lead, Pb_3O_4, was originally prepared by heating white lead,

$$3\,Pb(OH)_2 + PbCO_3 + O_2 \longrightarrow 2\,Pb_3O_4 + 3\,HOH + 3\,CO_2$$

It is made at present by heating metallic lead to produce litharge, PbO, followed by further oxidation to Pb_3O_4. The litharge may be prepared from lead in a furnace at 375° C (710° F), or from molten lead forced by compressed air into fine droplets which burn like an oil spray. Litharge, the product of the lead "flame," is a fine powder. The particle size of the red lead produced from the litharge "fumes" is approximately one half that of "furnace" red lead.

The chief use of red lead is as a prime coat for metal surfaces because it is a corrosion inhibitor. In the presence of Pb_3O_4, $Fe°$ becomes Fe_2O_3. It also acts as a drier. It is not used for the final coat, as it would be gradually converted to white lead by the action of moisture and carbon dioxide.

Chrome red is a basic lead chromate. Synthetic reds of different shades contain cadmium and selenium oxides. Copper ferrocyanide is a maroon pigment.

There are a number of red organic colors and pigments. Some of the latter are salts in which the metal ion is usually barium or calcium, and the acid radical is a complex organic dye. None of the organics have the heat resistance of the inorganic reds. Some of the organic reds, while satisfactory for interior work, are not suitable for exterior paints since they are sensitive to light and will fade.

Blue Pigments. There are not many blue pigments. The principal ones are modifications of Prussian blue, called the iron blues, and of ultramarine blue.

Prussian blue may be made by reacting a ferric salt with a ferrocyanide. In practice however, related pigments are usually prepared in two steps from ferrous sulfate, often in the presence of ammonium sulfate.

$$FeSO_4 + Na_4Fe(CN)_6 + (NH_4)_2SO_4 \longrightarrow Fe(NH_4)_2Fe(CN)_6 + Na_2SO_4$$
Ferrous ammonium ferrocyanide (white)

$$Fe(NH_4)_2Fe(CN)_6 + NaClO_3 + H_2SO_4 \longrightarrow 6\ Fe(NH_4)Fe(CN)_6 + NaCl + H_2O$$
Ferric ammonium ferrocyanide
(an iron blue) $+ 3\ (NH_4)_2SO_4$

The coloring power of these blues is very great. One-half ounce of Prussian blue will color twenty pounds of zinc white a decided blue. While stable to acid, the iron blues should not be used with basic pigments, on fresh plaster, or in other alkaline environment, owing to the formation of $Fe(OH)_3$.

Ultramarine blue is a complex sulfide and silicate of sodium and aluminum. It is found in nature as lapis lazuli, but the pigment has been made synthetically for 125 years by fusing clay, sodium sulfate, and carbon. Some of the sulfate may be replaced by carbonate. The color can be varied from pale robin's egg blue to a violet blue by changes in the process.

The pigment is excellent for wood, but, because of its sulfur content, it is not recommended for metals. It should not be mixed with lead white or lead chromate pigments, as reaction with the sulfide would cause darkening and change of color. It is stable to alkalies, but not to acids.

Other blue pigments are cobalt blue (30 to 35 per cent Co_3O_4 and 65 to 70 per cent Al_2O_3), medium blue, containing cobalt, alumina, and chromium oxides, and copper phthalocyanine blue in which the copper is at the center of a spider's web organic structure.

Yellow Pigments. The principal yellow pigments are chrome yellow, $(PbCrO_4)$, zinc chromate, barium chromate, cadmium sulfide, and naturally occurring yellow ochre and sienna.

Lead chromate pigments may be produced in a number of shades. When coprecipitated with sulfate, it gives light shades such as lemon. In the presence of excess OH, basic lead chromate is formed. This pigment is orange, the shade depending on the proportion of $PbO:PbCrO_4$ and also on particle size. In the presence of some molybdate, the mixed $PbMoO_4$ and $PbCrO_4$ is also orange. All the lead pigments darken on exposure to hydrogen sulfide and light.

Zinc yellow is a light-yellow chromate pigment widely used as a prime coating for galvanized iron and other metals. It is a corrosion inhibitor not attacked by sulfide or basic pigments. Barium chromate finds similar uses. In the United States approximately $6\frac{1}{2}$ tons of lead chromate pigments are used for each $1\frac{1}{2}$ tons of zinc chromate and each ton of molybdatechrome.

Yellow ochres are minerals containing clay and/or calcium carbonate colored by hydrated iron oxide, which usually amounts to around 20 per cent. If the pigment is roasted, the color changes to red due to oxidation of the iron. Cadmium sulfide is a permanent yellow, unaffected by sulfide gases. Metal derivatives of organic *azo* compounds are recent additions to the "permanent yellow" pigments.

Green Pigments. The commonest green pigments are mixtures of chrome yellow and Prussian or iron blue. The mixture is green because each color absorbs the light reflected by the other, except for the green which is partly reflected by each. These greens, of which "shutter green" is an example, suffer from the shortcomings of the components. The color weathers to a blue tone. However, chrome greens are relatively cheap and possess good hiding power and gloss retention. Permanent green is Cr_2O_3, a brilliant dark green. It not only withstands atmospheric attack, but is also stable at high temperatures. A light green made by mixing zinc or barium chromate and ultramarine, is also much more stable than chrome green. Zinc chromate and phthalocyanine blue produce bright greens, such as jade. Turquoise and blue-greens may be formulated from cobalt blues and zinc chromate.

Brown Pigments are mostly minerals which develop a brown color on roasting. The umbers contain manganese in addition to iron. Heating converts these compounds to the higher oxides.

Black Pigments. The pigment in most black paints is lamp black, although graphite and other carbonaceous blacks are also used. Copper chromate and manganese dioxide form a heat-stable black pigment which is better for metal primers than the carbon blacks.

Any shade of paint can be obtained by blending the basic colors discussed above. However, the chemical properties of the pigments must be kept in mind in order that the mixture will not contain incompatible components.

REINFORCING PIGMENTS AND EXTENDERS

These are powdered materials which may improve the properties of the paint, although they have low opacity themselves. They may serve to fill voids in the film, to increase random arrangement of the primary pigment particles, to act as carriers of the pigment color, or to improve the brushing qualities of the paint. Clay, asbestine, and talc, when ground in with pigments and oil, tend to lighten or dilute the color. Gypsum, chalk, silica, and diatomaceous earth have very little effect on the color, since the refractive index is in each case very close to that of the vehicle.

HIDING POWER

The two most important factors determining the hiding power of a paint are the refractive index of the pigment and the particle size. If the pigment has the same refractive index as the vehicle, it will have practically no hiding power. This is illustrated by immersing a piece of pyrex tubing and a piece of soft glass tubing in a mixture of carbon tetrachloride and benzene having the same refractive index as pyrex glass. As shown in Fig. 19-3, there appears

Figure 19-3 The glass jar contains a long piece of pyrex tubing and a shorter (vertical) piece of soft glass tubing, partially immersed in a liquid mixture having the same refractive index as the pyrex glass. The immersed portion of the pyrex is invisible.

to be only one tube in the liquid, although two tubes can be seen above the liquid surface. The pyrex does not obscure the ridged background at all.

The hiding power of pigments or paint may be measured in a number of ways. One A.S.T.M. method is to determine the area of black and white contrast design obliterated by a pound of pigment. This is illustrated in Fig. 19-4. The values for "complete hiding" for common white pigments are given in Table 19-2. The refractive indices are also given for comparison. It will be noticed that the extenders which have low hiding power have also low indices, whereas the best extenders have high refractive indices.

The fraction of light reflected at the interface between a particle and the vehicle is called the *reflection coefficient*.

$$R = \frac{(n_p - n_m)^2}{(n_p + n_m)^2}$$

Figure 19-5 shows the refractive index of some white pigments plotted against

Figure 19-4 A demonstration of the hiding power of TiO_2. The black, sandy material is Ilmenite, $FeTiO_3$, an important source of titania. [Courtesy *C.I.L.*, Montreal.]

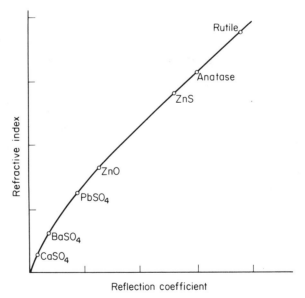

Figure 19-5 The relation between reflection coefficient and refractive index for a number of white pigments.

the reflection coefficient in an oil of which n_m equals 1.50. The pigments occupy positions on a smooth curve in the same order as their hiding power in the paint.

Scattering of light by pigments increases with the fineness of the particles to a maximum, beyond which further grinding would decrease the opacity of the suspension. A compounded paint is usually more satisfactory than one containing a single pigment type if the particles leave fewer voids in the film.

For the comparison of the hiding power of different paints, the weight of paint per unit area is determined for complete hiding of the test design or alternatively to reduce the contrast to a given value. Since, however, light scattering increases with concentration in different proportions for different pigments, comparison of amounts required to reduce the contrast to a series of values may give inconsistent results. Thus the number of uniform coats of the several paints necessary for complete hiding of a black and white checkerboard design may not be in the same order when tested on a design of lower contrast, such as grey squares on a lighter grey background.

A new method is based on the obliterating power of one coat of standard thickness (0.075 mm) applied to a test chart bearing discs of graded contrast. These are arranged on (a) a black background and (b) a white background. Figure 19-6 shows such a chart with the numerical values of the density of the grey semicircle and the contrast between it and the background. The density is given by the log of the ratio of the intensity of the incident and reflected light as determined by a photometer. Contrast is the difference between the density of the grey and the background. Positive values indicate that the background is darker; negative values indicate that the background is lighter than the grey spot; that is, $\Delta D = \log I_b/I_g$. The hiding power of the paint is determined by the numerical value of the greatest contrast obliterated.

OIL ABSORPTION

The flow properties of a paint depend to a great extent on the volume and nature of the pigment present. The oil absorption value of a pigment is the quantity of oil (linseed is taken as a standard) required to wet a standard weight of pigment, so that it will flow or form a fluid suspension. The oil absorption is usually expressed as grams of oil per 100 grams of pigment. Values for some white pigments are given in Table 19-3. These vary from a high of 27 for an anatase titania to a low of 7 for some white leads. The same variation occurs among the colored pigments. Thus, pigment E, yellow $BaK_2(CrO_4)_2$, has an oil absorption of 11.6, while for cadmium sulfide yellow, the value is 56.0. Oil absorption increases with the fineness, that is, the specific surface of a given pigment.

High pigment and low vehicle concentration give maximum hiding and

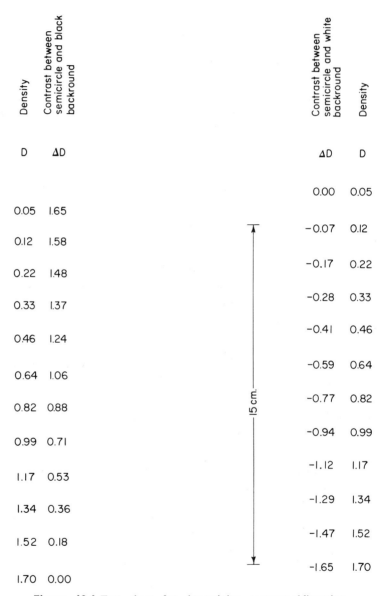

Figure 19-6 Test chart for determining contrast-obliterating power. [From P. F. Luft, *Ind. & Eng. Chem.*, **18** (1946) 484, by permission.]

"priming," and a "flat" type of paint. Lower concentration of pigment in the same vehicle will give a semigloss or glossy paint.

CHALKING

When a paint film weathers, the polymer film is broken down by oxidation and hydrolysis activated by ultraviolet light. This disintegration of the film exposes successive layers of pigment which will rub off like chalk or will be washed away by the rain. The "self-washing" whites are examples of this. Excessive chalking can be prevented by the addition of a pigment which absorbs ultraviolet as soon as it enters the first pigment layer instead of reflecting it back through the film, as is the case with Titanox A. White lead has high reflectance in all of the ultraviolet.

Thixotropic Paints

Certain colloidal systems, which set to a gel, may be reconverted to a fluid by mechanical agitation. On standing, the solution again forms a gel. This reversible breakdown of gel structure by agitation is called *thixotropy*. Thixotropic paints become fluid under the pressure of the brush and form a paint film which has less tendency to drip and spatter. They also have better shelf life since the pigment remains in suspension. Thixotropy should be such that resetting of the film will not take place before the brush marks level out.

Thixotropic properties may be imparted to a paint by the addition of resins, soaps, by adjusting the interfacial tensions, and by the incorporation of small amount of water (1%).

19-2 Water Paints

The earliest type of paint used for protective or decorative coatings had water as the vehicle. The Egyptians and Greeks made a "whitewash" from freshly burned lime and sour milk. These would react to form calcium caseinate and lactate which acted as the binder. The addition of fine earths and minerals gave color to the suspension. The tempera paints developed in the middle ages used egg white as the protective colloid and adhesive, while the water paints of the first part of this century used glue or powdered casein.

The great revolution in water paints came in 1949 with the marketing of the first water emulsion paint. In ten years, annual production in the United States reached 54 million gallons with a value of $300,000,000 and is still increasing. These paints are oil-in-water type emulsions. The vehicle is an aqueous solution or sol containing (1) protein, such as soybean protein, (2) protein "solvents" or peptizing agents, (3) thickeners, (4) preservative,

(5) mildew inhibitor, (6) anti-foamer, and an (7) emulsifying agent. The pigment or color (8) may be suspended in the vehicle. Interfacial tensions are controlled by surface-active agents so that the pigment goes to the interface, coating the surface of the droplets of drying oil (9).

In rubber-based or latex paints, the suspended droplets are rubber, or a synthetic resin such as polyvinyl acetate or an acrylate. More than 70 per cent of latex paints are of the buna S type. Polyvinyl acetate of many different formulations accounts for 19 per cent and the acrylates about 9 per cent of present production. The latter two are somewhat more expensive than the synthetic rubber latex.

Acrylate emulsion paints have been developed for *external* use. They can be applied to wood, stucco, cement, and other surfaces. Unlike oil paint, they can be applied to a damp surface. Surfaces have been successfully painted with polyvinyl acetate emulsion paint at 35° F, three degrees above freezing!

Water enamels have been marketed. These differ from emulsion paints in that the pigment is suspended in the oil enamel droplet.

Some of the advantages claimed for water emulsion paints are a short drying period, lack of odor, ease of application, excellent adhesion to fresh plaster, cement, and wood, no fire hazard, water can be used as thinner, brushes and rollers are easily cleaned, and spattered spots can be wiped clean with a damp cloth. Emulsion paints have enhanced hiding power, due to the arrangement of pigment in the dried film. The latex film is washable when dry and has high chemical resistance. The acrylate film is particularly resistant to yellowing by ultraviolet shown by drying oils. One-coat emulsion paints which give two or more colors superimposed on the basic color have been developed.

19-3 Special Paints

In addition to the common types of paint described above, there are paints designed for special or specific uses, such as heat-resistant, fire-retardant, and temperature-indicating paints, luminous paints, antifouling and fungus-resistant paints, and coatings to prevent or reduce icing, condensation of moisture, or penetration of porous surfaces.

Heat-Resistant Paints

Elevated temperatures cause the breakdown of ordinary paint. The heat may first cause blisters from the expansion of the softened film by vapors liberated at the increased temperature. A further increase in temperature causes a charring and disintegration of the film. Modern heat-resistant paints and enamels are based on silicone vehicles, metallic powders, and heat-stable pigments. These are used as finishes for ovens, furnaces, space heaters, smoke stacks, oil stills, diesel exhaust pipes, aircraft combustion chambers, and shrouds for jet after-burners. A properly formulated silicone-based coating has been found to reduce the oxidation of a mild steel sheet heated to 930° F for 380 hours, to one-seventh of the normal value. The coating was unaffected at that temperature. Metal powders, such as aluminum, zinc, and tin, protect the film by heat conduction and reflection. Graphite, mica,

Figure 19-7 Coating the compressor turbine blades with heat resistant silicone varnish. [Courtesy Orenda Engines Ltd.]

titania, chromic oxide, antimony oxide, red iron oxide, and cadmium selenide, cobalt oxide blue, barium sulfate, and other pigment compounds give heat-stable colors. The suitability of the many silicone compounds for the vehicle or binder of heat resistant paints and enamels depends on chemical structure. The methyl and phenyl silicones have the best heat resistant properties. If all the radicals are methyl, the resulting film is fast drying and hard but not as adherent or flexible as the softer polyphenyl silicones. Silicones containing both methyl and phenyl groups are more stable. Unsaturated groups give lower resistance to heat. For exposures under 650° F, primers based on silicone resins, zinc chromate, and oxide pigments may be used under silicone topcoats. The silicone resins may be modified by admixture with many other resins.

Figures 19-7 and 19-8 show the application of a silicone finish to aircraft turbine blades and as a heat resistant coating on an exhaust stack.

Figure 19-8 Silicone paint at surface temperature 350°-700° F after two years is still bright and undamaged. [Courtesy Dow-Corning Corp.]

Fire-Retardant Paints

Combustile materials may be rendered less flammable by impregnation with suitable compounds or by applying a fire-retardant paint. The paint is not heat resistant in the sense that it is unaltered when subjected to high temperatures. Indeed, the effectiveness of the protective coating depends in large measure on the decomposition of various paint components by the heat. Such compounds as calcium ammonium phosphate, magnesium ammonium orthophosphate, zinc ammonium ortho- and pyrophosphate and tungstate, various borates and boro-tungstates, antimony oxychloride, chalk, basic metallic oxides, and chlorinated organic compounds evolve ammonia, water, carbon dioxide, chlorine, or hydrogen chloride, which are extinguishing agents.

A second protective measure is to incorporate in the paint, materials which fuse, forming an impervious glass-like layer of foam, stabilized by the charred material of the film. Such materials are called *intumescent*. Several of the gas-producing materials listed above are used in intumescent paints. Fire-resistant and noncombustible vehicles such as silicones and chlorinated biphenyl, and solutes such as chlorinated resins, metholyl urea, and others with heat-stable plasticizers are used.

Heat conduction is decreased and the film strengthened by mica powder, clay, silicates and asbestos. High pigment volume is advantageous.

Water based paints may also be fire retardant. Three component anti-flame materials are used. These are (1) inorganic salts such as borax or sodium or ammonium silicate, (2) organic nitrogen compounds, such as urea and its derivatives, along with (3) carbonaceous starch, glucose, or other sugars, and pentaerythritol. Examples of two formulations of such water emulsion paints are given below (Table 19-4). This type of paint has good scrub resistance.

Table 19-4. COMPOSITION BY WEIGHT OF FIRE-RETARDANT EMULSION PAINTS

A.			B.		
Monoammonium phosphate	56.0%		"Borotherm"	10.0%	
Urea	10.0		Pigments	...	
Mannitol	21.2		Lithopone	10.0	
Pigment (TiO_2)	12.0		Clay	6.0	
Polyvinyl latex	35.5		$CaCO_3$	2.5	
Protective colloid	0.3		TiO_2	4.0	
Water	50.0		Mica	2.5	
			Polyvinyl acetate	15.0	
			Water	50.0	

Flame resistance is tested in the standard apparatus illustrated in Fig. 19-9. Test specimens of cellulosic wall board, painted or impregnated with the material under test, are supported at an angle of 45 degrees. One milliliter of ethyl alcohol (absolute) is pipetted into a standard, fixed brass cup and ignited. The area of the charred section at a definite time is inversely proportional to the flame resistance of the paint. The degree of intumescence is judged by the thickness of the solid char foam produced. Polyvinyl chloride-vinylidene chloride latex is suitable when the paint is dried at temperatures near the softening point of the polymer. Figure 19-10 shows the improvement in fire resistance when polyvinyl acetate is substituted for the usual Buna S-type latex, and the further improvement on the addition of soluble borates. The effect of varying the proportions of three components is shown in Fig. 19-11.

Wood, fabric, and other combustible materials may be impregnated with fire-retardant chemicals. It is estimated that treating the wood for a house to

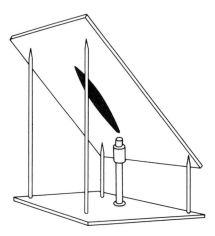

Figure 19-9 Apparatus for testing fire resistance and intumescent qualities of coatings. [Cf. U.S. Dept. of Commerce, CS-42-49 and British Standard Specifications, 476 (1932).]

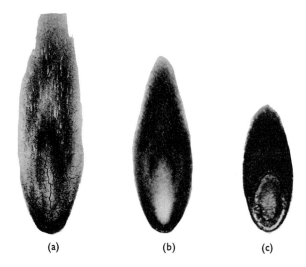

(a)   (b)   (c)

Figure 19-10 Effectiveness of Borotherm-PVAc coatings compared with PVAc coating and a non-fire resistant water-base paint. (a) Char area (32 sq in.) on a commercial water-base paint. (b) Char area (17.6 sq in.) obtained on a polyvinyl acetate latex with no borate added. (c) Char area (10.4 sq in.) when "borotherm" is present with the polyvinyl acetate. [Courtesy American Potash & Chem. Co.]

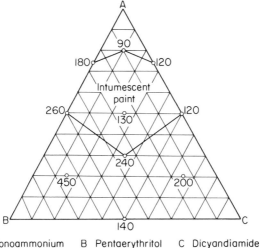

A Monoammonium   B Pentaerythritol   C Dicyandiamide
  phosphate

Figure 19-11 The effect of variation in proportions of three components on the fire-retardant and scrub-resistance properties of a latex paint.

The numbers on the figure represent the number of cycles in standard abrasion apparatus required to expose 10 per cent of the surface.

In every case components ABC totaled 87.2 parts by weight. The other components of the fire-resistant paint were TiO_2, 12.0; latex solids, 17.7; water, 50 parts by weight. [From I. J. Cummings, *Industrial and Engineering Chemistry*, **46** (1954), 1989, by permission.]

render it flameproof would only increase the costs of the dwelling by about 5 per cent. Attention is being given to the development of flame-resistant polyester resins for laminates and coatings. Esters of hexachlorocyclopentadiene, (HET) are much less flammable than the glyptals.

Temperature Indicating Paint

Paints or coatings containing materials which undergo a color change at definite temperatures can be used to indicate hot spots on equipment, the efficiency of insulation, and so on. Various combinations of components are used, which make it possible to cover a range of from 113° to 2500° F with a tolerance of 1 per cent of the temperature rating. The compounds used include double salts and amine salts of iron, cobalt, manganese, nickel, copper, chromium, molybdenum, and uranium. Hydrogen sulfide in the atmosphere will interfere. A few of the colors are affected by sulfur dioxide and ammonia. The thermal indicating coating must therefore be protected against these gases and other interfering substances by a coat of clear lacquer. To obtain maximum accuracy in the use of these temperature indicating paints, the duration of exposure to the particular temperature must be considered, since the color change observed in one minute at one temperature may perhaps be achieved by exposure for 30 minutes at a somewhat lower temperature. In one case a thermochrome which changed color in one minute at 842° F gave the same color change in 30 minutes at 824° F. When the color change is due to the melting of the indicator, the time factor is much less important.

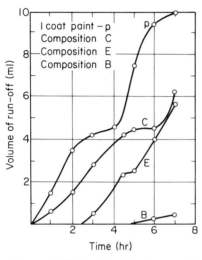

Figure 19-12 Results of tests run with anticondensation coatings. [From C. Y. Hopkins and T. H. G. Michael, "Evaluation of Marine Anticondensation Paints," *Can. Chem. & Process Ind.*, **28** (1944), 629, courtesy of authors and publisher.]

Anticondensation Paint

Marine anticondensation paint is designed to decrease the "sweating" of walls and ceilings especially below decks and on "outside" walls in ships' cabins, wardrooms, and other spaces during cold weather. This type of coating is applied in a relatively thick layer or film (0.08 in.). It consists of a fire-retardant, fibrous paste which gives a layer having a very high specific surface. This increased surface adsorbs a considerable amount of moisture before becoming wet. It also acts as an insulating layer. Figure 19-12 shows the run off obtained when a test metal surface maintained at 32° F was exposed to an atmosphere of 65 relative humidity and 68° F. When the protective coating was ordinary paint, condensation started immediately. The run off was approximately 2 ml/hr. Preparation C showed some insulating properties but no adsorption of water vapor. Preparation E gave no run off for 2.5 hours, indicating greater surface and higher adsorptive qualities. Product B exhibited high adsorption and insulation.

These fire-retardant and anticondensation paints replace the cork-dusted paint formerly used.

Water-Repellent Coatings

Latex paints are suitable for concrete and stucco surfaces. A colorless coating, which makes porous materials like masonry, stucco, cinder block, leather, and even paper, waterproof, is provided by the silicones. Water vapor can pass through the treated surface, but liquid water cannot penetrate.

Figure 19-13 Treating the Burlington (Ont.) Skyway with silicone to protect the roadway from de-icing salt. [Courtesy Dow-Corning Silicones Ltd.]

This prevents damage by freezing and thawing, known as "spalling." The antiwetting properties of the silicones have recently been put to use in the preparation of a de-icing lacquer. Water and sleet have much less tendency to adhere to this new coating material than to ordinary lacquers or varnishes. If ice does form, it does not stick so tenaciously. The lacquer contains 10 per cent nitrocellulose, 5 per cent plasticizer, 20 per cent oil modified alkyd resin, 1.5 per cent vinylacetate resin, 1.5 per cent silicone, and any small amounts of microcrystalline wax in a suitable solvent. This type of coating is of special value for aircraft and ships' superstructures.

The use of silicones as a water-repellent coating is illustrated in Fig. 19-13 which shows the Burlington Skyway near Hamilton, Ont., being treated to protect the concrete from the brine produced by the use of de-icing salt in winter.

Antifouling and Fungicidal Paints

This class of paints is of special interest to engineers concerned with marine construction. These paints prevent or greatly retard the fouling of ships and piers by barnacles, marine worms, fungi, and other organisms. Both pigments and vehicle contain substances toxic to the fungus or marine growth. Cuprous oxide, methyl mercury oleate, copper and zinc naphthenates, mercury oxide, mercurous chloride (calomel), and phenyl mercury naphthenate are commonly used. Mercury is much more effective than copper against seaweeds, while barnacles are more sensitive to copper than to mercury.

One of the best additives to the vehicle is pentachlorophenol

$$
\begin{array}{ccc}
 & \text{OH} & \\
\text{Cl} & | & \text{Cl} \\
 & \bigcirc & \\
\text{Cl} & & \text{Cl} \\
 & \text{Cl} &
\end{array}
$$

This not only prevents rot due to fungus growth in damp situations, but it is also effective against chewing and boring insects. It has been found that wood protected by a hard film containing this compound is much less subject to attack by termites. Other fungicidal vehicles or impregnates are salicyl anilide, creosote, and tar acids.

Fungi produce a variety of acids, alcohols, and fats in their catabolism and these reagents attack ordinary paint films, destroying gloss, film strength, and adhesion and abrasion resistance. Pretreatment of the surface with a 0.03 per cent solution of mercuric chloride (corrosive sublimate) kills fungi and any adhering spores. The dry surface is then painted with the fungicidal paint. Care should be taken when handling mercury compounds and other toxic materials. Chlorinated phenol may produce dermatitis on prolonged contact with the skin.

The addition of 5 to 6 per cent DDT in the form of a solution in mineral oil to outside paints is said to help to control spiders and other crawling insects. Enough insecticide diffuses to the surface of the film to keep the paint active for at least two years. A patented clear lacquer for coating screens contains

2%	resin (alkyl phenol-formaldehyde)
6%	DDT
4%	polybutylene solvent
29%	xylene
59%	mineral spirits

Other insecticidal compounds may be used.

Luminous Paints

Luminous paints may be divided into two groups, fluorescent and phosphorescent. Fluorescent paints absorb ultraviolet or violet radiation and emit light in the visible spectrum only while irradiated. Phosphorescent paints continue to glow for several hours after the radiation has ceased. The activating light may be sunlight or light from any other good source.

FLUORESCENT PAINTS

The principal fluorescent pigments are zinc sulfide and combined zinc and cadmium sulfides with small amounts of color-modifying elements. Zinc sulfide with silver gives blue fluorescence; zinc sulfide with copper gives green; 80 per cent zinc sulfide with 20 per cent cadmium sulfide and copper is yellow; 70% zinc sulfide and 30% cadmium sulfide gives orange and the 50 per cent material, a deep red.

The color of the paint in visible light will not be the same as the fluorescent color unless appropriate pigments or organic colors are added. This addition will of course reduce the intensity of the fluorescence.

Many dyes and some organic pigments give brilliant colors if exposed to ultraviolet light. These are not as stable for exterior use as the inorganic pigments.

This type of luminous paint is used for instrument dials, maps, inks, and for charts, identification of products, blackout signs, advertising signs, and novelties.

PHOSPHORESCENT PAINT

Phosphorescent paints may be divided into two types of phosphors, those which have a bright but short afterglow, and those that have a persistent but low-intensity phosphorescence.

The first type contains relatively coarse "impure" zinc sulfide or zinc and calcium sulfides. Pigments in this group usually have a green, yellow, or even orange phosphorescence. They resemble lithopone in visible light, but have poorer hiding power on account of the large particle size. These materials give maximum phosphorescence after exposure to light for from ten seconds to one minute depending on the light source. They continue to glow for several hours. When used indoors they are quite stable.

The second type of phosphors has lower brightness but longer afterglow. They are chiefly calcium or strontium sulfides or mixtures of these. The phosphorescence is usually violet, blue, or bluish green, but a variety of luminescent colors may be secured according to the choice of activating salts: bluish violet with uranium salts, yellowish red with cerium salts, greenish yellow with antimony salts, green with mercury salts, golden yellow with manganese sulfide, green with gold or copper salts, blue green with lead sulfide, and orange with molybdenum sulfide.

These sulfides must be protected from hydrolysis by a vehicle which is not only transparent but must also have low permeability to water vapor. They require longer illumination than the first type of phosphors, from one to ten minutes, but the phosphorescence lasts approximately three times longer. The duration of the glow and the color depend on the nature and distribution of the "impurities" and imperfections in the sulfide pigments.

Phosphorescent paints are used for black-out markers, for signs, guide lines, to mark obstructions, and safety devices, in industrial plants, ships, hotels, and public buildings in case of power failure. These paints are not used very extensively out of doors.

Instrument and watch dials have radioactive materials mixed with the pigment to act as a continuous source of irradiation. Mesothorium with a half-life of 6.7 years or radiothorium with a half-life of 1.9 years is commonly used. Thorium and bismuth salts are sometimes added as activators in the preparation of the second type of phosphors.

19-4 Varnish, Lacquers, and Enamels

Varnishes are solutions of natural or synthetic gums or resins in a vehicle. The vehicle may be a drying oil or a volatile solvent or "spirit." Shellac is a solution of a resin from the lac insect, dissolved in methanol, and it may be classed as a spirit varnish. Spirit varnishes have been displaced by modern lacquers.

Enamels are made of varnishes or lacquers with pigment added. The natural resins used in oil varnish are fossil gums, some of which are as old as coal. Nodules and lumps of the fossil resin sometimes weighing 50 pounds are recovered from swampy areas. Several of the natural resins are named for the locality from which they come, for example, Zanzibar gum, Congo, and so on. These differ somewhat in properties.

Rosin, the primary resin which remains after the distillation of turpentine, represents a low state of polymerization. It does not give a stable film. When combined with glycerol, the "ester gum" so formed has better properties. Hydrogenation of the rosin saturates about half of the double bonds, and when combined with pentaerythritol, it yields a hard, heat-stable resin, suitable for paints and varnishes. The coating has good gloss, color, hardness, and adhesion.

The fossil resins vary in complexity and degree of polymerization and therefore in hardness and solubility in organic solvents. The youngest and most soluble are the *dammar* gums. The *copals* are less soluble; they are broken down and caused to dissolve and react with fatty oils by heating to

300° C (570° F) in the varnish kettle. Kauri resins from New Zealand are even more stable.

A new era in varnish, enamel, and lacquer manufacturing followed the development of bakelite and other synthetic resins, many of which are well known materials for plastics. Recent statistics from Great Britain show that, of the synthetic resins used in these products, the alkyds comprised over 53 per cent of the total, phenolaldehyde 10.5 per cent, modified resin compounds 12.5 per cent, urea and amino compounds 7.7 per cent, styrene and vinyl 6.3 per cent, and miscellaneous polymers the remainder.

The properties of the varnish will depend on the nature of the resin and fatty oil with which it is combined or dissolved. A hard resin mixed with soybean oil gives a film with properties similar to that obtained from a soft resin and tung oil. A varnish containing a high proportion of oil to resin is softer and more flexible than one having a small percentage of oil. The former is referred to as a "long oil" varnish, and the latter a "short oil" varnish. These terms do not refer to polymer size or the length of oil component.

With the variety of synthetic resins available today and the modifications possible by choice of oils and methods of compounding, varnishes and lacquers can be prepared for many different and specific uses, for example, the silicone varnish, Fig. 19-7. It is always wise to employ the type of varnish or lacquer designed for the particular use. A varnish having superior water resistance may be too brittle for a floor varnish. A satisfactory interior varnish may be unsuitable for exterior surfaces.

Lacquers consist of a (1) volatile vehicle, (2) synthetic resin, (3) a plasticizer, (4) an extender, and sometimes (5) a dye or color. The solvents usually employed are esters such as "banana oil" (amyl acetate), ketones, for example, acetone and methylethyl ketone, cellosolve ($C_2H_5OCH_2CH_2OH$), dioxane, a cyclic diether,

$$\begin{array}{ccc} & CH_2-CH_2 & \\ O & & O \\ & CH_2-CH_2 & \end{array}$$

and alcohols.

Extenders are low-cost liquids, often nonsolvents for the resins. They are added to decrease the viscosity of the medium, acting as thinners. Alcohols and hydrocarbons are commonly used; plasticizers are also added to give a smooth, flexible film. They act as internal lubricants of the resin. Dibutyl phthalate, phosphate, castor oil, polyesters of chosen molecular weight, and tri-o-cresol are examples.

The first large-volume lacquer was made by dissolving nitrocellulose in a suitable solvent. The nitrocellulose was prepared by the partial denitration of surplus guncotton left from World War I. This lacquer proved a great boon to the automobile industry, as it gave a tough, durable, glossy coating that could be applied easily and dried in a very short time. The use of other cellulose derivatives and synthetic resins of the plastic type followed.

The following represents the composition of a high quality white enamel:

Titanium dioxide	8.3%
Alkyd resin (pentaerythritol + phthalic A, 50% solids)	69.8%
Petroleum thinner	21.5%
Drier (5-cobalt naphthenate)	0.4%
	100.0%

Some lacquers and enamels are "cured" by heating or "baking" the applied film. The resins in these are usually thermosetting; that is, condensation polymerization is induced by the elevated temperature. Many cross-linkages are formed with the production of a harder and more stable film.

An interesting application of this type of coating is the use of epoxy resin enamel for protecting the interior of tank cars. The lining is built up by five successive coats, each of which is dried and partially baked. Hot air is circulated through the tank from a special furnace having a capacity of 1,500,000 Btu/hr. The final curing temperature is 450° F. The applied coating has excellent chemical resistance and physical properties. Cars so treated may be used to transport caustic soda, salt solutions, alcohols, glycerol, petroleum, dilute acids, and aromatic hydrocarbons. Epoxy enamel is also used to coat food storage tanks. The final thickness of the resin lining is only one-third that required when neoprene is used.

Recently, a methacrylate lacquer has been developed for automobiles that exhibits high gloss which is not dimmed by weather, a water emulsion type of lacquer which deposits a film that is then baked and bonded to the metal, and epoxy resins in which silicones have been combined across unsaturated bonds, thus imparting heat resistance and high moisture resistance to the coating.

19-5 Methods of Application

Paints and related protective coatings are commonly applied with a brush, roller, spray, or by dipping. Industrial spray methods make use of colloid chemical principles to save time, labor costs, and from 45 to 75 per cent of the paint.

A paint spray is a typical aerosol in which the droplets are charged negatively. These particles will be attracted to a positively charged surface and repelled by a negatively charged object. Movement of a colloidal particle under an electric field is called *electrophoresis*. The article to be painted is suspended from the positively charged monorail and moves between two wire frames or electrodes charged negatively where it meets the spray from a fixed spray gun. Potentials of 100,000 v are used. The paint droplets, therefore, converge on the work so that even the far side of the object is coated. Practically no supervision is required for the spraying operation. (Figure 19-14 illustrates this procedure.)

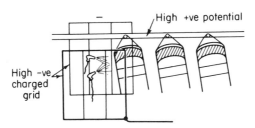

Figure 19-14 Paint application by electrophoresis.

When articles are coated by dipping, the draining of the excess paint or lacquer often leaves "tears" after the surface coat is dry. "Detearing" makes use of a similar phenomenon. After the dipped article passes the drip pans, it moves over a charged insulated grid. This pulls off the tiny droplets or tears of excess paint. Most of the droplets pass through the oppositely charged grid and are recovered.

19-6 Nonvehicle Coatings

In paints, varnishes, lacquers, and enamels, the vehicle is required as a carrier and film-forming agent. However there are several types of protective films such as metal, resin, rubber, vitreous enamel, and glaze, which can be classified as nonvehicle coatings. Plastics and synthetic rubber are commonly extruded over metal wire to form a continuous insulating film, and previously formed sheets may be bonded to a surface by heat or adhesives. Vitreous enamel and glass coatings are formed by fusing the components on the surface of the underlying metal. Metal films are formed as indicated below. A vehicle is not required in any of these examples.

Metal Coatings

Metal films may be applied by dipping, plating, rolling or "cladding," spraying, "sherardizing," and vacuum evaporation and condensation. For any of these processes the surface to be coated must be scrupulously clean.

HOT DIPPING

Hot dipping was one of the earliest methods used to put a metallic coating on sheet iron. The first tinned iron is said to have been produced about

1600 A.D. Mild steel is fed in a continuous sheet through zinc chloride flux, through molten tin, and then between rollers in an oil bath where excess metal is squeezed off, the oil forming a temporary film that protects the hot metal from oxidation. The thickness of the tin coating is approximately 10^{-4} in. The alloy, $FeSn_2$, is formed at the interface.

Galvanized iron has been used for over two hundred years. The zinc coating may be brightened by the addition of aluminum metal to the molten bath. The average thickness is 0.002 in. or 1.2 oz/sq ft.

Ternplate is produced like tin plate. The coating metal is an alloy of lead and tin melting between 280° and 300° C and containing between 75 and 88 per cent lead. In a corrosive atmosphere it has a longer life than galvanized iron.

ELECTROPLATE

Films of many metals can be formed by electroplating. These include copper, nickel, chromium, silver, gold, platinum, rhodium, tin, cadmium, zinc, lead, and brass.

The physical character of the deposit depends on the composition of the plating bath as well as on the current density, temperature, and time. The presence of protective colloids or "addition agents" and complex ions of the metal, aid in the formation of dense, smooth coatings.

Nickel plate is usually deposited on an undercoat of copper. Much chromium plate consists of an extremely thin coating electroplated over successive layers of tin, copper, and/or nickel. Although a piece of chromium metal will scratch glass, chromeplate will show scratches, the reason being that when a hard object moves against the plated metal, it creates a furrow in the softer underlying surface. The decorative coat of chromium is so thin that it cannot conform to the increased area of the depression, and the metal underneath is exposed. Thick chromium plate (0.04 in.) is used to provide smooth, hard-wearing surfaces.

Silverplate is not only used for cutlery and household articles, but because of its chemical inertness, finds use in the food and brewing industries. Tarnishing of silver plate is diminished by superimposing an extremely thin layer of rhodium.

Cadmium plate is used chiefly for small metal parts. These may be plated in a cathode "basket" in a complex-cyanide bath.

ROLLED COATINGS

Rolled plate is an adaptation of the jeweler's art. A layer of gold was welded to a cheaper base metal and the two rolled into a thin sheet. Sheffield Silverplate is made in a similar manner. Nickel-clad steel is formed by rolling nickel and steel billets together at around 1200° C, producing a strong bond. A layer of pure aluminum is bonded to various aluminum alloys to give a corrosion-resistant coating. Stainless steel sheet which has been plated on one side with iron, can be bonded to clean steel plate. Brass, copper, and monel-clad steel can be obtained by casting the metal around a heated iron ingot and rolling the casting at a lower temperature. In this case both sides of the sheet are clad with the thin protective coating.

Sprayed metal coatings are more porous than the films obtained by other methods and are therefore made thicker. The spray method is, however, preferred for coating a finished structure. The metal is fed into a spray pistol in the form of a wire where it is melted by gas flame or by the formation of an arc. Compressed air, or other gas, drives the metal droplets against the surface. The solidified coating contains varying amounts of oxide depending on the metal and the gases used. Successful adherence requires a clean but roughened surface. All the easily fused metals are used for spray coating. Monel metal, nickel, iron, stainless steel, brass, and others have also been employed for special work.

VACUUM METALIZING

Practically all the reflectors for automobile lights are made by the vacuum distillation of aluminum metal onto a methacrylate plastic moulded to the required shape. Small "hairpins" of aluminum wire are hung on heating wires opposite the surface to be coated. The rack, after being loaded, is put into a cylindrical chamber which is then evacuated and flashed.

For ornamental work such as horn buttons, radio dials, etc., the aluminum may be colored with a clear-colored lacquer. Other metals may be coated in the same way.

SHERARDIZING

A protective metal film can be formed on small objects by tumbling them in a rotating drum with metal powder at a temperature somewhat below its melting point. Zinc is the coating most commonly applied. The protective film produced at $360°$ C (mp $419°$ C) is chiefly $FeZn_7$. Cadmium is also applied by this method.

Vitreous Coatings

Vitreous or porcelain "enamels" are modified glass coatings bonded to a metal surface, commonly used on bathtubs, stoves, glass-lined tanks, chemical equipment, and various types of machinery. These coatings are formed from various combinations of silica sand, feldspar, clay, borax, and soda ash, with lead or tin oxides, fluorite, titania, and other pigments to make the film opaque. The composition used depends on the function of the equipment, for example hot water or chemical tanks may be lined with a boro-silicate glass, whereas a bathtub has a surface coating of an opaque soda glass. The choice of constituents also depends on the coefficient of expansion of the underlying metal. Bonding of the coating to steel or cast iron is achieved by the formation of iron silicate during fusion of the powdered material on the hot metal surface.

Vitreous coatings are chemically resistant and will stand higher temperatures than many other types of coatings. Like any glass, these thin coatings are easily fractured by impact, and except in special cases, by thermal shock. Even microscopic cracks in the coating will become the sites of intense corrosion.

Glazes are low-melting glass coatings applied to ceramic tiles and porcelain to prevent the diffusion of liquid through the porous material. Colored glazes are obtained by the incorporation of various metallic oxides.

Review Questions

1. Name the principal constituents of an oil paint.

2. Name five fatty oils used in paints.

3. Distinguish between blown and boiled linseed oil.

4. How is the iodine number of an oil determined?

5. What is the significance of a low iodine number?

6. What is saponification number?

7. What does a high saponification number indicate?

8. Show by formulas what happens during the drying of a paint film.

9. What is the chemical nature of oleic, linoleic, linolenic, and stearic acids?

10. Name three paint oils used in gloss paints.

11. Name three dryers in order of activity.

12. What is meant by Japan drier?

13. What is the function of a thinner?

14. Why is turpentine a better thinner than petroleum spirits?

15. What determines the covering power of paint?

16. What qualities determine hiding power?

17. Give the chemical composition of three white pigments.

18. What are the good and poor qualities of each of the above?

19. What chemical tests would distinguish ZnS, ZnO, and white lead?

20. What is the chemical composition of chrome yellow, Prussian blue, and Venetian red?

21. What is the function of $BaSO_4$, clay, and asbestene in paint?

22. Distinguish between varnish, lacquer, and enamel.

23. Define copal gum, glyptal resin, and alkyd resin.

24. Name the constituents of a lacquer.

25. What type of coating would you use for steel, concrete, and diesel exhaust pipes?

26. What are the components of a water paint?

27. How does this differ from a latex base water-enamel?

28. What principles of colloid chemistry are used in modern spray painting of manufactured articles?

29. What are the active components of (a) antifouling paints (b) fire-retardant paints?

30. What causes paint blisters?

Further Readings

Chatfield, H. W., *The Science of Surface Coatings* (London: Benn, 1962).   Chapters 6, 14, and 17.

von Fischer, W., *Paint and Varnish Technology* (New York: Reinhold, 1953).

20

Water for Domestic Uses

Water is an engineering material as well as one of life's necessities. It serves as a solvent, a suspending and transporting medium, a fire extinguisher, a heat-transfer agent, a source of power in the liquid and vapor state, and as a chemical reagent.

An oil refinery uses four tons of water per barrel of oil. It takes 300 tons of water in the manufacture of one ton of steel. A paper mill uses as much water as a city of 50,000 people. Many other industries require tremendous volumes of water as well. The average urban dweller uses 50 gal/day. With the increasing use of automatic washers, garbage disposal units, and other appliances, this figure will doubtless increase. Indeed, so prodigal is our present use of water that throughout the eastern United States and in some areas in Canada, seasonal, and, in some cases chronic, scarcity has developed. Industry and government realize that fresh-water sources are not limitless, and research is now being directed towards economic methods for obtaining potable and industrial water from the oceans and for purification and reuse of water.

20-1 Characteristics of Natural Water

Water is never chemically pure in nature. Rain collected at the end of a shower in a rural area probably is the purest form of natural water. The alchemists of old collected dew for their experiments. But dew, rain, and snow—nature's distilled water—all contain impurities such as dissolved gases, salts, oxides, and suspensions of dust, pollen, and spores from the atmosphere.

Water from rivers and lakes contains larger amounts of materials than rain water. If the soil of a region contains gypsum ($CaSO_4 \cdot 2\ H_2O$), the natural water will contain much more calcium than water from an area where the underlying rocks are igneous. Water from swampy areas or from soils in which there is decomposing organic matter or humus, will contain a variety of organic acids and carbon dioxide. Acidic waters readily attack carbonates such as limestone, dolomite $MgCO_3 \cdot CaCO_3$, and $FeCO_3$, forming soluble bicarbonates. Water containing CO_2 acts on feldspars to form a solution of potassium carbonate, and clay which often remains in suspension, causing turbidity. The reaction may be represented by the equation

$$K_2O \cdot Al_2O_3 \cdot 6\ SiO_2 + 2\ H_2O + CO_2 \longrightarrow K_2CO_3 + Al_2O_3 \cdot 2\ SiO_2 \cdot 2\ H_2O + 4\ SiO_2$$

Dissolved carbonic acid can also act upon pyrites (FeS_2) and other sulfide minerals liberating hydrogen sulfide. Dissolved oxygen converts insoluble sulfides to soluble sulfates and sulfurous or sulfuric acid; e.g.,

$$3\ FeS_2 + 3\ H_2O + 10\ O_2 \longrightarrow 3\ FeSO_4 + 2\ H_2SO_4 + H_2SO_3$$

Water from deep wells may contain relatively high concentrations of common salt. Sea water is a 3.1 per cent solution of various salts, principally (80 per cent) sodium chloride.

The usefulness of the natural water will depend on the nature and concentration of the suspended and dissolved substances. In some cases natural water may be used for domestic or industrial purposes without any treatment. In other instances, if water is to be used for high-pressure steam or in the manufacture of TV tubes, complete removal of dissolved and suspended material is required.

Since the requirements and therefore the treatment of water for domestic use may differ markedly from the necessary qualities and proper conditioning in industrial applications, the latter topic will be dealt with in the next chapter.

Fresh water is better than 99.9 per cent pure. The concentration of total solids present is therefore not expressed as percentages but as parts per million (ppm). This is equivalent to milligrams/liter or approximately pounds/100,000 Imperial gallons.

20-2 Qualities Required in Domestic Water

Domestic water should be colorless, odorless, free from harmful bacteria and suspended matter, and have an acceptable taste.

Turbidity

Turbidity in water indicates the presence in suspension of fine particles. The turbidity, which is roughly proportional to the amount of solid material in suspension, is measured by the reduction in transmission of light in a photoelectric colorimeter, or by the intensity of scattered (Tyndall effect) light at right angles to the incident beam (*nephelometry*). The latter method is valuable when dealing with dilute suspensions of colloidal material. A scale of turbidities is based on the optical properties of a standard silica powder, 1 mg SiO_2/liter, which equals one unit of turbidity.[1] Relative turbidity measurements are useful in determining when the water should be treated with a flocculating agent, the efficiency of filtration or sedimentation, and even the type of filter bed necessary.

Color

Color in natural waters is primarily due to extracts from decaying leaves, bark, and other vegetable material. These extracts contain tannins, humic acids and their salts, with various colloidal color bodies, which usually color the water a brownish yellow. Some intensification of color occurs by chemical reaction between the tannic acid and minerals dissolved in the water. In India a river containing iron salts from a mineralized region joins a stream which drains a jungle area. The resulting confluence produces a "black" river. One of the recipes for ink contains iron salts and tannic acid or "extract of gallnuts."

Contamination of water by trade wastes may result in undesirable color. Effluents from pulp and paper processing contain colored lignin compounds. Textile dyeing plants may add acid or basic dyes to the water. The color bodies from natural sources are negative colloids. These can be removed by treatment with a coagulant such as alum, which furnishes an effective trivalent positive ion. Activated charcoal, coke, or other adsorbents are also efficient decolorizing agents.

Color in natural waters is evaluated by comparison with a series of standards made by diluting a stock solution of potassium chlorplatinate (K_2PtCl_6) and cobaltous chloride ($CoCl_2 \cdot 2 H_2O$). The stock solution is prepared by dissolving 1.245 g of K_2PtCl_6, 1.00 g $CoCl_2 \cdot 2 H_2O$ with 100 ml of concentrated HCl and diluting the solution to 1.0 liter. This solution contains 500 mg of Pt and has been assigned a color score of 500 units. To prepare a standard for five color units, 0.5 ml is pipetted into a 50 ml graduated tube or flask, and made up to volume with distilled water. Solutions of 1.0, 1.5, 2.0, 2.5 ml diluted to 50 ml give standards for 10, 15, 20, and 25 color units,

---

[1] *Standard Methods of Water Analysis* (10th ed.; Philadelphia: A.S.T.M., 1955), Table 15.

respectively. The color value of a water having a shade of color between any two standards can be evaluated by appropriate dilutions of the stock solution. The upper limit recommended for drinking water is twenty units.

Color values are also measured by comparison with a series of graded glass color discs, simulating the color of the Pt-Co solutions.

Taste

Good drinking waters may differ in taste depending largely on the amount and nature of dissolved salts. Objectionable tastes can arise from high concentrations of magnesium or iron salts, chlorine in the presence of phenolic compounds, excess chlorine with certain nonphenolic compounds, and organisms such as certain algae which impart a fishy taste or "grassy" taste.

Tastes other than those caused by mineral salts can usually be removed by overchlorination with subsequent destruction of the excess chlorine. Aeration of the water supply may also be effective. Taste and odors, as well as color, can also be removed by activated carbon.

Sterilization of Drinking Water

The most important consideration in providing domestic water is the assurance of its freedom from harmful bacteria. Chlorine is now used universally for sterilizing drinking water. Concentrations of 0.1 to 0.2 ppm are effective. Concentrations of more than 0.4 ppm impart a taste to the water. Chlorine reacts with water to produce hypochlorus acid, a strong oxidizing agent.

$$Cl_2 + HOH \rightleftharpoons HOCl + H^+ + Cl'$$

This same agent is obtained from chloride of lime, bleaching powder, or sodium hypochlorite solution. Each of these can be used for sterilizing drinking water. Campers' kits, for making sure a water is safe for use, are solutions of the latter or a chlorine-containing organic compound related to the chloramines.

It was discovered in 1910 that more effective use of chlorine was obtained when the residual chlorine was in the form of a compound of ammonia called *chloramine*. One or more of the hydrogens of the ammonia may be replaced by chloride. The chloramines do not impart a taste to the water.

$$NH_3 + Cl_2 \rightleftharpoons NH_2Cl + H^+ + Cl'$$

or $$NH_3 + HOCl \rightleftharpoons NH_2Cl + HOH$$
$$\text{Monochloramine}$$

and $$NH_2Cl + Cl_2 \rightleftharpoons NHCl_2 + H^+ + Cl'$$

or $$NH_2Cl + HOCl \rightleftharpoons NHCl_2 + HOH$$
$$\text{Dichloramine}$$

and $$NHCl_2 + HOCl \rightleftharpoons NCl_3 + HOH$$
$$\text{Trichloramine}$$

This represents a maximum of combined Cl. Further amounts of chlorine oxidize some of the trichloramine to nitrogen or nitrous oxide, and free hydrogen chloride.

It will be noted from the equations above that ammonia removes excess chlorine or hypochlorous acid, but since the reactions are reversible, the chloramines act as chlorine reserves, killing any spores or organisms that were not destroyed during the initial treatment. Bacterial "kill" increases with concentration and time of contact ($K \propto Ct$). The presence of chloramines increases t. The equations also show that a lowering of the hydrogen ion concentration favors the formation of HOCl and chloramines. Swimming pools, which always present a sanitary problem, are best controlled by chloramines at pH 8.

Since any reducing substance in the water (for example, H_2S, NO_2', Fe^{++}, algae, and other organic material) will use up chlorine, overchlorination is often practiced. After sufficient time has elapsed, excess chlorine is reduced to the desired residual concentration by reaction with sulfur dioxide or sodium thiosulfate:

$$SO_2 + Cl_2 + 2\,HOH \longrightarrow H_2SO_4 + 2\,HCl$$

$$2\,Na_2S_2O_3 + Cl_2 \longrightarrow Na_2S_4O_6 + 2\,NaCl$$

Calculation from the molecular weights indicates that 9 lb of SO_2 will remove 10 lb of Cl_2.

Chlorine Demand

Chlorine demand is the amount in ppm necessary to give a final residual concentration of 0.1 ppm after 10 min contact. Residual chlorine may be present as chlorine, hypochlorite ion, or hypochlorous acid. These are called *free chlorine residuals* to distinguish them from the *combined chlorine residuals*, the chloramines. The concentration of each type of residual can be found by taking advantage of the fast oxidation and yellow color formation with the "free" chlorine and orthotolidine (5 sec), and subtracting this reading from the value after the slow reaction of the chloramines with the reagent has been completed (5 min).

Ozone and ultraviolet radiation are used for sterilizing water, particularly on shipboard. Figure 20-1 shows a photograph and diagram of an ultraviolet sterilizer. These are available for domestic and industrial uses to handle up to 7000 gal/hr with 99 per cent reduction in bacterial count.

The final criterion of satisfactory sterilization of domestic water is the reduction in the bacterial concentration to a very low value. Bacteriological examination of drinking water uses a particular organism, *B. coli*, as an indication of the purity of the water. The *B. coli*, as is the case with many other microorganisms, are not necessarily pathogenic, but they are easily

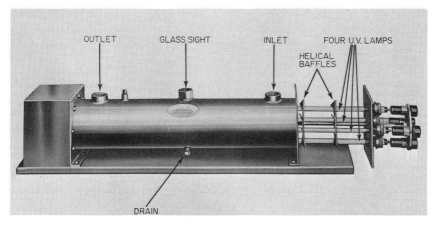

Figure 20-1 Ultraviolet water sterilizer with one end housing removed and assembly withdrawn to show U.V. lamp and mixing baffles. [Courtesy Rode Photo Service, Los Angeles.]

identified, and their presence is taken as an indication of the presence of other organisms of intestinal origin, and hence the degree of contamination of the water. No *B. coli* should be detectable in a volume of less than 10 ml. Results are reported as "*B. coli* absent in 1 ml, present in 10 ml," or "*B. coli* absent in 10 ml, present in 100 ml," and so on. A complete bacterial analysis gives the total number of organisms of all kinds by counting the number of colonies developed after twenty-four hours in a sterile agar nutrient medium, when innoculated with 0.1 ml, 1.0 ml, and so on, of the water being tested. A good water will show less than 10 per ml.

Other Health Aspects of Domestic Water

In times past *lead* pipe was used for domestic water systems. The word plumber means a worker in lead, from the Latin word for the metal, *plumbum*. Lead conduits have now been abandoned in favor of copper or iron pipes. Polyethylene tubing is replacing metal for cold-water systems. There are, however, a large number of old houses which still have lead water pipes. This metal is appreciably soluble in water containing carbon dioxide or

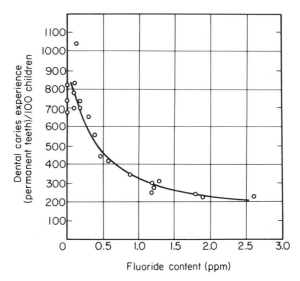

Figure 20-2 Relation between dental caries and fluoride content
of drinking water. (After Dean, *J. Am. Water Works Assn.*, **35**,
1161, 1943.) A more recent study of 1709 children in Czecho-
slovakia (c.a. 1955) confirms the beneficial effect of even 0.1 ppm F.
[By permission, from C. Sawyer, *Sanitary Chemistry for Engineers*
(New York: McGraw-Hill, 1960).]

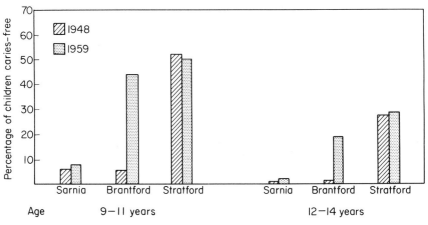

Figure 20-3 The percentage of children caries-free in two age
groups in a low fluoride area (Sarnia, 0.05 ppm F), in an area with
1.6 ppm in the water (Stratford), and in a third area (Brantford)
before and after fluoridation to 1.0 ppm F. Data for children 9–11
years old are from 1608 children in 1948 and 1550 in 1959; for
children 12–14 years old, from 1450 children in 1948 and 1468 in
1959. [From *Dental Effects of Water Fluoridation*, 7th Report,
Dept. of National Health and Welfare, Ottawa, Canada, Sept. 1959.]

organic acids. The chloride is also soluble to a considerable extent. Cases of chronic lead poisoning have been observed, due in some instances to the habitual use of water that had stood in the lead pipes overnight.

The presence of *fluoride* in natural waters in concentrations greater than 4 ppm has been shown to cause a brownish discoloration or mottling of tooth enamel. It was observed that such teeth were singularly free from cavities. Much research in different countries has shown that there is a direct

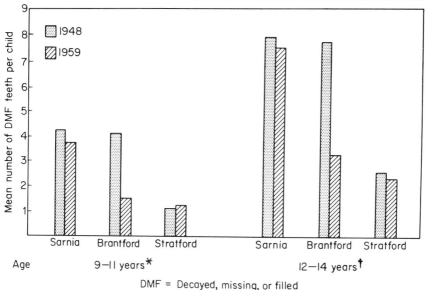

Figure 20-4 DMF permanent teeth per child. [From *Dental Effects of Water Fluoridation*, 7th Report, Dept. of National Health and Welfare, Ottawa, Canada, Sept. 1959.]

* 1948—1608 children   † 1948—1450 children
  1959—1550 children   1959—1468 children

correlation between the fluoride concentration in the domestic water and the "soundness" of the teeth. In 1943 Dean published a summary of data available at that time (Fig. 20-2). Subsequent research has confirmed the beneficial effect of fluoride addition to civic water supplies, in concentrations of 1.0 to 1.5 ppm, in reducing the incidence of dental caries. Figure 20-3 gives a comparison of the percentage of children ages 9 to 11 and 12 to 14 years having *no* dental caries in Sarnia, Brantford, and Stratford, Ontario. In Sarnia the water contains less than 0.05 ppm, the Brantford water supply has been fluoridated to 1.0 ppm, and in Stratford 1.6 ppm of fluoride is present. The striking improvement in the dental health of Brantford children who had fluoridated water during the whole period of tooth development (1959 groups) is indicated in the figure. The number of diseased, missing, and filled teeth per child (DMF) for the two age groups in the three cities is plotted in Fig. 20-4. In the 9 to 11 year group a reduction of 62.7 per cent in DMF occurred during this period of fluoridation of the Brantford water. For the twelve to fourteen-year olds, the improvement was 58 per cent. Children in the fluoride-free area had three times the DMF as those in the 1.6 ppm area. It will be noted that the best teeth were developed in Stratford where the drinking water contains 1.6 ppm.

Similar results have been obtained elsewhere. Ten-year studies have been carried out in several cities in the United States. The city of Washington, D.C., reported (March 1961) that an eight-year fluoridation period there had reduced the dental caries in the seven-year old group by 63.5 per cent. Numerous investigations have shown that fluoride in concentrations of 1.0 ppm is harmless and that there is no difference in mortality rates in low and high fluoride areas attributable to the concentration of fluoride. Public Health Bodies, Medical Associations, and Dental Colleges and Associations recommend the addition of fluoride to water supplies deficient in this element. In 1957 over 1500 public water supplies serving over 30,000,000 people in the United States received supplementary fluoride. In 1963, 2,455 communities representing 45,000,000 people in the United States and 188 communities in Canada representing 3,800,000 people used fluoridated water. Many other communities use water containing more than 1.0 ppm of fluoride derived from the soil or rocks. In 1959 over 1900 cities and towns in the United States with 7 million people used water containing 0.7 or more natural fluorides. The data for Canada is incomplete. In Ontario 50 municipalities or some 200,000 people have water supplies containing more than 0.7 ppm F'.

The citizens of certain areas having water supplies deficient in fluoride have rejected fluoridation. This is to be expected when it is recalled that the chlorination of water supplies met the same kind of opposition. In 1909 chlorination was fought in the courts of the United States. The judge ruled that chlorination was in the public interest—and chlorination has now become accepted by all but a few "natural food" faddists. In most cases opposition is based on fear generated by ignorance of elementary chemical facts. Any science student should be able to correct the most common misconceptions concerning fluoridation.

(1) "Sodium fluoride is a poison." So is chlorine. So is common salt in high concentrations. Cobalt and molybdenum are essential elements for human nutrition, yet their salts in very modest concentrations are poisonous. It is all a matter of concentration. Oxalic acid is a poison, yet people who eat cranberries or rhubarb in moderation are not poisoned, although both of these foods contain this "poisonous" substance. Sodium fluoride in concentrations used for fluoridation is not poisonous either.

(2) "Natural fluoride is all right, but not artificial fluorides." This displays ignorance of the dissociation of salts. The effective agent is the fluoride ion. Its original partner does not matter. At a concentration of one part per million, the sodium fluoride will be completely dissociated into sodium and fluoride ions, and no one can differentiate these ions from those found in a

natural water which had dissolved some calcium fluoride mineral along with some sodium salts.

(3) "When the water evaporates in the tea kettle, the sodium fluoride will be concentrated to much higher, even toxic amounts." This ignores the presence of calcium ions or any hardness in the water. It will be seen by applying the solubility product principle, that as the steam evaporates, calcium fluoride scale will precipitate on the walls of the kettle, removing fluoride ion from the water.

Probably the best answer to those who fear fluoridation is the healthiness of the people who have used water containing F' for many years.

20-3 Chemical Analysis of Natural Water

Since fresh water is a very dilute solution, the salts present are completely ionized so that analyses report the concentration of the individual ions present. These include the cations calcium, magnesium, iron, aluminum, sodium, and potassium, and the anions chloride, sulfate, carbonate, and bicarbonate, and for domestic water, sulfites, nitrites and nitrates, and fluorides. Silica, total solids, free ammonia, organic matter, dissolved oxygen, and pH are also determined.

The calcium ions may have come from dissolved $CaSO_4$, $CaCl_2$, $CaCO_3$, or $Ca(HCO_3)_2$. The identity of the original salts would involve a knowledge of the minerals present in the drainage area. "Guestimates" are made from the analysis of the water by pairing equivalent amounts of positive and negative ions in descending order of the solubility of the possible salts. This simply indicates the probable way in which the solutes would be deposited on evaporation of the water. Whiie the latter information is or may be important, it *does not* identify the original solutes. For example, fluoride ions from any source would, in the presence of appreciable Ca^{++}, be precipitated as calcium fluoride.

"Hardness" is due chiefly to calcium and magnesium ions. These and the small amounts of iron and aluminum ions present react with soap to form water-insoluble, sticky compounds—the ring around the bath tub in hard water areas!

When bicarbonate is present, heating the water causes the liberation of carbon dioxide, leaving a carbonate ion and water. This results in the precipitation of an equivalent amount of calcium or magnesium

$$Ca^{++} + 2\,HCO_3' \longrightarrow CaCO_3 + CO_2'' + H_2O$$

This is called *temporary* or *carbonate hardness*. The residual hardness is called permanent or noncarbonate hardness.

Since *one* calcium ion is equivalent to one magnesium or one ferrous ion, in this reaction with soap or a softening agent, such as sodium carbonate, the hardness is calculated on the basis of ppm of equivalent calcium carbonate, $CaCO_3$. Thus 40 ppm or Ca^{++} (at. wt $Ca^{++} = 40$), or 24.3 ppm of Mg^{++}, or 55.9 ppm of Fe^{++} equals, or is equivalent to 100 ppm of $CaCO_3$ (40 + 12 + 48). In terms of dissolved salts,

$$\begin{aligned}
\text{1 millimole of } MgCl_2/\text{liter (95.3 mg/liter)} &= \text{1 millimole of } CaSO_4/\text{liter (136 mg/liter)} \\
&= \text{1 millimole of } Ca(HCO_3)_2/\text{liter} \\
&\quad \text{(162 mg/liter)} \\
&= \text{1 millimole of } CaCO_3/\text{liter (100 mg/liter)} \\
&= \text{100 ppm of hardness}
\end{aligned}$$

Table 20-1. CONVERSION FACTORS FOR HARDNESS OF WATER[a]

Unit	ppm	Equivalent			
		Grains/ U.S. gal	Clark degrees	French degrees	German degrees
One part per million	1.0	0.058	0.07	0.10	0.56
One grain per U.S. gal	17.1	1.0	1.20	1.71	0.958
One grain per Imp. gal	14.3	0.829	1.00	1.43	0.80
One French degree	10.0	0.583	0.70	1.00	0.56
One German degree	17.9	1.044	1.24	1.78	1.00

[a] Definitions:

Parts per million = mg per liter as $CaCO_3$
Clark degree (G.B.) = 1 grain per Imperial gallon (9.98 lb)
1 grain per U.S. gal = 1 grain per 8.34 lbs
French degree = 1 part per 100,000 as $CaCO_3$
German degree = 1 part per 100,000 as CaO

Other methods of expressing the hardness of water and their equivalence in parts per million, are given in Table 20-1, and the analyses of some typical waters are given in Table 20-2.

Table 20-2. THE CHEMICAL ANALYSIS OF SOME REPRESENTATIVE NATURAL WATERS

Source	St. Lawrence River (Montreal)	Lake Ontario	Niagara River	Detroit River	Lake Superior	Red River	Regina City
pH	7.6	8.1	8.0	8.1	7.4	···	···
Dissolved O_2, ml/l.	6.5	5.4	6.0	4.9	7.5	···	···
Dissolved solids	143.0	157.8	170.4	114.6	68.0	864.0	1128.0
Ca	27.6	36.4	37.7	26.1	14.3	98.0	163.6
Mg	6.8	8.4	8.2	7.4	4.6	40.0	86.5
Fe	0.06	0.06	0.05	0.05	0.06	0.34	0.12
Na and K	6.1	9.5	4.6	2.6	2.9	134.0	···
SiO_2	9.2	2.5	7.0	5.0	8.0	14.8	21.0
$(HCO_3)'$	89.4	105.0	122.0	105.0	47.0	223.0	543.0
$(SO_4)''$	17.6	20.7	18.1	10.9	4.3	202.0	424.0
$(Cl)'$	13.1	16.5	13.5	5.3	11.8	211.5	9.0
$(NO_3)'$	0.2	1.9	0.5	1.2	0.2	0.9	0.5
Total hardness	96.9	125.4	128.0	95.6	54.7	409.0	622.3

In general, surface waters adjacent to the East and the Northwest Coasts are soft; for example, Halifax, 17 ppm; Catskill, N.Y., 16 ppm; and Vancouver, 17.4 ppm. Waters in the mid-continent region are hard. Various systems have been suggested for grading water according to its hardness. The classification given in Table 20-3 is based on that adopted by the United States Geological Survey and the Canadian Mines and Geology Branch. A fifth class has been added.

Table 20-3. WATER HARDNESS CLASSIFICATION (IN PPM): AVERAGE VALUES

Class A, soft	60	Nova Scotia, New Brunswick, New Hampshire, Massachusetts, Rhode Island, Connecticut, Virginia, North Carolina, South Carolina, Georgia, Mississippi, Alaska, British Columbia, Washington, Oregon, Delaware
Class B, medium hard	61–120	Quebec, Prince Edward Island, Vermont, New York, Pennsylvania, West Virginia, Kentucky, Tennessee, Arkansas, Louisiana, Montana, Idaho
Class C, hard	121–180	Manitoba, Ontario, Alberta, Michigan, Ohio, Minnesota, Missouri, Wisconsin, Oklahoma, Texas, Wyoming, Colorado, Utah, Nevada, California, Florida
Class D, very hard	181–350	South Dakota, North Dakota, Nebraska, Kansas, Iowa, Illinois, Indiana, Arizona, New Mexico
Class E, saline, brackish, or "bad"		Saskatchewan and some areas in Classes C or D

Methods for Determining Hardness

The hardness of water can be determined in a number of ways. Clark's method measures the volume of a standardized soap solution necessary to produce a stable froth when shaken with 50 or 100 ml of the hard water. From this the *total hardness* is calculated. The volume of soap solution necessary to produce a permanent froth with 50 or 100 ml of boiled water gives the *permanent hardness*. The "temporary" or bicarbonate hardness is obtained by subtracting the latter from the total hardness.

A more accurate method due to Hehner consists of determining the amount of alkali carbonate required to react with the Ca^{++} and Mg^{++} in a given volume of water. The reactions may be represented by the equation

$$Ca^{++} + SO_4'' + Na_2CO_3 \longrightarrow 2\,Na^+ + SO_4'' + CaCO_3\downarrow$$

$$Mg^{++} + 2\,Cl' + 2\,NaOH \longrightarrow Mg(OH)_2\downarrow + 2\,Na^+ + 2\,Cl'$$

EXAMPLE

One hundred milliliters of water is pipetted into a beaker and 50.0 ml of $N/50$ alkali carbonate added by pipette. The precipitated hardness is removed by filtration. The filtrate contains the unprecipitated ions from the water and the excess reagent. This is titrated with $N/50$ acid.

Suppose that the filtrate required 32.50 ml of $N/50$ acid in the titration (T). Hence 17.5 ml of the $N/50$ alkali carbonate must have been used in reacting with the Ca and Mg. Now 17.5 ml of $N/50$ reagent is equivalent to 17.5 ml of $N/50$ $CaCO_3$ or,

$$17.5 \text{ ml of } M/100 \text{ } CaCO_3 = \frac{17.5 \times 100}{1000 \times 100} \text{ grams} = 17.5 \text{ mg}$$

Since the sample was 100 ml and hardness is expressed as ppm, which is the same as mg/l., the hardness of this sample is

$$\frac{17.5 \times 1000}{100} = 175 \text{ ppm}$$

That is, using 100 ml of water and 50 ml of $N/50$ reagent the total hardness equals $(50 - T) \times 10$ ppm.

To determine temporary and permanent hardness, 100 ml of the water is first boiled and filtered before treatment with the standard alkaline reagent. Back titration of the filtrate from the alkali carbonate gives the permanent or noncarbonate hardness.

INDICATOR METHOD

The most-recent method makes use of titration of the water with a special reagent and an indicator which changes color when all the Ca and Mg have reacted. The method is rapid, convenient, and accurate. The reagent is known by various names: Complexione, Versene, Ethylenediamine tetra acetic acid (EDTA), or simply hardness titrating solution (BDH).

The usual procedure is to add 10 ml of a buffer solution (pH 10), three drops of the indicator (Eriochrome Black T) to a 50 ml sample of water. Titration is carried out with the standard hardness reagent (1 ml = 1 mg $CaCO_3$). The end point is a color change from wine-red to blue. The total hardness equals milliliters of reagent used times 20.

EXAMPLE

50 ml of Lake Ontario water required 6.20 ml of reagent, which is equivalent to 6.20 mg of $CaCO_3$. Therefore, 1000 ml of the water contains

$$\frac{6.20 \times 1000}{50} = 124 \text{ mg}$$

That is, the hardness is 124 ppm.

Titration kits containing buffer, indicator, and reagent can be obtained from any scientific supply house.

The chemistry of the indicator method depends on the formation of a complex, in which the Ca and Mg ions become surrounded and bound in a claw-like structure by the reagent. Reagents which form this type of compound are called chelating (claw-forming) agents. EDTA is one of these. This is not as formidable as it sounds, as will be seen below. Ethylene diamine

$$CH_2{=}CH_2 \qquad H_2NCH_2CH_2NH_2$$
Ethylene   Ethylene diamine

is simply ethylene with two added amino groups. Hence EDTA is ethylene diamine in which all four of the amino hydrogens are replaced by an acetic acid radical $-CH_2COOH$.

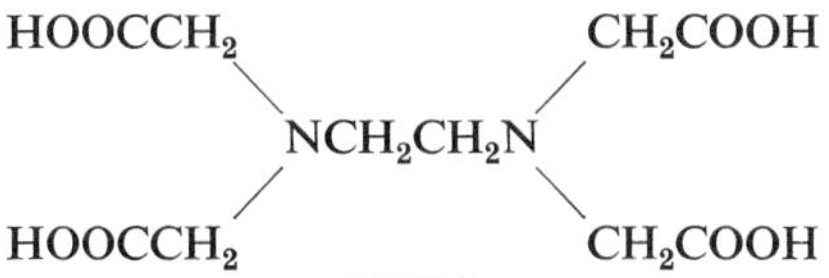

$$\begin{array}{ccc} HOOCCH_2 & & CH_2COOH \\ \diagdown & & \diagup \\ & NCH_2CH_2N & \\ \diagup & & \diagdown \\ HOOCCH_2 & & CH_2COOH \\ & EDTA & \end{array}$$

The reagent may be used as the sodium salt.

Everyone will remember that when a little ammonium hydroxide (ammonia and water) is added to a copper salt in solution, a pale blue precipitate is formed. This precipitate disappears when more ammonia is added, forming a deep blue solution. The royal blue color is due to the formation of a complex ion

$$\begin{array}{ccc} NH_3 & \cdots & NH_3 \\ & \diagdown \quad \diagup & \\ & Cu^{++} & \\ & \diagup \quad \diagdown & \\ NH_3 & \cdots & NH_3 \end{array}$$

It has been noted (see Chapter 4) that the amines behave chemically like their parent ammonia. If, then, ethylene diamine is added to the copper salt instead of ammonia, an amine group will occupy similar positions. In this case, however, two pairs of terminal amines are joined, so that the copper ion is caught in a claw-like structure.

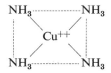

$$\begin{array}{ccc} & CH_2{-}CH_2 & \\ \diagup & & \diagdown \\ NH_2 & & NH_2 \\ & Cu^{++} & \\ NH_2 & & NH_2 \\ \diagdown & & \diagup \\ & CH_2{-}CH_2 & \end{array}$$

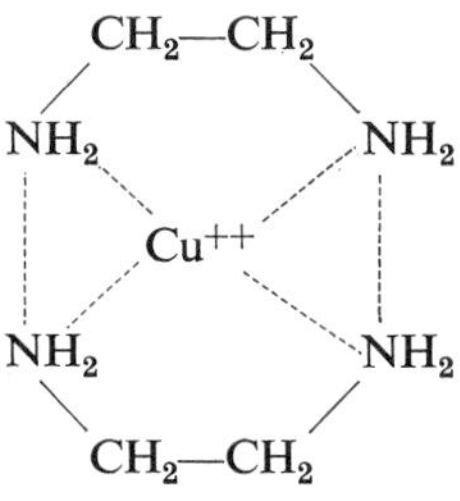

A structure that is even more claw-like is obtained with EDTA derivatives, since two of the acetate ion ends form an "internal" salt with the copper.

$$Na^+ \ O'OCCH_2 \quad CH_2CH_2 \quad CH_2COO' \ Na^+$$

$$
\begin{array}{c}
N \qquad\qquad N \\
H_2C \qquad\qquad CH_2 \\
| \qquad Cu^{++} \qquad | \\
OC \qquad\qquad CO \\
O{-} \qquad {-}O
\end{array}
$$

Calcium and magnesium are caught in the organic claws in a similar fashion. Their disappearance is signalled by the color change of the indicator.

In addition to their use in determining hardness, these chelating agents are employed in metal cleaners, rust and scale removers, and in many other applications.

Removal of Hardness in Domestic Waters

Domestic water supplies are usually softened by means of ion-exchange materials. The first substances used for this purpose were naturally occurring alumina silicates called *zeolites*. Synthetic zeolites have been used for over half a century. The reaction which takes place on the surface or within the framework of the gel may be represented by the example

$$Na_2Z + Ca^{++} + 2 \ Cl' \longrightarrow 2 \ Na^+ + 2 \ Cl' + CaZ$$

The cations causing hardness of the water may thus be removed, but the softened water contains an equivalent amount of sodium salts.

When the efficiency of the zeolite becomes low due to replacement of most of the original Na^+ by Ca^{++}, concentrated sodium chloride brine is forced through the zeolite; the softener is regenerated by the reversal of the equation above. The displaced $CaCl_2$ is flushed to the sewer. For optimum operation of the softener, regeneration should be carried out before the efficiency of the zeolite has dropped too low. Frequent regenerations prevent plugging of the internal structure with the alkali-earth elements and permit shorter contact time with the brine. The regeneration process consists of three steps: (1) backwash to clean the sand and gravel filter at the bottom of the Zeolite bed until the effluent is perfectly clear; (2) draw the brine by venturi injector from the brine tank (20 to 30 min); (3) rinse to flush out the displaced calcium, magnesium, and iron salts (35 minutes).

The cost of soft water is determined by the cost of the equipment amortized over ten or twenty years, and the cost of the salt. The latter in turn depends on the hardness of the water.

With the advent of synthetic detergents ("syndets") which, unlike soap, form *soluble* compounds with calcium and magnesium ions, the hardness of the water is not as important as it used to be in the domestic laundry. Toilet soaps are still widely used, but synthetic toilet bars are available. However, hardness in the water is the cause of scale formation on utensils, in heating systems, and car radiators so that an increasing number of households and municipalities are softening the water.

The chemistry of detergents and their action, wetting agents, penetrating oils, and waterproofing materials, will be found elsewhere.

20-4 Drinking Water Conversion from Sea Water

During World War II, emergency kits were developed which permitted the preparation of small volumes of drinkable water from sea water. The kit consisted of a briquet of a silver-zeolite, a plastic bag, and a filter. After pouring a quantity of sea water through the special zeolite, silver ions were displaced by sodium, calcium, and magnesium ions present in the sea water. The silver ions formed a precipitate with the chloride and sulfate ions. For more complete removal of the sulfate, some $Ba(OH)_2$ was later incorporated in the briquet, $BaSO_4$ being very insoluble. The precipitates and used gel were removed by filtration. Each packet produced about a pint of potable water.

In several areas, such as Kuwait, on the Persian Gulf and Aruba in the Netherlands Antilles, drinking water is obtained by the *distillation* of sea water. At Aruba a new distillation plant produces 2.7×10^6 gal/day at a cost of $1.30/1000 gal. Costs in other installations run from $3.50 to about $1.00/1000 gal. This is still undesirably high. The United States Government recommended figures are $0.38 for domestic water and $0.12/1000 gal for water of sufficient purity for irrigation.

Other methods used to purify sea water are a *compression distillation* in use at Gibraltar, and *electro-dialysis* in use at Tobruk, North Africa. Desalting of brackish waters by *ion exchange resins* is also in use. Small solar stills have been designed for emergency equipment for ships and aircraft. Larger installations are feasible for certain areas.

20-5 Conservation of Surface Water

Chemistry assists in the conservation of surface waters. Polyethylene plastic film is used to line catchment basins, preventing seepage through the soil (Fig. 20-5). Loss by evaporation may be greatly reduced by the addition of very small quantities of a waxy alcohol, cetyl alcohol, $C_{17}H_{35}OH$, related to spermaceti wax. This polar compound forms a molecular layer over the water with the hydrocarbon end uppermost and the —OH group in the

Figure 20-5 Lining a million gallon catchment basin with water-proof polythene film. [Courtesy C.I.L. and A.E.C.L.]

surface. Neither material affects the taste or other properties of the water. The prevention of evaporation of water from storage basins which often have a large area but little depth, is very important. In such cases, loss by evaporation may cause an increase in salinity or hardness of the water even when the inflow keeps the level of the reservoir constant. The accumulation of dissolved material will continue year by year, except in special areas where a volume equal to the loss by evaporation is returned as rain or snow.

Further Readings

Elwell, K. R., and Easlick, K. A., *Classification and Appraisal of Objectives to Fluoridation* (Ann Arbor, Michigan: University of Michigan, 1960).

Report of the Ontario Government Committee on Fluoridation (Toronto, 1961), with bibliography of 120 references.

Sawyer, C., *Chemistry for Sanitary Engineers* (New York: McGraw-Hill, 1961).

Taylor, E., ed., Thresh, J. C., Beale, J. F., and Suckling, E. V., *The Examination of Waters and Water Supplies* (6 ed; London: J. & C. Churchill, Ltd., 1949).

Water Analysis, Bulletin No. 11. Solvay Technical and Engineering Services (New York: 1959).

21

Industrial Water

21-1 Treatment of Water for Engineering Uses

For some engineering or industrial purposes, natural water, even sea water, is used without any treatment. In other cases the water must meet far more stringent specifications than those required for domestic water. In the manufacture of television tubes and transistors, water of extreme purity is required. The same is true for water used as a coolant in nuclear reactors or in steam generators operating above the critical temperature of water.

For many years water used in heat exchangers and in boilers has been treated or "conditioned" to prevent the formation of deposits or scale. Improper treatment of water may be disastrous, as is illustrated by Fig. 21-1. Any method of treatment which depends on the removal of the offending ions by precipitation involves the chemical principle known as the *solubility product principle*. It is derived from the mass law.

The Mass Law

It was recognized for a long time that the speed of a chemical reaction is determined by the temperature, the presence or absence of a catalyst, and the nature of the reactants. Guldberg and Waage pointed out that the velocity of a chemical reaction also depends on the product of the molar

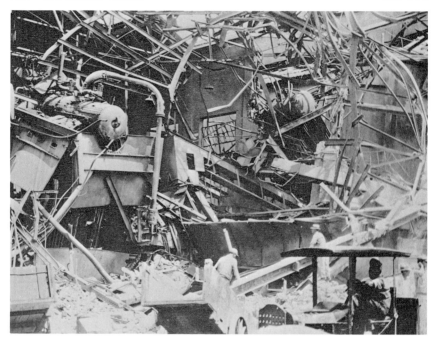

Figure 21-1 Disaster caused by improper water conditioning. While not as spectacular as this boiler explosion, improper water treatment may be just as costly over a period of years because of resulting corrosion, impaired heat transfer, lower quality of product, shut-downs, descaling, and lower efficiency of equipment. [Cf. E. P. Partridge and H. Purdy, *I.E.C.*, **30** (1939), 394, by permission.]

concentration of the reacting substances or as they stated it, "The rate is proportional to the *active masses* of the reacting substances." This has become known as the *law of mass action*, or the *mass law*. For reactants in dilute solution the "active mass" may be expressed as moles or formula-weights per liter.

For the reaction $A + B \rightarrow C + D$ the velocity of the forward reaction $V' \propto [A] \times [B]$ or $V' = k'[A] \times [B]$, where the square brackets indicate the molar concentration and k' is the proportionality constant.

If the reaction is reversible, that is, $A + B \rightleftharpoons C + D$, the velocity of the reverse reaction V'' will be proportional to the product of the concentrations of C and D in g ions/liter, that is, $V'' = k''[C] \times [D]$.

At equilibrium

$$V'' = V' \quad \text{or} \quad k''[C] \times [D] = k'[A] \times [B]$$

that is,

$$\frac{[C] \times [D]}{[A] \times [B]} = \frac{k'}{k''} = K_{eq},$$

the equilibrium constant. The solubility product is a special case of an equilibrium constant.

A salt or hydroxide in the solid state consists of a lattice of ionic groups. Crystals dissolve if the attraction between the solvent and the ions in the crystal is greater than the forces holding the ions in the lattice. If one stirs some calcium carbonate in a small volume of water, calcium ions and carbonate ions are pulled from the solid. However, the concentration of these ions does not become very large before the water becomes saturated; that is, the rate of ions rejoining the solid $CaCO_3$ becomes equal to the rate at which ions dissolve. This equilibrium can be represented

$$CaCO_3 \text{ (solid)} \rightleftharpoons Ca^{++} + CO_3^{--}$$

although this does not show the number of water molecules associated with each ion. Since this is an equilibrium we may write

$$\frac{[Ca^{++}] \times [CO_3^{--}]}{[CaCO_3]} = K$$

and because the solution is saturated, the value of the denominator ($CaCO_3$) (solid) remains constant. Hence

$$[Ca^{++}] \times [CO_3^{--}] = K \times k$$
$$= \text{the } solubility \ product \ constant, \text{ or } K_{sp}.$$

This means that the product of the concentration of the ions of a slightly soluble substance expressed as gram ions or formula weights is a constant.

In the derivation of the K_{sp} above, the presence of any dissolved salt "molecules" (ionic pairs or associated ionic pairs) has been ignored. Even if some of these were present in this dilute solution, they would be in equilibrium with single ions and therefore

$$\frac{[Ca^{++}] \times [CO_3^{--}]}{[CaCO_3] \text{ (dissolved)}} = K$$

The concentration of these dissolved ionic pairs would be very small and constant, so

$$[Ca^{++}] \times [CO_3^{--}] = K \times k' \quad \text{or} \quad [Ca^{++}] \times [CO_3^{--}] = K_{sp}$$

Again the conclusion is that the product of the formula or gram-ion concentrations is a constant.

If the ionic product $> K_{sp}$, precipitation occurs. Should the concentration of one of the ions be lowered so that the ionic product $< K_{sp'}$, the concentration of the other ion must increase. This is achieved by some of the solute going into solution.

K_{sp} IN TERMS OF SOLUBILITY

If the solubility of the slightly soluble substance is expressed in moles/liter, the K_{sp} can be readily calculated. For example, a compound AB having a solubility of S moles/liter will give S formula weights of A and S formula weights of B. The expression for the solubility product is therefore

$$[A] \times [B] = S \times S = S^2$$

The solubility of calcium carbonate at $15°$ C is 18 mg/l. This is

$$18 \times 10^{-3}/\text{mol wt}, \quad \text{moles/liter} = 18 \times 10^{-3}/100, \text{ or } 1.8 \times 10^{-4}M/\text{liter}$$

The K_{sp} of $CaCO_3$ at $15°$ is therefore

$$(1.8 \times 10^{-4})^2 = 3.2 \times 10^{-8}$$

For a precipitate having the general formula ABC, which gives equal quantities of each of its ions in solution, for example $MgNH_4PO_4$, then

$$K_{sp} = [A] \times [B] \times [C] = S^3$$

If C is replaced by another B giving the compound AB_2, the expression for the K_{sp} becomes $[A] \times [B] \times [B]$. If the solubility of the compound is S moles/liter the concentration of A will also be S. The *total* concentration of B will be $2 S$. Since the concentration of B occurs twice in the product, the K_{sp} for such a compound is $S \times 2 S \times 2 S = 4 S^3$. The chances of forming the compound AB_2 are four times greater than the chances of forming ABC, since (1) A now requires only one kind of partner and (2) there are twice as many B atoms available as in the compound ABC.

For a substance A_2B_3 the K_{sp} equals

$$[A]^2 \times [B]^3 = (2 S)^2 \times (3 S)^3 = 108 S^5$$

For compound $A_nB_mC_y$ giving n A $+ m$ B $+ y$ C, the K_{sp} is

$$(n S)^n \times (m S)^m \times (y S)^y = n^n m^m y^y (S)^{n+m+y}$$

Anything that affects the solubility, such as a change in temperature, the nature or concentration of foreign electrolytes, and the degree of hydration of the ions, will alter the numerical value of the K_{sp}. However, the solubility product remains constant if the environment is kept constant and can be used to predict the approximate concentrations required for the formation of a precipitate. It may also be used to predict the order and extent of precipitation of two slightly soluble substances by a common reagent. It enables one to predict whether scale can be removed by treatment with a given reagent.

These and other applications are illustrated in the examples and problems.

EXAMPLE 1

A natural water containing 40 ppm of Ca^{++} was treated with Na_2CO_3. If the equilibrium concentration of CO_3^- after treatment was 10^{-4} M, (1) what would be the hardness of the treated water? (2) How many pounds of soda ash would be required per 100,000 Imperial gallons (120,000 United States gallons) to reduce the hardness to this value? The K_{sp} of $CaCO_3$ for the given conditions $= 7.0 \times 10^{-9}$.

(1) Since

$$[Ca^{++}] \times [CO_3^-] = 7 \times 10^{-9}$$

$$\text{and the final } Ca^{++} = \frac{7 \times 10^{-9}}{10^{-4}} = 7 \times 10^{-5} M$$

$$= 7 \times 10^{-5} M \text{ of } CaCO_3$$

$$= 7 \times 10^{-5} \times 100 \text{ g of } CaCO_3/\text{liter}$$

$$= 7 \text{ mg/liter or ppm}$$

the hardness of the treated water is therefore 7 ppm.

(2) The original concentration of Ca^{++} equals

$$40 \text{ ppm} = 40 \text{ mg } Ca^{++}/\text{liter} = 10^{-3} M/\text{liter}$$

$$10^{-3} M \, Ca^{++}/\text{liter} = 10^{-3} M \text{ of } CaCO_3/\text{liter} = 100 \text{ ppm of hardness}$$

The final hardness is 7 ppm. The soda ash (Na_2CO_3) required is the amount equivalent to 93 ppm of hardness plus the residual carbonate in solution. This is 93×10^{-5} M/liter (or 9.3×10^{-4} M/liter) $+ 1 \times 10^{-4}$ M/liter equals

$$10.3 \times 10^{-4} M/\text{liter} = 10.3 \times 10.6 \text{ mg/liter}$$

(Since MW of Na_2CO_3 is 106) $= 109$ ppm or 109 lb/100,000 Imp. (120,000 U.S. gal)

EXAMPLE 2

What is the pH of water saturated with $Mg(OH)_2$ at 25° C if $K_{sp} = 8.9 \times 10^{-12}$?

$$[Mg^{++}] \times [OH']^2 = K_{sp} = 8.9 \times 10^{-12} = 4 S^3$$

$$S^3 = 2.23 \times 10^{-12} \quad \text{so} \quad S = 1.3 \times 10^{-4}$$

$$[OH'] = 2 S = 2.6 \times 10^{-4}$$

and

$$[H^+] = \frac{10^{-14}}{2.6 \times 10^{-4}} = 3.9 \times 10^{-11}$$

$$pH = 10.4$$

EXAMPLE 3

Lead iodide and calcium carbonate have approximately the same value for their solubility products, namely, 1×10^{-8}. What is the ratio of their solubilities and hence the ratio of Pb^{++} to Ca^{++} in saturated solutions of the salts?

The K_{sp} for PbI_2 is

$$4 S^3 = 10 \times 10^{-9}, \qquad S = 1.36 \times 10^{-3}$$

for $CaCO_3$ is

$$S^2 = 1 \times 10^{-8}, \qquad S = 1 \times 10^{-4}$$

Therefore, the solubility of PbI_2 to the solubility of $CaCO_3$ equals

$$13.6:1::Pb^{++}:Ca^{++}$$

EXAMPLE 4

Barium chloride is added to remove sulfate from a water containing $10^{-3}\,M\,SO_4^{--}$ and $10^{-4}\,M\,CO_3^{--}$. Which precipitate will form first and what will be the ratio of CO_3 to SO_4 at equilibrium? K_{sp} of $BaCO_3$ at 25° C is given as 8.1×10^{-9}; K_{sp} of $BaSO_4$ is 1.1×10^{-10}.

$$[Ba^{++}] \times [CO_3^{--}] = 8.1 \times 10^{-9}$$

$$[Ba^{++}] \times 10^{-4} = 8.1 \times 10^{-9}$$

Therefore, the $[Ba^{++}]$ required to exceed $K_{sp} = 8.1 \times 10^{-5}\,M/$liter.

The $[Ba^{++}]$ required to exceed K_{sp} for $BaSO_4$ equals

$$\frac{1.1 \times 10^{-10}}{10^{-3}}, \text{ or } 1.1 \times 10^{-7}\,M/\text{liter}$$

Thus, $BaSO_4$ will precipitate first.

The ratio $CO_3^{--}:SO_4^{--}$ equilibrium equals

$$\frac{8.1 \times 10^{-9}}{1.1 \times 10^{-10}} = 74:1$$

Additional examples are given in the chapter on antifreeze and radiator compounds.

Treatment of Water Containing Bicarbonate Hardness

Temporary or bicarbonate hardness precipitates when the water is heated. As a result, the tubes in heat exchangers may become encrusted and blocked by these deposits, and heat transfer will be cut down by the porous scale. Chemical treatment can prevent the formation of this type of scale.

PRECIPITATION BY LIME

One of the reagents commonly used to remove hardness due to calcium or magnesium bicarbonates, is slaked lime, $Ca(OH)_2$. This seems a paradox— to remove calcium ions by adding calcium ions, or as is often said (inexactly), "To add lime to remove lime." The reaction may be written

$$Ca(OH)_2 + Ca(HCO_3)_2 \longrightarrow 2\ CaCO_3\downarrow + 2\ HOH$$

When $Mg(HCO_3)_2$ is present, twice as much lime is needed to remove the hardness. The reaction does not produce $MgCO_3$, but rather $Mg(OH)_2$.

$$Ca(OH)_2 + Mg(HCO_3)_2 \longrightarrow Mg(OH)_2\downarrow + Ca(HCO_3)_2$$

That is, the hardness due to the Mg^{++} is removed, but an equivalent amount of Ca^{++} takes its place. This requires another mole of $Ca(OH)_2$ for its removal, so the final equation is

$$2\ Ca(OH)_2 + Mg(HCO_3)_2 \longrightarrow Mg(OH)_2\downarrow + CaCO_3\downarrow$$

The different behavior of $Mg(HCO_3)_2$ and $Ca(HCO_3)_2$ is explained by the values of the solubility products of $Mg(OH)_2$ and $MgCO_3$ which are 9×10^{-12} and 1×10^{-5} respectively. For $Ca(OH)_2$ and $CaCO_3$ the corresponding values are approximately 1×10^{-6} and 1.0×10^{-8} respectively.

PREVENTION OF DEPOSITS FROM BICARBONATE HARDNESS:
THE THRESHOLD TREATMENT

Instead of removing the bicarbonate hardness, as shown above, deposition of calcium carbonate can be prevented in condensers or heat exchangers by adding a substance called *hexametaphosphate* $(NaPO_3)_{6n}$. This glassy phosphate acts as a sequestering agent and as a protective colloid. Either action keeps the calcium carbonate from forming a sludge or precipitate when the concentration of Ca^{++} is less than 200 ppm and the metaphosphate is present in concentrations of 2 ppm. This treatment is sometimes referred to as "threshold treatment." It is used in feed-water make-up systems or where the water is preheated before introduction to the boiler. Higher temperatures convert metaphosphate to the orthophosphate, and the calcium comes out as the carbonate and orthophosphate which can be removed by "blow down," that is, the forced ejection at intervals of the suspension and concentrated solutions of salt and also the sludge from the lower part of the boiler.

Starch, tannin, and other colloids may be used to give an adsorbed layer around the particles of calcium carbonate as they are formed and thus prevent their growth. Such protected particles tend to remain in suspension instead of settling to form sludge or scale. Hexametaphosphate apparently exerts the same type of suspending action.

TREATMENT WITH SODIUM ALUMINATE

Sodium aluminate made by dissolving scrap aluminum or hydrated aluminum oxide in caustic soda solution will remove bicarbonate hardness along with magnesium or calcium ions present as noncarbonate hardness.

$$2\,Al + 6\,NaOH \longrightarrow 2\,Na_3AlO_3 + 3\,H_2$$

or $\qquad 2\,Al + 2\,NaOH + 2H_2O \longrightarrow 2\,NaAlO_2 + 3\,H_2$

Hydrolysis takes place producing gelatinous alumina flocks and alkali.

$$Na_3AlO_3 + 3\,HOH \rightleftharpoons Al(OH)_3 + 3\,NaOH$$

or $\qquad NaAlO_2 + 2\,HOH \rightleftharpoons Al(OH)_3 + NaOH$

The high concentration of $(OH)^-$ present causes the precipitation of $Mg(OH)_2$, and carbonate from the bicarbonate precipitates calcium hardness.

$$2(OH)^- + Ca(HCO_3)_2 \longrightarrow \underline{CaCO_3} + CO_3^{--} + 2\,HOH$$

$$2(OH)^- + MgSO_4 \longrightarrow \underline{Mg(OH)_2} + SO_4^{--}$$

$$(CO_3)^{--} + CaSO_4 \longrightarrow \underline{CaCO_3} + SO_4^{--}$$

The sodium carbonate precipitates any remaining calcium ions as calcium carbonate

$$Na_2CO_3 + CaCl_2 \longrightarrow \underline{CaCO_3} + 2\,NaCl$$

The precipitating aluminum hydroxide is an excellent clarifying agent.

Treatment of Water Containing "Permanent" or Noncarbonate Hardness

The reagents most commonly used for the removal of noncarbonate hardness are sodium carbonate, disodium hydrogen phosphate, and trisodium phosphate. Other phosphates, such as sodium pyrophosphate, are converted to the orthophosphate Na_2HPO_4 by hydrolysis

$$Na_4P_4O_7 + H_2O \longrightarrow 2\,Na_2HPO_4$$

While precipitation reactions between electrolytes take place almost instantaneously in concentrated solutions, the rate of reaction in cold dilute solutions may be very slow and a precipitate may not appear for some time. Most natural waters are dilute solutions. The formation of such a precipitate depends on the formation and *growth* of crystal nuclei of the "insoluble" substance. Thus when the solubility product of any calcium carbonate is exceeded and aggregates of calcium and carbonate ions are formed, it is assumed that each positive ion joins the crystal, accompanied by or closely followed by the negative ion. In cold dilute solutions the slow migration results in the production of very small particles of colloidal dimensions. These may carry some unpaired ions adsorbed on the surface. These extra ions impart a charge to the particle and help to prevent precipitation by agglomeration. The charge on the fine particle depends on the sign of the excess ion. Thus one can have a negative or positive sol of silver iodide x AgI, y I′ or n AgI, x Ag$^+$ depending on whether I′ or Ag$^+$ is present in more than equivalent amounts.

Furthermore, the solubility of a very fine particle is greater than that of the larger particles, so that in such a suspension, the concentration of dissolved solute would for the time be greater than the true equilibrium value, and the solution would be supersaturated. A precipitate would eventually form because the smallest particles tend to dissolve, and the excess would then crystallize on the larger ones. This process can be hastened by warming the mixture. As the particles grow larger, they settle out.

The conditions described above often apply in the treatment of natural waters. The supersaturation and delayed precipitation result in "after deposits" in feed lines. For clarification by settling, large sedimentation basins are required to afford time for sedimentation. Sand filters used to remove the ultrafine particles become cemented, forming an impervious mass.

Equipment to prevent "after precipitation." These troubles can be overcome by modern conditioning equipment based on the physico-chemical principle that when a supersaturated solution comes into contact with bulk solute, equilibrium is established, and the solute held in metastable condition separates out. This principle can be demonstrated by adding a crystal of sodium thiosulphate to a supersaturated solution of the substance.

In equipment such as the *Accelator*, illustrated in Fig. 21-2, raw water and chemicals enter a primary mixing and reaction compartment formed by the conical part of an inverted funnel. Further agitation and mixing takes place as the solution flows upward through the wide stem of the funnel into the secondary reaction zone. The liquid and suspended particles are forced through the space between the skirting of the inverted cylinder, forming the secondary reaction vessel and the sloping sides of the primary reactor. Part of the mixture flows upward towards the outlet and part is recycled through the primary reaction zone.

The rate of sedimentation of a particle depends on its size, its density, and the viscosity of the medium. The rate can be calculated from Stokes' equation

$$V = \frac{2r^2(d_p - d_m)gf}{9n}$$

where r is the radius of the particle, d_p the density, d_m the density of the medium, n the viscosity in cgs units (poise), g is the gravitational constant, and f is a shape factor, since the equation was derived for spheres. Heavy particles having a rate of sedimentation greater than the linear upward flow of the medium, will sink and collect in the sump, but the fine particles having a sedimentation rate less than the upward flow of the water will move upward. There will be one size of particle which has a velocity of settling just equal to the rate of the moving water. Such particles will form a stationary layer which acts as a barrier or floating filter. The finer particles are entrapped and form aggregates with the suspended particles in the stationary layer. The agglomerates, being larger than the critical size, are removed by sedimentation.

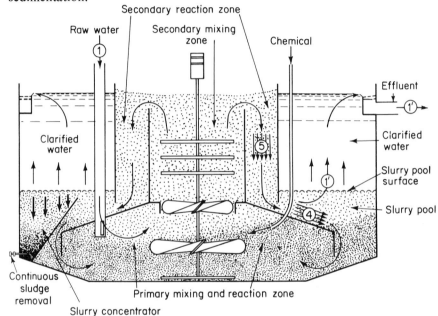

Figure 21-2 Functional section drawing of typical Accelator for softening.

The position and thickness of the surface slurry layer can be controlled by the rate of flow of the raw water and effluent, the rate of circulation, and by a *skimming* process whereby an area of the filter layer is removed by the draining of sludge from the sump. The intimate contact between the solution and the very large surface of the solid reaction products brings about rapid attainment of equilibrium with consequent prevention of any supersaturation. Such equipment eliminates the necessity for large sedimentation basins and filters, to take care of "after precipitation."

Boiler Scale: Formation, Prevention, and Removal

Boiler scale is the name applied to bonded deposits which form on the walls or heating surface of the boiler. Calcium carbonate scale is derived chiefly from untreated water containing bicarbonate hardness. It tends to form near the injector where it first meets the hot water in the boiler. The carbon dioxide released in the decomposition of the bicarbonate is carried into the steam lines, and the reaction

$$Ca^{++} + 2\,HCO_3^- \longrightarrow CaCO_3 + HOH + CO_2$$

proceeds with the removal of the carbonate ion by the precipitation of $CaCO_3$. This tends to form a sludge which can be removed by regular blow down. It may also form a porous, relatively soft scale, sometimes cemented by other substances present in the boiler water.

Carbonate scale is often the cause of failure of domestic water heaters where the electric heater is placed in an external circulatory loop outside the hot water tank. The deposited calcium carbonate acts as a heat insulator. A layer only $\frac{1}{16}$ in. in thickness will cut down the efficiency 12 to 15 per cent. The deposited scale also reduces the flow of water around the heater. The insulating layer may become so thick and the heat transfer so poor that the heater burns out.

The solubility curves for most salts indicate a rapid increase in solubility with rising temperature. Unfortunately the reverse is true for the compounds formed in water conditioning. The solubilities of $Mg(OH)_2$, $CaSO_4$, $Ca(OH)_2$, and $Ca_2(OH)_2SO_4$ all decrease with increasing temperature. For example the solubility of the hemihydrate from gypsum is about 1650 ppm at $100°\,C$. It decreases to 150 ppm at $200°\,C$, corresponding to a steam pressure of only 250 psi. At the higher temperatures encountered in high-pressure boilers, the solubility of the anhydrous $CaSO_4$ falls to a few parts per million. Substances which have this negative temperature coefficient tend to precipitate on the hottest parts of the boiler, that is, on the heating or "steaming" surfaces.

MECHANISM OF CALCIUM SULFATE SCALE FORMATION

When a bubble of steam forms on the heating surface, any salts which were held in solution by the water precipitate in the form of a ring-shaped deposit. If the water in the boiler is already saturated, this deposit will not be redissolved when the bubble leaves the surface. The adhering particles of calcium sulfate or other scale-forming compounds will be hotter than the water and therefore less soluble than before. As the evolution of steam proceeds, the successive rings build up a network over the surface and form nuclei for the crystallization of solute from the heated film of solution adjacent to the hot metal. A hard insulating scale is built up by the continued formation of rings and crystals.

The higher the rate of steam production and/or boiler pressure, the greater is the probability of scale formation. A 1200 hp boiler may evaporate 100,000 gallons of water per day. For a steam pressure of 600 psi, the water temperature is 254° C (489° F); at pressures of 1000 psi, the corresponding steam temperature is 286° C (546° F). Under these conditions the concentration of both scale-forming and soluble salts should be kept low. In very high pressure steam generators such as the Eddystone Station of Philadelphia Electric Co., which operates at 5000 psi and a steam temperature of 1200° F, pure water free from any solute must be used.

The most serious aspect of boiler scale is its poor heat conductance. For the scale discussed above, the conductivity is about 3 one-hundredths that of steel. In a boiler operating with a net input of 100,000 Btu/ft²/hr, the temperature of a clean ¼ in. steel plate on the heated side will be approximately the same as on the water side (4° F higher). If the inner surface is covered with a layer of scale, the temperature difference between the heated surface and the water is greatly increased. As scale builds up, higher and higher temperatures are required to produce the necessary energy transfer. The temperature of the steel may reach the softening point, and being subjected to boiler pressure, bulges will be formed on the tubes with thinning of the metal. This will lead to blow-outs or boiler failure.

If 900° F is taken as the softening point of mild steel or the maximum safe temperature, a boiler operating at 600 psi (steam 489° F) would have a safety margin of 410° F. With an input of 100,000 Btu/ft²/hr a layer of $CaSO_4$ scale 0.076 in. thick will cause the plate or tube temperature to exceed 900°. At 1000 psi the safety margin of 354° will be exceeded in the presence of 0.061 in. of hard scale.

The heat conductance of a silicate scale is so low that boiler failure would be caused by a film less than 0.002 in. thick. The special problem of silicate scale will be discussed later.

Iron oxide tends to bind solids to hot spots. It may form a dense insulating layer of Fe_3O_4 which may also cause boiler failure.

When condensed steam forms the major portion of "make-up" water, significant amounts of cylinder oil may be introduced into the boiler. The internal surfaces become coated with a thin film of oil. Since the thermal conductance of oil is very low, about one five-hundredths that of steel, this film is dangerous. Oil present in boiler water may also be a contributing factor to foaming and priming (see page 364).

SCALE PREVENTION

The formation of boiler scale may be prevented by pretreatment to remove hardness or by the addition of reagents directly to the boiler. The reagents are sodium carbonate or phosphates. The orthophosphates are preferred because of the hydrolysis of sodium carbonate at the temperatures found in boilers operating above 500 psi.

$$Na_2CO_3 + HOH \longrightarrow 2\,NaOH + CO_2\uparrow$$

The high alkalinity produced by the loss of carbon dioxide to the steam lines is the cause of intergranular corrosion called *caustic embrittlement*. The attack is worse on the portions of the metal under strain, such as around rivet holes or where plates overlap. It is thought that corrosion proceeds along the grain boundaries because of the reaction with iron nitrides. It has been shown that at high concentrations of alkali ($OH' \neq 0.1\ N$), ferrites may be formed.

Caustic embrittlement does not occur when phosphates are used, because the alkalinity can be regulated by the proportions of the various phosphates in the conditioner. Sodium dihydrogen phosphate, NaH_2PO_4, is acid; disodium hydrogen phosphate Na_2HPO_4, is slightly alkaline; and trisodium phosphate is much more alkaline. Hydrolysis of these phosphates produces various proportions of H_2PO_4', HPO_4'' and PO_4''' depending on the pH. Thus for pH 10 the proportion of the ions above present are 0.2:98.8:01.0 respectively. At pH 11 the figures are 0.0, 90.1, and 9.1. Calcium phosphate, $Ca_3(PO_4)_2$, has a solubility product so small (approximately 10^{-25}) that at pH 10.5 the mixed phosphate reagents will provide adequate concentration of PO_4^{---} ion to prevent the formation of $CaSO_4$ scale. Calcium phosphate sludge is removed by blow down. It does not normally form a scale unless left in the boiler for a relatively long time. Basic calcium phosphate, referred to as the "hydroxyapatite" type scale, is sometimes formed.

If magnesium hardness is present, the pH is adjusted so that magnesium hydroxide rather than magnesium phosphate is precipitated, since the latter readily forms scale.

The use of protective colloids to prevent the deposition of suspended particles of scale-forming materials has been referred to earlier in the chapter. Water conditioning mixtures for ships of the navy and for locomotives in the days of steam, always contained some such colloidal components. One of the old ferries operating on Lake Ontario used potatoes in the condensed steam tank as its sole "water conditioner."

Oil scale or film can be prevented by treating the condensed steam with a coagulant such as $Al(OH)_3$ or by mechanical means. Some oil is adsorbed by sludges high in iron oxide and silica, but low in MgO; it is thus removed during disposal of the sludge.

REMOVAL OF SCALE

Carbonate and phosphate scale can be removed by treatment with acid. An inhibitor is added to the acid to prevent or minimize any attack on the exposed metal (see page 233). Other calcium or magnesium scale, with the exception of silicates, yield to treatment with complexing agents. Hexametaphosphate has been found to reduce the layer of scale in feed lines.

The most successful method of treatment is by a mixture of EDTA (page 348) and its tetrasodium salt. The proportions are 14 parts of the acid to 100 parts of the salt. The concentration of the mixture in the boiler is kept at a minimum of 2.0 per cent for a period of 12 to 24 hours. The pH is maintained between 7.5 and 8.0. In this pH range any phosphates tend to be converted to soluble acid phosphates. The calcium and magnesium ions from any scale are grabbed by the "chelating" or complexing agent, and the scale dissolves to keep up the concentration of the Ca^{++} and Mg^{++} ions according to the solubility product principle. During treatment the boiler temperature should be kept below 400° F.

While iron oxide is not chelated at a pH of 7.5 to 8.0, any rust in the mixed scale will be dislodged during treatment and flushed out with the other suspended and dissolved materials during blow down.

Foaming and Priming

Foam consists of bubbles of gas surrounded by a film. They are sometimes produced by design for specific engineering uses such as in the collection or separation of minerals, the flotation of coal "fines" or in extinguishing of an oil fire. Solidified foams are our best insulating materials. In most instances however, for example, in antifreeze, lubricating oil, paints, aeration tanks (page 394), and certainly in the steam boiler, stable foams can be a source of trouble. Conditions favorable to their formation should be avoided.

Foams may be formed when there is a difference in concentration of solute or suspended matter between the film and bulk of the liquid. Substances which increase the viscosity of the film favor foam production. The bubbles may also be protected by finely divided solids forming a "shell" around each of them. Any material which lowers the surface tension of the water will collect at the interface and thus increase the tendency of the liquid to foam.

In steam raising, the bubbles of steam may be stabilized because of the accumulation of soluble salts in the water. Clay or organic matter in natural water, oil or grease in condensed make-up water, and finely divided particles of sludge may be responsible for foaming.

If the steam bubble does not collapse on reaching the surface of the water, the foam may be drawn into the preheater or steam lines. The liquid film will carry with it the salts, solids or other stabilizing materials which will be deposited on the cylinder walls, turbine blades, or in the steam lines. If the stability of the bubble is such that it breaks near the steam outlet, small droplets of liquid from the collapsing film may be swept along into the lines giving "wet" steam.

During high steam demand and rapid steaming, stable bubbles may increase the volume in the boiler so that a relatively large amount of water is pushed into the steam lines. This is usually referred to as "priming," although the terms foaming and priming are now being used synonymously.

Foaming and priming can best be prevented by removal of the foaming and stabilizing agents from the water. Clay and other suspended solids as well as droplets of grease and oil can be removed by treatment of the feed water with clarifying agents such as hydrous silicic acid and aluminum hydroxide. The concentration of salts and sludge in the boiler can be controlled by repeated or continuous blow down. Spiral or "cyclone baffles" or a series of baffle plates near the steam outlets help to prevent water droplets from entering the steam lines. Antifoaming agents can also be used.

Since foaming and/or priming may be caused by different factors, an antifoaming agent which is effective in one case may be ineffective in another. The formation of a concentrated layer of solute or a protective film of solid particles around the steam bubble depends on the surface tension and interfacial tensions. A chemical which suitably alters the surface tension will be an antifoam reagent. Research has shown that small, stable bubbles are produced on a heating surface in the presence of a foaming agent. The addition of a small concentration of polyamide antifoamer alters the surface tension and large unstable bubbles are produced at the same heat input.

When the foam owes its stability to a viscous film, a reagent which lowers the film viscosity will render it unstable. Antifoaming agents may act by reducing the charge on the protective film or its components. A foam may be destroyed by the addition of another good foaming agent. This paradox is explained by the difference in charge on the colloidal particles of the two foams. The antagonistic effect of two wetting agents of different types is pictured in Fig. 21-3. The figure shows the foam obtained with (A) a solution of an anionic detergent (Aerosol OT), and (B), a cationic detergent (Ethyl Cetab). On mixing the solutions no foam is obtained (C).

Corrosive Agents in Natural Water

Untreated water may contain substances which cause boiler corrosion. Water dissolves air, and, although the atmosphere is 21 per cent oxygen by volume, the dissolved "air" is 35 to 38 per cent oxygen. Fresh rain water contains about 7 cc of oxygen per liter. Carbon dioxide, which may be present in varying amounts in feed water, causes corrosion in steam lines. The concentration of oxygen in boiler water should be below 0.05 ppm for boilers operating at low pressures and less than 0.01 ppm for pressures above 500 psi.

The solubility of these gases varies inversely as the temperature. Everyone has observed the bubbles which collect on the inside surface of a glass of cold water as its temperature rises to the temperature of the room. At 90° C the solubility of oxygen in water is only one-ninth the solubility at 0° C. The solubility of a gas is proportional to the pressure (Henrys' law). "Deaerators" make use of these two principles. The water may be flashed into steam at reduced pressure, or water in the form of a spray may be heated and scrubbed by a counterjet of steam. The steam and liberated gases are pumped off at low pressure through a condensing system which removes the condensed steam. The gases are not redissolved at the reduced pressure.

Pitting by dissolved oxygen can be prevented by the use of reducing agents. For small installations, the feed water may be passed through a tank containing iron turnings. Much better results are obtained by the addition of reducing chemicals such as sodium sulfite (Na_2SO_3) or hydrazine (NH_2NH_2) to the boiler water.

(A)   (B)   (C)

Figure 21-3 The antagonistic action of two different types of foaming agents: (A) a cationic type—Aerosol OT; (B) an anionic reagent—Ethyl Cetab; and (C) a mixture of the two.

Sodium sulfite is suitable for boilers operating below 650 psi. The sulfite reacts with the oxygen in the water to form sulfate. Above 650 psi, some SO_2 is formed by decomposition of the sulfite.

Hydrazine, which is usually added as a 40 per cent solution, has the advantage that the products of oxidation are an inert gas and water:

$$NH_2NH_2 + O_2 \longrightarrow N_2 + 2 HOH$$

The molecular weight of hydrazine and oxygen are the same (32), so that complete elimination of 1 ppm of oxygen would require only 1 ppm of the reagent, one-eighth of the necessary concentration of sodium sulfite. At temperatures in excess of 350° C, hydrazine decomposes into nitrogen and ammonia:

$$3 \text{ NH}_2\text{NH}_2 \longrightarrow 4 \text{ NH}_3 + \text{N}_2$$

Residual hydrazine can be measured easily by a colorimeter. Care should be taken in handling hydrazine, as the amine may cause dermatitis.

Magnesium and calcium chlorides are also corrosive agents. Magnesium chloride hydrolyzes completely at 200° C (392° F).

$$\text{MgCl}_2 + 2 \text{ HOH} \longrightarrow \underline{\text{Mg(OH)}_2} + 2 \text{ HCl}$$

Calcium chloride also hydrolyzes, but to a lesser extent. At 600° C, hydrolysis is about 25 per cent. Silicic acid catalyzes the reaction so that in water containing silica, appreciable quantities of HCl may be formed at lower temperatures.

Natural waters may be acid due to the wet oxidation of sulfide minerals (see the previous chapter). Acid waters may be neutralized by alkali, by sodium carbonate, or by phosphate.

Treatment with Ion Exchange Resins

Water for use in steam plants operating near or above the critical temperature, or for use as a coolant in nuclear power reactors, must have a degree of purity far in excess of that necessary for most other uses. A satisfactory purification may be achieved by distillation or more cheaply and efficiently by the use of ion exchange resins.

Some twenty years ago, chemists synthesized organic resins which had the ability to exchange hydrogen ions for any cation present in the water. Similar anion exchangers were also prepared. These trade hydroxyl ions for other negative ions or acid radicals. If a solution of a salt is passed through a bed of *cation* exchanger and then through a bed of *anion* exchange resin, both of the salt ions will be removed and the effluent will be pure water.

$$\text{Rz—H} + \text{Na}^+\text{Cl}^- \longrightarrow \text{RzNa} + \text{H}^+\text{Cl}^-$$

$$\text{H}^+\text{Cl}^- + \text{Rz—OH} \longrightarrow \text{Rz—Cl} + \text{HOH}$$

Water treated in this manner is often referred to as "deionized" water. The degree of purity or freedom from ionic contaminants can be determined by the conductance (1/resistance) of the water. An instrument for the purpose is shown in Fig. 21-4. In this model, the scale divisions indicate the conductance as equivalent ppm of sodium chloride with supplementary readings in ohms.

Distilled water has a resistance of 500,000 ohms/cm. Water of this quality is not sufficiently pure for some engineering purposes, such as in the manufacture of transistors, TV tubes, and other electronic equipment. Table 21-1

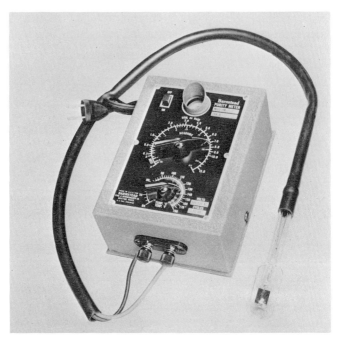

Figure 21-4 A convenient way to test the removal of ionic or conduction impurities. On immersing the dip cell in the sample, the dial indicates the conductance in terms of ppm of NaCl or as micromhos. [Courtesy Barnstead Still & Sterilizer Co.]

(based on water obtained from various sources) indicates that much higher purity can be obtained by the use of ion exchange resins.

There are several types of ion exchange resins. The earliest organic cation exchanger was made by treating bituminous coal with fuming sulfuric

Table 21-1[a].

Method of purification	Resistance, in ohms/cm
Water after a single distillation in glass	500,000
Water in equilibrium with CO_2 in air	700,000
Water after three distillations in glass	1,000,000
Water after three distillations in quartz	2,000,000
Water treated by Monobed ion exchange (strong acid-strong base system)	18,000,000
Water redistilled 28 times in quartz (Kohlrausch 1894)	23,000,000
Theoretical maximum	26,000,000

[a] Adapted from *Deionization by Amberlite Monobed Ion Exchange Resins* (Philadelphia: Rohm & Hass Co.).

acid. Sulfonic groups ($—SO_3H$) were thus introduced into the framework of the coal (Fig. 21-5). The resulting resin in the form of black angular granules can exchange the hydrogen ion of the acid for positive ions such as Ca^{++}, Mg^{++}, Fe^{++}, Mn^{++}. Regeneration of the acid form of the resin is effected by treatment with 2 per cent sulfuric acid.

Synthetic resins formed by copolymerization of styrene and divinyl benzene also provide a gel framework to which exchange groups may be affixed

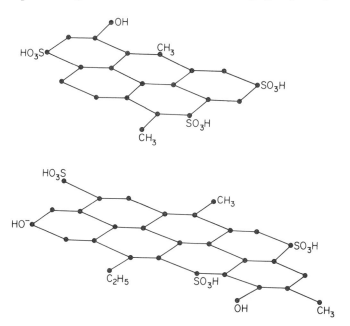

Figure 21-5 Hypothetical structure of sulfonated coal.

chemically. The porosity and density of the resins can be regulated by the degree of cross-linking of the styrene chains and the divinyl benzene. Increased porosity gives a higher rate of exchange and a greater capacity to the gel. The resin structure must, however, have good mechanical stability and be resistant to the solvent action of water, acids, and alkali. These properties are enhanced by cross-linkages. For cation exchange, the acid form of the resin, containing $—SO_3H$ or $—COOH$ groups is used.

Another type of cation exchanger is prepared by the condensation of phenol and formaldehyde (see Bakelite, page 266) with subsequent sulfonation. Both styrene and phenolic-type cation resins are sold in the form of tiny spheres. Cation exchange not only takes place on the surface but also within the pores of the gel. The capacity of the resin is the amount of cation removed per unit volume or mass of the resin before regeneration is necessary. If much calcium ion has been absorbed, hydrochloric acid gives more rapid and more efficient regeneration than sulfuric acid, since calcium sulfate is only slightly soluble. *Dilute* sulfuric acid ($<$ 2 per cent) may be employed, but the rejuvenation of the resin will be much slower.

Anion exchange resins contain strongly basic or weakly basic groups. Strongly basic resins contain quaternary ammonium ions and may be represented by the formula $(Rz)_3NHOH$ or $(Rz)_4NOH$ where Rz is the resin attached to the exchange group. Such basic resins can remove even weak acids from the water. They require a strong alkali (NaOH) for regeneration.

Exchange:

$$(Rz)_4NOH + H_2SiO_3 \longrightarrow (Rz)_4NHSiO_3 + HOH$$

Regeneration:

$$(Rz)_4NHSiO_3 + 2\,NaOH \longrightarrow Na_2SiO_3 + (Rz)_4NOH + HOH$$

Weak anion exchangers resemble polyamines. Amine groups are attached to a styrene, bakelite, or other three-dimensional polymer. The weakly basic resins will remove strong acids such as HCl, HNO_3, or H_2SO_4 but not weak acids from solution. Weak bases, such as soda ash, Na_2CO_3, or ammonia, will regenerate the resin.

Exchange:

$$RzNH_2 + HCl \longrightarrow RzNH_2HCl$$

or

$$RzNH_3OH + HCl \longrightarrow RzNH_3Cl + HOH$$

Removal of Carbonic Acid

When a water containing bicarbonates is passed through an acid cation exchanger, the hydrogen ions liberated by the resin during exchange for some other positive ion will unite with the bicarbonate ions to form carbonic acid. This breaks up into water and carbon dioxide, and the CO_2 is removed from the water in a degasifier (page 365).

$$2\,RzSO_3H + Ca(HCO_3)_2 \longrightarrow (RzSO_3)_2Ca + 2\,HOH + 2\,CO_2\uparrow$$

This is a cheaper method of removing bicarbonate than treatment with a strong anionic resin.

Deionization by Mixed Bed Exchangers

Deionization of water to a conductivity of 10^{-7} mho can be obtained by a single treatment by a mixed bed of strong cation and strong anion resins. A typical monobed arrangement is illustrated in Fig. 21-6.

Raw water enters the tank at *A* and flows through the uniformly mixed resins. The deionized water is delivered at *B*. When regeneration is necessary, rapid reverse flow of water agitates the resin bed so that the lighter anion beads and the heavier cation resin form two layers. Caustic soda is then pumped into *A*. This regenerates the anionic resins, and, as the caustic or sodium salts flow through the cation layer in the bottom of the tank, this resin is converted to the sodium form. The displaced salts are flushed by rinsing water to the drain.

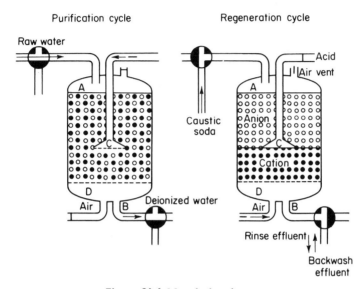

Figure 21-6 Monobed exchanger.

Acid is then introduced through the pipe, *C*, changing the cation resin to the acid form. The acid is followed by a rinse with pure water. A strong air blast forced through the resins from the bottom of the container (*D*) causes violent agitation of the small resin spheres and completely mixes them. The monobed is now ready for reuse.

For some purposes the cheaper weak basic exchange resin may be substituted for the quaternary ammonium type component.

Silica Scale Prevention

Silicate scale was first noticed in 1933 in boilers operating at higher pressures. It forms a very hard porcelain-like coating on the heating surfaces and on turbine blades. Its thermal conductivity is much less than that of other types of scale. For boilers operating at 600 psi, tube failure may occur if the thickness reaches 0.0015 in. Very low concentrations of silica must be assured (<0.02 ppm) for water used in boilers generating steam above 1000 psi.

Silicate scale arises from the presence of silica, colloidal clay, and other siliceous minerals in natural waters. It may also be due to the formation of sodium silicate by the action of alkaline treated water on sand filters or reaction with the silicates of calcium, magnesium, or aluminum precipitated during pretreatment. Since sodium silicate is soluble, it enters the boiler in the feed water. Analysis of siliceous scale shows the presence of calcium and magnesium silicates. Some silicate scale approximates the composition of the mineral *analcite*, $Na_2SiO_3 \cdot Al_2(SiO_3)_3 \cdot 2 H_2O$. Various methods for removing silica and silicates are in use.

1. *Removal by ferric sulfate and alkali.* Ferric sulfate is added to the water and the *p*H adjusted to 9.0-10 with alkali. The gelatinous ferric hydroxide adsorbs and reacts with collodial silicate, reducing the silica concentration to 2 to 3 ppm.

2. *Magnesia process.* Magnesium hydroxide, formed from a magnesium salt or magnesia (MgO), is the reagent in this process for removing silica. The reaction may be represented by the equation

$$Mg(OH)_2 + H_2SiO_3 \longrightarrow \underline{MgSiO_3} + 2 HOH$$

Most effective removal is obtained by heating the water during treatment in an "accelator" type of mixing equipment (page 360). The silicate content (as silica) can be reduced to approximately 1 ppm. Calcination of dolomite, $CaCO_3 \cdot MgCO_3$, gives both lime and magnesia. The lime serves to remove temporary hardness and the magnesia, the silicates.

3. *Fluosilicate anion exchange.* This method depends on the conversion of the silica to a fluosilicon complex ion $(SiF_6)''$ which can be removed by an anion exchange resin. Sodium fluoride is added to the raw water and the solution passed through an acid form of a cationic exchanger. The sodium and other positive ions are replaced by hydrogen. The effluent contains HF and the other acids corresponding to the kind of salts in the natural water. The hydrofluoric acid reacts with the silica or silicic acid to produce the soluble complex fluosilicate ion.

$$6 HF + H_2SiO_3 \longrightarrow 3 H_2O + H_2(SiF_6)$$

The acid solution is then put through an anion resin which removes the acid radicals in exchange for hydroxyl ions, reducing the silica content to less than one part per million.

4. *Direct removal by strongly basic resins.* Hydrous silicic acid and silicates can be removed by either of the procedures illustrated in Figs. 21-6 and 21-7. Water from either of the chemical treatments (1) and (2) above, may have the residual silica reduced still further by the strong anionic resin.

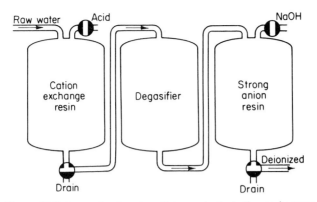

Figure 21-7 System for de-mineralizing water including carbonates and silicates.

WATER FOR NUCLEAR REACTORS

Deionized water is used as a coolant and heat transfer agent in certain types of nuclear reactors (page 148). The water is kept free of impurities by continuous recycling of a portion of the water through a cationic or mixed resin bed. This is necessary because even pure water is corrosive at temperatures of 400° F or higher and at high pressures. Metallic ions from the pipes absorb neutrons and become radioactive. Some of the water itself may be decomposed by absorbed radiation. Nitrogen dissolved in the water may be converted to nitric acid. The pH can be maintained at a suitable value by having some lithium or potassium as exchangeable cations in the resin.

Intrinsic or "Polished" Water

Water used in the manufacture of transistors, TV tubes, and some other types of electronic equipment must be very carefully purified—to a conductance of 0.2×10^{-6} to 0.05×10^{-6} mho. Water of such high purity has been called "intrinsic" or "polished" water. Intrinsic water is prepared in two stages. The initial treatment through columns of cation and anionic resins produces water having a resistance of 400,000 to 500,000 ohms, equivalent to distilled water. It is delivered by stainless steel pipes to another purification unit consisting of a monobed of mixed exchange resins at the work site. The intrinsic water is prepared as needed and is used immediately. Contamination of the cleaned surfaces of the transistors is prevented by rigid air-conditioning of the enclosed dust-free work space because the smallest trace of foreign matter can spoil the performance of transistors. Final rinsing with high purity water has been found to increase quality and decrease the number of rejects.

Water from Brine by Electrodialysis

Polymeric materials in the form of fabrics or membranes can be converted into ion exchangers by the incorporation of appropriate chemical groups. One of the important uses for such membranes is in the preparation of drinkable water from saline sources or industrial water from sea water, by electrodialysis. A simple electrodialysis cell is shown in Fig. 21-8.

The salt water enters the center portion of the cell which is separated from the electrode compartments by ion exchange membranes. The cationic exchange membrane is adjacent to the cathode and the anionic exchange resin near the anode. When a potential is applied, the positive ions move

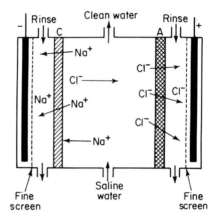

Figure 21-8 Single electrodialysis cell.

toward the cathode. They come in contact with the cationic membrane and are passed through it from one exchange group to another in a manner somewhat similar to the diffusion of a gas through a metal. The anions are pulled toward the cathode and are passed through the anion exchange membrane. Random thermal collisions of oppositely charged ions do not result in any appreciable diffusion through the membranes. The membranes remain practically unaltered and thus do not have to be regenerated.

Rinse water flows through each of the electrode compartments to remove the products of electrolysis, alkali [NaOH, $Ca(OH)_2$] at the cathode and chlorine and acids at the anode.

In industrial installations the electrodes are separated from the first membrane by a fine screen to keep solid particles from contaminating the electrodes. Many cells formed by alternating cationic and anionic membranes are interposed between the electrodes. These dialysis cells increase the efficiency of the electrodialysis.

One such commercial installation converts 3,000,000 gal/day of brackish water to an acceptable water for $0.35 per 1000 gal. Other plants for desalting sea water by electrodialysis are in operation in South Africa, Tobruk, North Africa, and California.

In 1961, 1100 communities in the United States restricted the use of water during the summer dry spells. The city of Los Angeles now brings water 625 miles by pipe line. For this reason, industry will shortly be forced not only to greater reuse of water, but also to more extensive use of electrodialysis and other methods to obtain industrial water from the sea.

Further Readings

Hefferich, F. G., *Ion Exchange* (New York: McGraw-Hill, 1962).

Kunin, R., and Meyers, R. J., *Ion Exchange Resins* (New York: Wiley, 1951).

Lewin, S., *The Solubility Product Principle* (London: Pitman, 1960).

Nordell, E., *Water Treatment* (2 ed; New York: Reinhold, 1961).

Partridge, E. B., "Your Most Important Raw Material," Edgar Marburg Lecture Reprint, *A.S.T.M.*, Philadelphia (1957).

Solner, K., "Membranes of High Ionic Selectivity," *Jour. Electrochem. Soc.*, **97**, 139 (1950).

Symposium on Saline Water Conversion, National Academy of Sciences (1957); and Publication 568, National Research Council, Washington, D.C. (1958).

Water Analysis, Bulletin No. 11. Solvay Technical and Engineering Services (4 ed; New York, 1956).

Wilson, J. R., *Demineralization by Electrodialysis* (London: Butterworth, 1960).

Review Questions

1. What impurities are found in rain water?

2. How does the composition of air differ from the mixture of gases in uncontaminated rain water?

3. Distinguish between total hardness and permanent hardness; colloidal impurities and suspended matter; ppm, and lb/100,000 gal.

4. Indicate the effect of surface water on each of the following: gypsum, limestone, marble, calcareous sandstone, a sulfide ore, and a feldspar.

5. List three methods of conditioning natural water for domestic use.

6. Write the equation for the reaction that occurs when alum is added to a water containing temporary hardness.

7. Does aluminum sulfate soften hard water?

8. What difference would there be in the result if sodium aluminate were used instead?

9. How does $Al(OH)_3$ clarify a turbid water?

10. Show by an equation how lime added to a natural water may remove "lime" from the water.

11. For what other purpose is slaked lime added to water?

12. How can bacterial contamination of water be overcome?

13. What causes taste in water?

14. How can this be overcome?

15. What is dichloroamine?

16. Show how it reacts with water.

17. What is the lime-soda process?

18. Where would magnesium hardness precipitate in the boiler?

19. At what part of the boiler is temporary hardness precipitated?

20. What is the chemical principle on which the accelator process is based?

21. What are some advantages of the accelator process?

22. Show by an equation how $BaCO_3$ removes dissolved solids from hard water.

23. How does the result differ when Na_2CO_3 is used?

24. What is a "syndet"?

25. The K_{sp} of CaF_2 is 3.4×10^{-11}; at. wt of F = 19 and Ca = 40. What is the concentration of fluoride ion in a *saturated* solution of the mineral in ppm?

26. If water containing calcium hardness was concentrated in a boiling kettle so that Ca = 160 mg/liter, what would be the maximum concentration of F' in ppm that could remain dissolved in the water?

27. What is the difference between a zeolite and a cation resin?

28. Indicate how "deionized" water could be prepared from a water containing $CaSO_4$ in solution.

29. Define and explain "threshold treatment" and "caustic embrittlement."

30. How does the solubility of $CaSO_4$, $Ca(OH)_2$, $CaCO_3$, and $Mg(OH)_2$ change with steam pressure?

31. How is silica scale prevented?

32. How can the oxygen content of a water be reduced?

33. Why is this desirable?

34. A hard water contains 160 mg of $Ca(HCO_3)_2$, 131 mg of $CaSO_4$, and 97 mg of $MgCl_2$/liter. What is the total hardness of the water? Given at. wt Ca $= 40$, Mg $= 24.3$, S $= 32$, Cl $= 35.5$.

35. The solubility product of $CaCO_3 = 1 \times 10^{-8}$, $Mg(OH)_2 = 1.2 \times 10^{-11}$, $CaSO_4 = 6.1 \times 10^{-5}$. Calculate the solubility for each in mg/liter.

36. Will calcium sulfate scale be removed by oxalic acid? (K_{sp} of $Ca(C_2O_4)$ is 1.3×10^{-9}.)

37. Give the K_{sp} of $Ca_3(PO_4)_2$ and $Al(OH)_3$ in terms of the solubility of the compounds.

38. What will be the concentration of Ca^{++} obtained when a $CaSO_4$ scale is treated by a solution of soda ash so that $CO_3 = 0.1\ M$?

39. Why does the United States Navy package water conditioner contain starch?

40. What is sodium hexametaphosphate?

41. What pH would start precipitation of $Al(OH)_3$ from a solution containing 1 lb $Al_2(SO_4)_3$/100,000 gal; at. wt Al $= 27$, $K_{sp} = 5 \times 10^{-33}$?

42. One hundred milliliters of water was treated with 50 ml of $\frac{N}{50}$ Na_2CO_3. The filtrate required 22.50 cc of $\frac{N}{50}$ HCl for titration. What was the total hardness of the sample in ppm?

43. A similar sample was boiled and filtered before the addition of Na_2CO_3. The titration of the filtrate this time was 35.75. What was the temporary and permanent hardness of the sample?

44. Name two other methods of determining hardness of water.

22

Sewage Disposal

In a scattered or primitive community the disposal of sewage is largely determined by the personal convenience of the individual. In urban areas however, even in ancient times, sewage disposal has been a problem in which the engineer was involved. In Egypt and Babylon canals were built to carry the sewage to the nearest river. Roman engineers constructed large conduits 14 × 17 feet in cross-section to carry the sewage and effluents from the private and public baths to the river Tiber.

The towns and cities of Europe were served by open drains until the nineteenth century. In Paris in the fourteenth century an ordinance required the housewife or chambermaid to call "Prenez garde! De l'eau!" three times before throwing fluid wastes to the street. It wasn't until the early 1800s—four hundred years later—that the great system of sewers made famous in French literature were constructed. Unfortunately they emptied into the river Seine often at the very place where the Parisians took their drinking water. Open sewage drains ran along the streets of London until little more than a century ago, dumping the filth into the Thames from which most of the city got its water supply. It is no wonder that from mediaeval times Europe suffered successive epidemics which decimated the population, although it must be remembered that the relation between bacteria and disease was unknown until the middle of the nineteenth century when the work of the French chemist Pasteur (1822–1895) not only proved the transmission of disease by germs, but also laid the foundation of immunology and antisepsis. In 1854 it

378

was proved that the source of a cholera epidemic in London was contaminated water from a single pump in Broad St. In 1858 a Sewage Commission in Great Britain reported that "the increasing pollution of rivers is an evil of national importance which urgently demands remedial measures . . . ." Ten years later it was shown that sewage was rendered innocuous by penetration into sandy soil. This lead to the development of filter beds of broken rock, coal, clinkers, coke, or other material. Filtration was preceded by removal of coarse particles in a settling tank. Such a system was first used in 1893 at Salsford, England, and it is the basis of many partial treatment plants in use today.

22-1 The Chemical Nature of Sewage

Sewage as it arrives at the treatment plant is 99.9 per cent water. It is a dilute suspension and solution of organic wastes, food particles, nitrogenous materials, fats, soaps, carbohydrates, detergents, cellulose fibers, salts, chiefly sodium chloride, but also sodium and ammonium sulfates and phosphates, and a great variety of bacteria. In addition to these components derived from domestic wastes, the average city sewage receives effluents from school, hospital, and university laboratories, from garages, dairies, and various industrial plants. Clay, sand, paper, metal foil, sticks, and other debris from surface waters are present unless separate storm sewers have been installed. Since most communities have combined sewers, the concentration or "strength" of the sewage will vary with the weather. Comparisons of data are usually made on Dry Weather Flow (DWF).

The screened sewage is subjected to certain tests, which are repeated and amplified in testing the final effluent. The minimal data to determine the strength of the sewage and to follow the purification are total solids, settleable solids, suspended solids, biochemical oxygen demand, and chemical oxygen demand. The fat and oil content, color, total and amino nitrogen, and pH are also of value. Supplementary tests including bacterial analysis are done on the effluent and processed sludge.

Total Solids

"Total solids" represents the dissolved and suspended solids in the sewage. The amount is expressed in parts per million or milligrams per liter, and is determined by evaporating a known volume and weighing the residue dried at 105° C.

Settleable Solids

The determination of the amount of settleable solids indicates the quantity of sludge that may be obtained in the primary settling tanks. It also gives a rough estimate of the strength of the sewage and the efficiency of the sedimentation units. The test is carried out by allowing a one liter sample to settle for one hour at 20° C in a tapered vessel called an Imhoff cone. The glass cone, 15 in. high, with a conical angle of 15°, is graduated in milliliters. The settleable solids are reported as milliliters per liter.

Suspended Solids

Suspended solids are determined by filtering a measured volume through a Gooch crucible previously ignited to constant weight. The increase in dry weight per volume is reported as parts per million or milligrams per liter. The percentage of *volatile solids* may be calculated from the loss on ignition at 600° C. Volatile solids may also be determined as a percentage of the total solids by ignition of the residue obtained on evaporation of a measured volume in a porcelain dish.

The composition and strength of sewage varies from city to city and from hour to hour. In the United States and Canada, sewage treatment plants handle 100 to 200 gal/person/day. This is more than double the volume per capita in Great Britain, and consequently the value for suspended solids is higher in Britain than here. The average American figure for suspended solids is 90 g per capita per day (0.20 lb), and for total solids, 250 g per capita per day. The increased use of garbage grinding or disposal units is expected to increase the quantity of suspended solids and total solids from 60 to 80 per cent in domestic sewage.

Dissolved Oxygen

The concentration of dissolved oxygen is used to indicate the freshness of the sewage and thus whether chlorination will be required to prevent odors from unwanted anaerobic decomposition during pretreatment. Dissolved oxygen determinations are required for the calculation of the BOD (see below). Fish and other aquatic organisms depend on the oxygen dissolved in the water to maintain life. If the dissolved oxygen is depleted, the fish and green plants die and the stream becomes septic. DO determinations of the receiving water are therefore also required.

Oxygen from the air dissolves in water to give concentrations from 14.5 mg/l. at 0° C to 8.8 at 20° C (68° F). The solubility decreases with increasing temperature. It varies directly with atmospheric pressure. At 4° C (39.2° F), the temperature of maximum density, the concentration is 12.7 mg/liter when the atmospheric pressure is 760 mm. The concentration of oxygen in sea water is less than in fresh water.

The essence of the analytical method for determining dissolved oxygen, is the alkaline oxidation of manganous ions or the precipitated manganous hydroxide, to hydrated MnO_2 by the DO. Iodide ions in the reagent (NaOH + KI) are not oxidized under these conditions.

$$Mn^{++} + 2\,(OH)' \longrightarrow Mn(OH)_2$$
$$\text{white}$$

$$2\,Mn(OH)_2 + O_2 \longrightarrow 2\,MnO_2 + 2\,H_2O$$

or $\quad 2\,Mn^{++} + 4\,(OH)' + O_2 + x\,H_2O \longrightarrow 2\,MnO_2 y\,H_2O$
$$\text{brown}$$

After thorough mixing followed by settling, the suspension is acidified with sulfuric acid. Oxidation of the iodide now occurs.

$$MnO_2 + 2\,I^- + 4\,H^+ \longrightarrow Mn^{++} + I_2 + 2\,H_2O$$

The concentration of free iodine is equivalent to the DO in the sample. The free iodine is titrated with standard thiosulfate, using starch as indicator.

Refinements in the method to eliminate interference by certain reducing substances are given in "Standard Methods."[1]

Biochemical Oxygen Demand (BOD)

Two samples of sewage having the same total or settleable solids may have very different effects on the receiving stream. The BOD represents the amount of oxygen consumed by the biological agents in oxidizing and stabilizing the organic matter in a measured sample, when kept at 20° C for 5 days.

Several dilutions of the sewage or trade waste are made with distilled water to which a small amount of "seeding" material (a mixed group of organisms in sewage) and small amounts of salts required by the organisms have been added. For raw sewage the dilutions should give a concentration from 1 to 5 per cent. The dissolved oxygen content of the diluted and stoppered sample is determined at the start; a second bottle of the sample is tested after 5 days. A blank is also run on the diluting water. The corrected decrease in oxygen concentration of the stoppered samples represents an equivalent amount of organic matter oxidized. The BOD is equal to the O_2 used times the dilution. For example, 3.0 ml of sewage was diluted to 300 ml. The initial concentration of dissolved oxygen was 8.8 mg/liter, and the final (5 day) concentration was 6.0 ml. The BOD was therefore $2.8 \times \frac{300}{3} = 280$ mg/liter.

According to American standards, an average sewage has a BOD of 100 to 150 mg/liter. A sewage having a BOD of 350 or greater would be listed as "strong."

$$\text{BOD} \times \text{U.S. gal/cap/day} \times 3.785 \times 10^{-3} = \text{gm/cap/day.}$$

1 *Standard Methods for Examination of Water, Sewage, and Industrial Wastes*, 10th ed. (New York: American Public Health Association, 1955).

According to British standards, a BOD if <210 would be considered as weak, of 350 would be average, and if >600, strong.

The BOD value is very sensitive to temperature changes. It is influenced by any material poisonous to bacterial organisms. Such materials may be present in trade wastes. With proper controls the BOD values check within 5 per cent. It is of more significance and utility in following sewage treatment than the total or settleable solids.

CHEMICAL OXYGEN DEMAND (COD)

The BOD (5 day) value indicates the rate and degree of oxidation of organic sewage by the biological agents in the receiving stream or lake. An estimate of the total oxidizable substances present, and hence the "strength" of the sewage, cán be obtained much more quickly by the use of chemical oxidizing agents. This is particularly suitable for certain types of industrial wastes. For many years potassium permanganate was used. Moore and others found that more consistent results and better oxidation were obtained with dichromate in the presence of silver sulfate as a catalyst. The reagent is added in excess and the unused dichromate in the measured sample is titrated with a standard reducing agent such as a ferrous salt. The amount of dichromate used gives by calculation the equivalent oxygen consumed. When dichromate is reduced

$$Cr_2O_7^{--} + 14\,H^+ + \xrightarrow{6\,e} 2\,Cr^{+++} + 7\,H_2O$$

That is, each dichromate ion is equivalent to three oxygen atoms in oxidizing power (six electrons). The oxidation of sugars and carbohydrates, cellulose, fats, organic acids, and hydrocarbons gives carbon dioxide and water. The equation for the destruction of the simple sugar glucose is

$$C_6H_{12}O_6 + 4\,Cr_2O_7^{--} + 32\,H^+ \longrightarrow 6\,CO_2 + 8\,Cr^{+++} + 22\,H_2O$$

That is, 1 mole or 180 g of glucose reacts with 4 moles of dichromate which equals 4×6 equivalents or 24×8 g of oxygen $= 192$ g of oxygen. A solution containing 180 ppm of glucose would therefore have a COD of 192 mg/l.

In determining the COD, the dichromate solution is usually made $N/4$ (that is, $M/24$ since each dichromate $= $ six equivalent weights). A liter of $N/4$ reagent is therefore equivalent to

$$\tfrac{8}{4}\,g \quad \text{or} \quad \frac{3 \times 16}{24}\,g = 2\text{ g O}_2/\text{liter}$$

Each milliliter is then equal to 2 ppm or 2 mg of oxygen.

For a solution containing 180 ppm of glucose/liter, a 100 ml sample would require dichromate equivalent to 19.2 mg of oxygen or 9.6 ml of the standard reagent. Thus if 10.0 ml of reagent were added to the sample, the back titration with standard $N/4$ reducer would be 0.4 ml.

EXAMPLE

Fifty milliliters of $N/4$ dichromate was added to a 100 ml sample of a distillery waste. The back titration with $N/4$ ferrous ammonium sulfate was 4.90 ml. What was the COD of the waste?

$$\text{Volume of standard used} = 50.0 - 4.9 = 45.1 \text{ ml}$$
$$1 \text{ ml reagent} = 2 \text{ mg oxygen}$$

so
$$\text{COD} = 45.1 \times 2 \times 10 = 902 \text{ mg/liter}$$

Relation between Biochemical and Chemical Oxygen Demand

Unfortunately, the BOD and COD do not measure the same things. The five day BOD represents about 80 per cent of the carbonaceous material capable of digestion. It does not indicate the oxygen absorbed later to convert nitrogenous materials to nitrates. The strong chemical oxidizing agent reacts with substances such as cellulose which is not destroyed by short time bacterial action. COD values are thus higher than the BOD. However, for sewage in which the proportion of biologically sensitive, to more stable reducing substances is moderately constant, COD data can be used to indicate approximate BOD values. Moore and Ruchhoft found that when gross particles such as cellulose fibers were removed from domestic sewage by filtration through cotton cloth, the ratio of COD to BOD for eight out of nine samples was 0.99 ± 0.05. This does not hold for industrial wastes, but where the nature of the waste remains the same, correlation factors between the two determinations may be established. This permits much more rapid detection and control of changing sewage strength or plant efficiency.

Grease

Sewage *grease* consists of fats, waxes, vegetable and mineral oil, and fatty acids from soaps. In amounts over 100 ppm, grease may cause trouble in the treatment of the sewage. Grease components tend to collect in the froth formed during aeration and to stabilize it. The presence of excess grease in sludge may prevent its sale as fertilizer. A low grease content is an important criterion of a satisfactory effluent.

The grease is extracted from an acidified and evaporated sample using a mixture of volatile hydrocarbons called "petroleum ether." From the weight of residual extract after evaporation of the solvent and the size of the sample, the grease content is calculated in ppm.

pH, Total Acidity or Alkalinity

Measurement of the pH serves to indicate the presence of acid or alkaline industrial waste. Normal domestic sewage has a pH of 7.2 to 7.4. The enzymes which cause the decomposition of the sewage in the treatment plant are affected by the pH of the medium. Chemical coagulation is also dependent on pH. Total acidity or alkalinity is determined by titration, the pH usually with a glass electrode-calomel instrument (pH meter).

Chlorine Demand

In periods of warm dry weather, the dissolved oxygen in sewage is usually low. If sewage flow is slow, wastes in the sewage system may become septic and "smelly." Such a sewage should be chlorinated. *Chlorine demand* is the amount of chlorine or its equivalent in chloramines or hypochlorite required to give a residual of 2 mg/liter after 15 min. Chlorine destroys hydrogen sulfide and other malodorous volatiles by oxidation;

$$H_2S + 4 H_2O + 4 Cl_2 \longrightarrow H_2SO_4 + 8 HCl$$

The bacterial concentration is also greatly reduced by the chlorination. Overchlorination should be avoided as it may interfere with subsequent sewage treatment.

22-2 Direct Disposal

Direct disposal of untreated sewage and industrial waste by discharge into the sea, lakes, or rivers is still practiced in many areas. It is the cheapest method. Untreated and inadequately treated sewage have converted some of our rivers and streams to nothing more than open sewers. Even large bodies of water such as the Great Lakes periodically develop pockets of pollution near the cities. Shell fish beds near the coast become contaminated and no longer serve as a source of food.

Direct disposal of screened material is allowable if certain conditions are fulfilled. The ratio of oxygen content of the receiving water to the oxygen demand of the added sewage must be >1. Rapid dispersion and a dilution of 500-fold or better are necessary to prevent localized deposits which would be oxidized slowly or become septic.

The resultant BOD can be calculated from the ratio $(S - WD)/(D - 1)$, where S and W are the BOD values of the sewage and water respectively, and D is the dilution factor.

The health of the stream depends on the rate of renewal of the dissolved oxygen. Aeration is hastened by waterfalls, rapids, and wind-driven waves. Green water plants produce oxygen during photosynthesis, assisting in the maintenance of oxygen balance.

Land disposal of screened sewage was first used in the United Kingdom a century ago. Intermittent saturation of the soil produced a harmless effluent.

In summer an acre of sandy loam can handle 10,000 to 20,000 gal/day. Such disposal of domestic sewage is not practiced to any degree in North America. Certain industrial wastes, for example, dairy and cannery wastes, can be dealt with satisfactorily by spray or shallow ditch irrigation of a porous soil.

Regulations by different levels of government and the sheer necessity for conserving water resources have forced many municipalities and industries to adopt treatment procedures for water reuse. There is still a long way to go, however, before the gross pollution of natural waters can be eliminated. According to a 1958 United States Public Health Report, less than half the population were served by sewage treatment plants. Urban areas are growing rapidly, and, as a result, treatment plants are overloaded. Because of this, during a period of heavy rain, for example, as much as 50 per cent of the sewage delivered by a combined sewage system may have to be dumped directly into the receiving stream as the total flow exceeds the capacity of the plant. It will take a lot of money—and time—to solve the problem of water pollution because the only answer is adequate treatment of all sewage and industrial wastes.

22-3 Sewage Treatment

The particular procedures and types of equipment adopted in a treatment plant depend on the economy of the area, the nature of the sewage, the presence or absence of industrial wastes, the size of the community, the type of sewerage system (separate or combined with storm sewers), and the degree of purification required.

The treatment may make use of some or all of the following:

Prechlorination	Chemical precipitation
Screening	Trickling filters
Disintegration or shredding of screenings	Activated sludge process
	Secondary sedimentation
Removal of grit	Sludge digestion
Grease removal by skimming or flotation	Secondary filtration
	Chlorination of final effluent
Flocculation	Sludge elutriation
Primary sedimentation	Residual sludge disposal

Classification of Sewage Plants

Sewage plants are classified according to the extent of the treatment given. A *primary* or *partial* treatment plant only removes 60 per cent of the settleable solids and 35 per cent of the BOD by primary sedimentation and primary filtration. Secondary treatment includes biological processes such as the activated sludge treatment, with supplementary removal of solids by

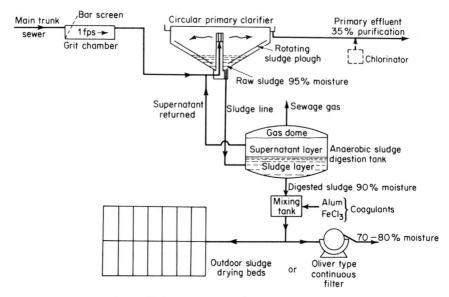

Figure 22-1 Sewage disposal—primary treatment.

secondary sedimentation and/or filtration. A *complete* treatment plant, using both primary and secondary processes, may remove 90 per cent of suspended solids and 90 to 95 per cent of the BOD. The bacterial count is also reduced 95 per cent, or if chlorine is applied to the final effluent, 98 to 99 per cent. Figure 22-1 illustrates the steps in a typical partial treatment plant. Secondary treatment is shown in Fig. 22-2a and b. Various procedures are followed in different localities. Some of these are indicated in Fig. 22-3.

Screening

Screens are used to remove large solid materials which would interfere with the operation of the plant. Several types of screens are in use that usually have mechanical cleaning devices such as brushes, blades, or rakes to remove screenings. Screen openings are generally 1 in. in width. A bar type screen with a rotating cleaner rake is shown in Fig. 22-4.

Screenings contain sticks, paper, and putrescible solids. These may be burned, buried, or disintegrated mechanically and added to the influent sewage.

Removal of Grit or Detrius

Grit or *detrius* consists principally of silt, sand, and fine gravel. The chief source of grit is storm water from street drains which empty into combined

Secondary treatment—trickling filter

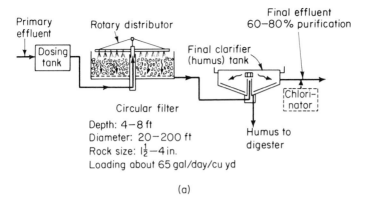

(a)

Secondary treatment—activated sludge

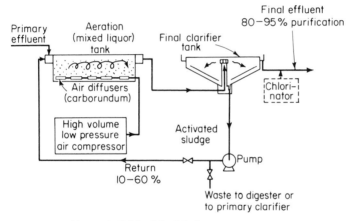

(b)

Figure 22-2

sewage systems. The term grit also includes relatively inert food refuse such as coffee grounds, broken egg shells, seeds, fruit pits, and so on.

The removal of detrius material depends on its high specific gravity and consequent high rate of settling. The velocity of sedimentation of spherical particles is given by the Stokes' equation,

$$V = \frac{2}{9} \frac{r^2}{\eta} (d_p - d_m) g$$

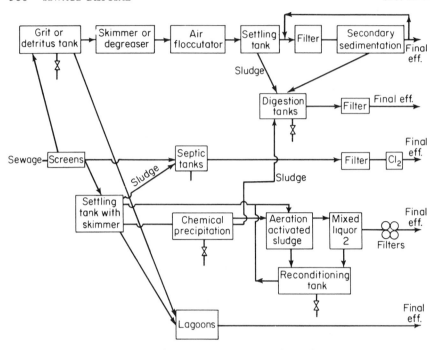

Figure 22-3 Methods of sewage disposal.

Figure 22-4 Bar screen with cleaning rake. [Courtesy Dorr-Oliver Inc.]

where V is the velocity of sedimentation in cm/sec r is the radius of the particle, d_p and d_m are the densities of the particle and medium respectively, g is the gravitational constant, and η is the viscosity in poise. For other than spherical or regular particles a "shape factor" is applied.

Grains of sand 1 mm in diameter settle from 5 to 300 times faster than sludge particles of the same size. Fine clay is not precipitated. Most grit (80 per cent) has diameters above 0.2 mm.

Detrius tanks are designed so that linear velocities of flow and hence

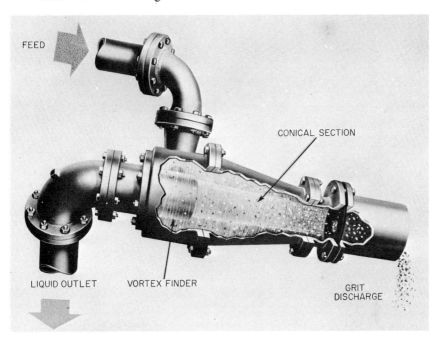

Figure 22-5 Grit separator. [Courtesy Dorr-Oliver Inc.]

retention time are kept constant. Too long a retention time would permit the settling of sludge, too short a period would result in the introduction of abrasive material into the disposal equipment. Some organic matter is brought down with the grit, and thus separation is improved by giving a swirling motion to the entering suspension by a tangential air stream or by a conical bottom on the grit tank. Centrifugal separation obtained by the device illustrated in Fig. 22-5, washes and separates grit particles >0.1 mm in diameter.

Skimming

Grease and some solids of sp gr < 1 form a scum on the surface of the sewage in the primary tank. This scum may be removed by skimming.

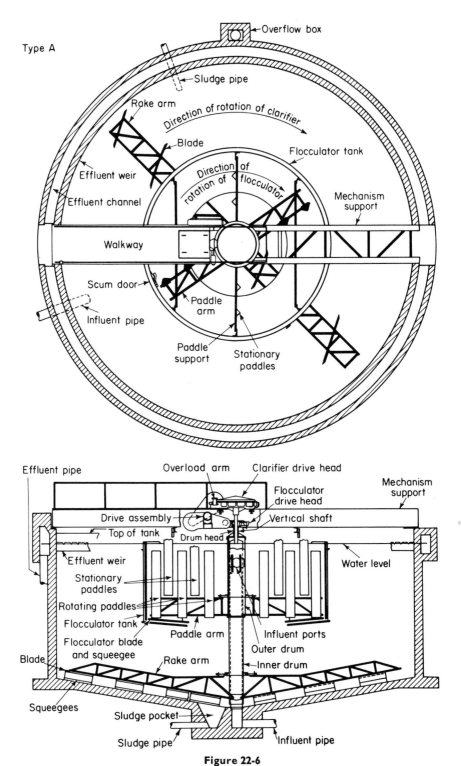

Figure 22-6

390

Skimmer blades with neoprene wipers force the scum into a disposal trough. Preaeration of the effluent from the detrius tank furthers the removal of grease, since it collects at the surface of the air bubbles. Detergents present in the sewage or added flotation agents may be used to "float" finely divided substances which would require a long settling time or even chemical treatment. This application of *flotation* has been most successful with certain industrial wastes.

Flocculation

Agitation of the sewage by air or mechanically by paddles, causes some of the very small suspended particles to agglomerate. The larger flocks will then settle as sludge. The diagram (Fig. 22-6) shows a combined flocculator and primary sedimentation tank.

Primary Sedimentation

In many plants the screened sewage flows directly to the primary settling tank or clarifier. There are various forms of primary tanks. A diagram of a circular tank with central flow is given in Fig. 22-6. Rectangular tanks with a sump and scrapers are also in common use (Fig. 22-7). Detention time is usually 2 to 3 hr. depending on whether the plant gives partial or complete treatment. About 40 per cent of organic matter and BOD is removed in primary sedimentation. The exact figure depends on the loading (gal/day/ft^2), flow rates, temperature, and the nature of the sewage.

The primary sludge is pumped to anaerobic digestion tanks (page 396). Some installations have combined sedimentation and digestion units such as the Imhoff tank (Fig. 22-8). These combined units are most frequently found in plants serving communities of 5000 or less.

Chemical Precipitation

Chemical coagulation and precipitation of sewage is similar in principle to the chemical clarification of water (page 357). Lime, alum, and ferrous and ferric salts precipitate negatively charged colloids by virtue of the trivalent and divalent cations. Lime increases the pH, and aluminum and iron salts form hydrous oxides which settle in large flocks, entrapping and adsorbing organic matter. The gelatinous "hydroxides" also act as coagulants, being themselves positively charged. Lime and ferrous sulfate are the cheapest of the precipitants. $FeSO_4 \cdot 7 H_2O$ is sometimes referred to by its old name "copperas," confusing to some since it contains no copper. Chlorinated copperas,

$$Fe{=}SO_4^{\nearrow Cl}$$

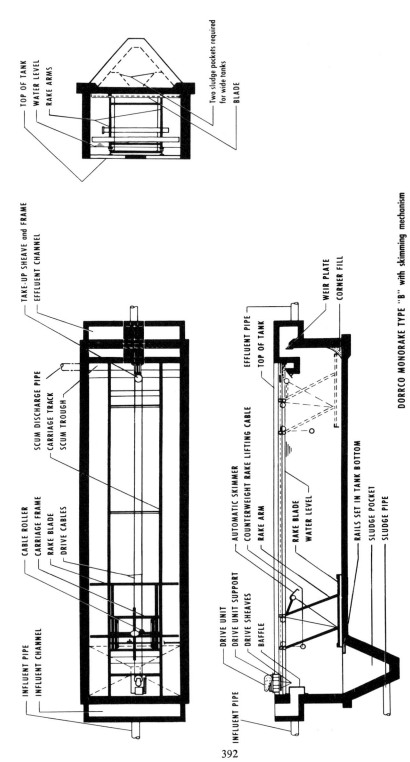

TOP OF TANK
WATER LEVEL
RAKE ARMS
Two sludge pockets required for wide tanks
BLADE

TAKE-UP SHEAVE and FRAME
EFFLUENT CHANNEL

SCUM DISCHARGE PIPE
CARRIAGE TRACK
SCUM TROUGH

CABLE ROLLER
CARRIAGE FRAME
RAKE BLADE
DRIVE CABLES

INFLUENT PIPE
INFLUENT CHANNEL

AUTOMATIC SKIMMER
COUNTERWEIGHT RAKE LIFTING CABLE
RAKE ARM

RAKE BLADE
WATER LEVEL

EFFLUENT PIPE
TOP OF TANK

WEIR PLATE
CORNER FILL

RAILS SET IN TANK BOTTOM
SLUDGE POCKET
SLUDGE PIPE

DRIVE UNIT
DRIVE UNIT SUPPORT
DRIVE SHEAVES
BAFFLE

INFLUENT PIPE

DORRCO MONORAKE TYPE "B" with skimming mechanism

Figure 22-7 Rectangular sedimentation tank.

392

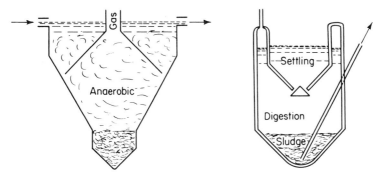

Figure 22-8 Imhoff tanks.

is cheaper than ferric chloride, $FeCl_3$. It can be prepared *in situ* from the hydrated ferrous sulfate by chlorinating the solution.

$$2\ FeSO_4 + Cl_2 \longrightarrow 2\ Fe^{+++} + 2\ Cl^- + 2\ SO_4^{--}$$

This is an effective reagent. In concentrations of between 40 and 120 ppm it is reported to remove 70 to 80 per cent of the BOD.

Ferrous salts, for example, $FeSO_4 \cdot 7\ H_2O$ react with bicarbonate or hydroxyl ion to give the corresponding ferric compound by the action of dissolved oxygen. For example,

$$FeSO_4 + 2\ (OH)^- \longrightarrow Fe(OH)_2 + SO_4^{--}$$

$$4\ Fe(OH)_2 + O_2 + 2\ H_2O \longrightarrow 4\ Fe(OH)_3 \quad \text{or} \quad 2\ Fe_2O_3\ x\ H_2O$$

Aluminum salts will hydrolyze at pH values greater than 5, producing flocculent aluminum hydroxide or hydrous oxide.

$$Al_2(SO_4)_3 + 6\ HOH \longrightarrow 2\ Al(OH)_3 + 6\ H^+ + 3\ SO_4^{--}$$

or $\quad Al_2(SO_4)_3 + 6\ (HCO_3)^- \longrightarrow 2\ Al(OH)_3 + 6\ CO_2 + 6\ H^+ + 3\ SO_4^{--}$

The chief virtue of chemical precipitation is its ability to remove colloidal material. It is an aid to other steps in the treatment and is used as a supplemental treatment when extra loads are imposed on the sewage plant. It is also of value in removing certain deleterious trade wastes. Since the resulting chemical sludge is more bulky than normal primary sludge, it presents a disposal problem.

Activated Sludge

It was shown back in 1877 that the purification of sewage by soil disposal was due primarily to the action of aerobic bacteria. About half a century ago experiments by Ardern and Lockett at the University of Manchester demonstrated that aeration of sewage promoted the growth of the organisms. The sludge produced during the oxidation process was loaded with thriving, active, aerobic bacteria. When some of this active sludge is used to "seed" or inoculate the primary effluent, its purification in the aeration tank proceeds rapidly. The bacteria and other organisms derive their food from the materials in the "mixed liquor," using oxygen in their metabolic processes. Oxidizable sewage components are thus converted to the cells of the organisms. Aggregates of these biological agents and undigested material form the active sludge.

Air is introduced into the aeration tanks in the form of streams of fine bubbles from pierced pipes or ceramic diffusers, or it may be beaten into the mixed liquor by rotating vanes or blades. If porous diffusers are used, the air from the compressors must be free from dust. Air from the blowers is cleaned by the methods discussed in the chapter on aerosols.

The effluent from the mixed liquor contains more solids than the original sewage. It flows to a clarifier or secondary sedimentation tank from which a portion of the active sludge may be recycled by air lift or pumps. In some plants the sludge is given a separate aeration to assure its aerobic activity before being added as inoculant.

A few years ago the process was carried on until nitrogenous substances were oxidized to nitrates. The BOD was reduced 90 to 95 per cent. Present practice tends toward a shorter aeration period, producing little or no nitrification. The faster but more economical process does not give as complete purification. Final effluents may be chlorinated.

Activated sludge contains 98.5 to 99.8 per cent water. Excess sludge is usually combined with primary sludge (8 to 12 per cent solids) for anaerobic digestion.

Aerobic filtration

When sewage effluent is sprayed on open ventilated filters, the filter media, broken rock, slag, or coke become coated with a gelatinous film of aerobic organisms akin to the activated sludge of aeration tanks. This biological material, called *zooglea*, thrives on the nutriment provided by the trickling effluent in the aerobic environment on the ventilated filter bed. Such filters do not give as great a reduction in BOD as the activated sludge process. Removal of 77 to 86 per cent of 240 mg/liter of BOD effluent is reported. Trickling filters are used for secondary treatment. They are also found in partial treatment plants where 20 to 30 mg/liter of BOD may be acceptable.

The operation of a high-rate filter is apparent from the diagram in Fig. 22-9. Sewage effluent flows to a vertical pipe in the center of the circular filter and is distributed by a sprinkler head rotated by the sewage flow or by motor. Ventilation is provided by perforated channels. The filtrate flows to a collection trough. High-rate filters treat 200 to 1000 gal/ft^2/day. Filter beds are

3 to 6 ft in depth. Organic loading ranges from 23 to 300 lb/1000ft³ of filter media per day.

Low-rate filters give a higher percentage of removal of BOD. The bed is usually 6 to 8 ft in depth. Filtration rates are 25 to 100 gal/ft²/day with BOD loads of 5 to 25 lb/1000ft³/day. Efficiency varies with temperature.

As the zooglea grows and dies, fragments of the film break off and are carried through the filter to "humus" settling tanks. With high-rate filters,

Figure 22-9 Diagram of a circular trickling filter. [Courtesy Dorr-Oliver Inc.]

secondary sedimentation may be followed by recycling the effluent to the first or second filter, while the humus sludge is piped to the primary sedimentation tank. In periods of minimum flow, recycling serves to keep the biofilm in good condition.

Trickling filters soon attract flies, worms, larvae, and insects which feed on and control the growth of the algae, fungi, and other organisms. Filter flies may become a nuisance. Chlorination is used to control them and also to prevent slimes which tend to clog the filter. DDT is used around the treatment plant.

Sludge Digestion

Sludge is the watery residue from the various sedimentation units. Primary sludge contains most of the original settleable solids. It is grey in color, has an offensive odor, and is difficult to dehydrate. Chemically precipitated sludge is bulkier and less odorous, and activated sludge has an earthy smell when fresh. It contains more nitrogen and phosphorus than primary sludge. Humus is greyish brown and consists of biological debris, unconsumed coagulum from the filters, and the remains of filter worms, and larvae. The water content of the different types of sludge varies from 99.5 to 88 per cent. Combined sludge has a solids content of approximately 4.5 per cent.

Much of the organic material in sludge can be digested by anaerobic microbes with the production of gases, chiefly methane and carbon dioxide. Components which can be converted to gas are called *volatile solids*.

Various types of digestion tanks are in use (Figs. 22-8 and 22-10), the optimum operation of which is obtained by maintaining the temperature at

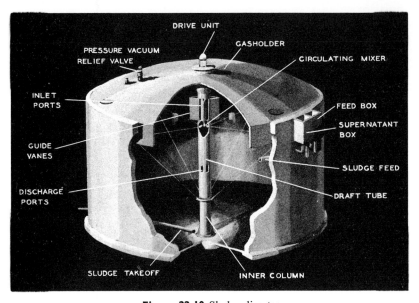

Figure 22-10 Sludge digester.

35° C (95° F) and at a pH of 7.0 to 7.8. Anaerobic digestion is a much slower process than aerobic oxidation. Retention time in heated tanks is 20 to 30 days. Longer periods of up to 60 days are required for tanks operating at 60° F.

The composition of the gas depends on the nature of the sludge. Proteins give a high proportion of CH_4 in the gas (69 to 76 per cent by volume). The aerobic oxidation of fats produces CO_2 and water. In contrast, the anaerobic decomposition first produces fatty acids of low molecular weight, which are then hydrolyzed to give methane and carbon dioxide. For example,

$$2 CH_3CH_2CH_2COOH + 2 H_2O \longrightarrow 5 CH_4 + 3 CO_2$$
butyric acid

Acetic acid, CH_3COOH, goes directly to CH_4 and CO_2. The equation for the butyric acid indicates that the mixture of gases will contain 62.5 per cent of CH_4. Carbohydrate digestion produces equal volumes of the two gases. A

Figure 22-11 1000 hp gas engines operated on sewage gas, supply compressed air for aeration tanks and heat for digesters and plant. [Courtesy Metropolitan Board of Works, Toronto.]

typical analysis of digester gas is CH_4, 67.8 per cent, CO_2, 25.1 per cent, N_2, 6.8 per cent, H_2S, 0.1 per cent, and H_2 and PH_3, traces. Hydrogen sulfide comes from sulfur-containing proteins and other organic wastes, or from sulfates by the action of a specific type of bacteria. Concentrations of methane vary from 65 to 78 per cent by volume.

The average yield of gas from primary sludge is 15 ft^3/lb of volatile solids. This is about 0.8 ft^3 per capita per day from primary sludge or 1.75 ft^3 per capita per day from combined sludge.

UTILIZATION OF DIGESTER GAS

The high content of methane makes digester gas a good fuel. In many plants the gas is used as a fuel for gas engines which drive blowers for the aeration tanks or to generate electrical power. Figure 22-11 is a photograph of a portion of the engine room of a 50 mgd plant. Four 1000 hp engines compress 20,000 cu ft of air per minute. The engines' exhaust furnishes the heat required to keep the digesters at the optimum temperature. Heat is also recovered from the engine cooling system to heat the building or for other purposes throughout the plant.

Disposal of Residual Sludge

The perennial problem of the sanitary engineer is the disposal of the residual sludge. While 50 to 55 per cent of the solids may have been digested, the residual sludge amounts to 115 to 120 lb per day per 1000 population, or 1200 lb of dry solids per million gallons of sewage treated. The material contains 90 to 93 per cent water. If it cannot be dumped or discharged into the sea, it must be given further treatment to remove a considerable portion of the water.

The most common method of dewatering residual sludge is to distribute it over a porous, drained, drying bed to a depth of about 8 in. Surface loadings recommended for the northern United States is 3.3 lb (dry solids basis) per sq ft per application. Seven or eight applications can be made per year. A glass, polyester, or plastic cover with open sides speeds the drying process.

Air-dried sludge cake contains about 40 per cent total solids and occupies $\frac{1}{4}$ to $\frac{1}{2}$ the original volume of the residual sludge. It may be used as fill or for soil conditioning. The dry solids contain 2.3 per cent nitrogen and 0.85 per cent phosphorus, and therefore they have some fertilizing action. Bagged fertilizer, Milorganite, and Torganite are prepared from powdered, heat-dried sludge cake, fortified by the addition of required elements, notably potassium. The presence of certain industrial waste residues may render the sludge unsuitable for soil conditioning.

In large treatment plants, vacuum filtration or centrifugal dewatering follows washing, chemical treatment, or thickening of the sludge. The sludge cake is then dried or incinerated.

ELUTRIATION

Sludge from the digester is alkaline. It contains 90 to 93 per cent water and dissolved salts, such as ammonium bicarbonate, produced during the digestion process, and others, as well as colloidal and volatile material. These can be removed and the residue rendered more suitable for chemical treatment and filtration, by countercurrent washing called *elutriation* (Fig. 22-12). The elutriated sludge is then coagulated chemically (see page 357) or thickened by mechanical stirring with paddles as in the flocculator, Fig. 22-6.

Sludge from the thickener contains 12 to 15 per cent solids. Vacuum

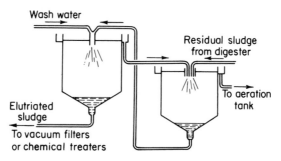

Figure 22-12 Two-stage elutriator.

drum filtration forms a sludge cake on the canvas or screen walls of the rotating filter. The cake is removed continuously by a scraper knife.

Thickened sludge may also be dewatered by a cyclone separator. The dried sludge may be fed directly to an incinerator as shown in Fig. 22-13. In the Dorr-Oliver Disposal System, the airborne material enters a special burner (Fig. 22-14) where it comes into immediate contact with a suspension of very hot fine sand. This fluidized bed of fine sand resembles the "fluid"

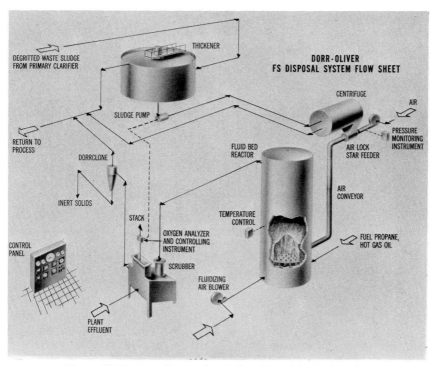

Figure 22-13 Flow diagram for sludge disposal by incineration. [Courtesy Dorr-Oliver Inc.]

catalyst of the cat cracker (page 78). Heat transfer is very rapid and the organic particles are all consumed within the sand suspension. The exhaust gases are scrubbed by bubbling through plant effluent. Ash is removed by a centrifugal separator (Fig. 22-5).

The sludge itself is a low grade fuel with a heating value of about 3500 Btu/lb (dry basis). Sewage gas, propane, or other fuel is used to preheat the fluidized bed and to assist in the combustion of sludge. Incineration is probably the most economical method of disposal for large inland cities.

A modern 50 million gal/day plant is pictured in Fig. 22-15. Pertinent data on the operation of the plant are given in Table 22-1.

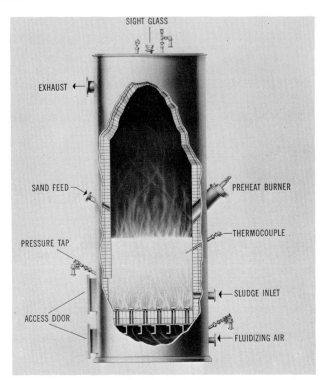

Figure 22-14 Fluidized bed sludge incinerator. [Courtesy Dorr-Oliver Inc.]

Lagoons or Oxidation Ponds

The domestic fish pond of ancient China was probably the original oxidation pond. Household wastes added to the shallow pond stimulated the growth of algae and aquatic plants, which produce oxygen during photosynthesis, providing a suitable environment for aerobic bacteria. Snails, worms, and other water bugs assist in the breakdown of organic material. The Chinese stocked the pond with fish, usually carp, which fed on the plant and animal growth. The fish supplemented the family's food supply, thus completing the cycle.

The *municipal* sewage lagoon first appeared in America as a "temporary" remedy for an overloaded sewage disposal plant. When it was found that the lagooned sewage reached a lower BOD than the final effluent of the disposal plant, the lagoon was kept in use with continuing satisfactory results for twenty years.

Since 1948 several hundred stabilization ponds or lagoons have been constructed in the United States and Canada. They are distributed from Florida to Manitoba and therefore operate under a wide range of climatic

Figure 22-15 Aerial photograph of the new 50 mgd Humber sewage treatment plant, Toronto. This is one of Metropolitan Toronto's smaller but most modern plants. Pertinent data on the plant are given in Table 22-1.

CHLORINE BUILDING

SLUDGE DIGESTION TANKS

GRIT TANKS

SCREENS

GAS ENGINES AND BLOWERS

ADMINISTRATION

RETURN SLUDGE PUMPING STATION

AERATION TANKS

FINAL SEDIMENTATION TANKS

PRIMARY SLUDGE

PRIMARY SEDIMENTATION TANKS

PRE-AERATION TANKS

401

Table 22-1. BASIC DESIGN DATA

ESTIMATED FLOW (million gallons/24 h):

	Immediate	Initial design	Ultimate design
Population	285,000	475,000	800,000
Average flow	27	50	100
Maximum monthly flow	34	63	25
Maximum peak hour (classification)	68	125	200
Maximum peak hour (secondary)	40	75	150
Minimum (for less than 1 hr)	14	28	60

ESTIMATED SEWAGE STRENGTH (based on industrial waste control):

	Raw sewage, ppm	Primary Treatment Per cent removal	Primary Treatment Settled sewage, ppm	Secondary Treatment Per cent removal	Secondary Treatment Final effluent, ppm
Estimated solids	210	47.5	110.0	95	5
Biochemical oxygen demand	260	30.0	182.0	93	13
Grease (ether soluble)	75	50.0	37.5	...	...

GRIT CHAMBERS (two units, each 40 ft square by 5 ft SWD):

Surface area . . . . 4040 sq ft
Surface loading, at 50 mgd . . . . 12,375 gpd/sq ft
Detention at 50 mgd . . . . 3.6 min

PREAERATION TANKS (two units, each two passes, each pass 237 ft long by 21 ft wide by 16 ft SWD):

Total volume . . . . .317,000 cu ft
Detention, at 50 mgd . . . . 57 min
Air supply, at 50 mgd . . . . 0.9 cu ft/gal

PRIMARY SETTLING TANKS (four units, each two channels, each channel 16 ft wide by 237 ft long by 11 ft SWD):

Total volume . . . . .354,550 cu ft
Detention, at 50 mgd . . . . 64 min
Surface loading, at 50 mgd . . . . 1550 gpd/sq ft
Weir overflow rate, at 50 mgd . . . . 25,000 gpd/lin. ft

AERATION TANKS (five units, each three passes, each pass 27 ft wide by 457 ft long by 16 ft SWD):

Total volume . . . . 2,900,000 cu ft
Detention, at 50 mgd . . . . .8.7 hr
Air (three blowers) at 50 mgd . . . . 1.2 cu ft/gal

FINAL SETTLING TANKS (eight units, each 95 ft square by 13 ft SWD):

Total volume . . . . .925,000 cu ft
Detention at 50 mgd . . . . .2.8 hr
Surface loading, at 50 mgd . . . . 690 gpd/sq ft
Weir overflow rate, at 50 mgd . . . . 900 gpd/lin. ft

Table 22-1. Basic Design Data (cont.)

SLUDGE DIGESTION (six tanks, each 110 ft dia. by 25 ft swD):
Total volume . . . . 1,425,000 cu ft
Unit volume per capita . . . . 3.0 cu ft
External sludge heaters
Gas holders on two secondary tanks, fixed covers with mechanical or gas recirculation
  on primaries
Approximate detention, at 475,000 persons. . . . . 40 days

SLUDGE ELUTRIATION (center-current provisions):
Two thickening tanks (plus one standby)
Ratio of effluent water to sludge . . . . 4 to 1
Digested sludge flow rate . . . . 145 gpm
Elutriation capacity . . . . 600 gpm
Detention period, at 600 gpm . . . . 4 hr
Surface loading, at 600 gpm . . . . 325 gpd/sq ft

SLUDGE DEWATERING (6 day week):
Four vacuum filters, each 11.5 ft by 14 ft (includes one standby)
Area, 3 by 500 sq ft . . . . 1500 sq ft
Digested sludge loading, dry weight . . . . 70,400 lb
Estimated moisture content of filter cake 70%
Average loading, dry basis . . . . 4.4 lb/sq ft/hr
Average operating period, at 475,000 persons . . . . 16 hr/day/6 days/week

CHLORINATION (prechlorination, sludge chlorination, post chlorination):
Four units, at 8000 lb/day . . . . 32,000 lb/day
Dosage, at 50 mgd at 10 ppm . . . . 5000 lb/day
Detention in outlet, at 125 mgd . . . . 17 min

conditions. The first installation in Ontario was constructed in 1954 for a military camp. In 1961, twelve out of 62 communities constructing sewage disposal facilities chose lagoons.

The great advantage of the stabilization pond for cities of less than 10,000 is the relatively low cost, one-quarter of the conventional treatment plant. The principal expenditure is for land, which is usually cheaper near the smaller cities. The lagoon area should be 1 acre for every 100 to 250 persons.[1] In spite of the large areas required, the city of Auckland, New Zealand, with a population over 380,000, is served by four lagoons.

Natural ponds can be used, but this is very exceptional. Lagoons can be constructed in most soil, although seepage may be too great if it is very sandy. Seepage can be decreased by lining the banks and bottom with clay or by treating the interior surface with sodium silicate followed by a spray of calcium chloride. Black polythene sheets, joined by thermal "sewing" as used to line catchment basins and storage ponds (Fig. 20-5), could be employed if covered with an inch of earth.

---

1 Depending on the climate.

Lagoons covering more than ten acres should be divided into smaller areas by dykes to cut down erosion by wind-driven waves. The dykes may be provided with openings to permit uniform circulation to each section, or each cell may be serviced separately.

Ponds may be located within one-quarter mile or more from the nearest dwelling. The only time any objectionable odors are observed, is during the early spring when a heavy ice cover may have caused anaerobic conditions. The change back to aerobic digestion takes place rapidly in sunny weather however.

Various lengths of time have been suggested for retaining sewage in lagoons, ranging from 120 to 200 days. The retention time depends on the strength of the sewage and the latitude. The pond should handle 20 to 30 lb BOD per acre per day.

Unlike the treatment plant, a stabilization pond practically runs itself. Maintenance consists in cutting the grass on the banks, elimination of weeds in the pond, and inspection of the submerged inlet and surface outlet. Mosquitoes can be controlled by stocking the pond with a species of surface minnow which feeds on the larvae.

The lagoon will play an increasing role in the battle against pollution of natural waters.

22-4 Industrial Wastes

Industrial wastes constitute a very important factor in stream pollution. The untreated wastes from a sugar refinery or a paper mill have an oxygen demand of a city of over 200,000. While the industry does not add any harmful bacteria, such an effluent can, and has, converted more than one stream to a septic sewer. During the last decade, industry has spent millions to improve waste recovery. The waste load from the paper mill was reduced 51 per cent per ton of paper during the period between 1943 and 1959. However during the same years the annual production of paper increased 100 per cent.[1] The total wastes reaching our rivers is still increasing. The same is true in other instances. More emphasis must be placed on waste removal and cooperative reuse of water.

Industrial wastes may be divided into four classes.

1. Organic waste high in BOD but amenable to standard sewage treatment.

2. Organic wastes containing substances not removed by ordinary procedures.

---

1 L. F. Warrick, Industrial Waste Conference, Honey Harbor, Ont., 1961.

3. Toxic wastes.

4. Acid, alkaline, or saline effluents.

Food processing industries produce wastes belonging to the first group. Many of these industries—except small dairies—have their own treating facilities. Some pork packing plants boast that they save everything but the squeal! Beet-sugar wastes require special treatment if sugar has been extracted by lime. Cannery and dairy wastes, after screening, may be disposed of by spray irrigation on grass cover or by ditching. Brewery wastes have a 90 per cent BOD, removed by aerating them for 3 to 6 hours.

Tanneries produce alkaline waste high in BOD and total solids of around 10,000. The character of chrome tan waste differs from that of the waste of vegetable tanning, the former containing toxic chromium compounds. As a general treatment, sedimentation, aerobic filtration, and secondary clarification are recommended. Spray disposal of the settled effluent is reported to give a BOD of 6 to 9 ppm in the field run-off from a primary effluent having 200 to 500 mg/liter BOD.

The second class includes wastes from oil refineries, creosoting, petrochemical, gas, coke, and dye plants. In some cases the waste is both acid and toxic. Special methods of treatment have been worked out which have been highly successful in removing phenolic compounds, oils, and sulfur compounds. A notable example is in the treatment of refinery waste for which a special variety of bacteria has been developed. The bacteria cause the oxidation of phenols in an activated sludge treatment. Final oxidation of traces of phenol is accomplished by treatment with ozone followed by activated charcoal. The effluent is purer than Lake Ontario water. Concentrated wastes are sometimes disposed of by incineration or by pumping them into deep wells drilled into porous strata which distribute the effluent over an underground area of many square miles.

Toxic wastes such as cyanide and various metal salts require special chemical treatment. Ag^+, Cu^{++}, Cr^{+++} are very toxic to fish. As little as 0.03 ppm of Cu^{++} is lethal for trout. Black bass can tolerate ten times this amount. The metal ions are concentrated in the sludge and poison the bacteria in the activated sludge process.

Laundries, textile plants, and other industries, in the second group, produce alkaline wastes. Effluents from coal mines and sulfide mines are acid. Acid pickling wastes also contain metal salts. The problem of seepage from abandoned coal mines is too great for adequate control, but the pH of industrial wastes can usually be controlled. The cheapest alkali for the neutralization of acid is limestone. Flue gas containing carbon dioxide has been used to neutralize alkali.

Laundry waste, like domestic sewage, may also add a type of detergents which is not susceptible to aerobic treatment. These accumulate as the water is used successively by cities along the river, until the final concentration may produce enough foaming to constitute a nuisance. The most intractable type is an alkylbenzene sulfonate which has a highly branched alkyl radical, for example,

It has been found that if the alkyl radical is in the form of a straight chain or one which is only slightly branched, such as in the compound

the detergent is broken up more readily by the aerobic bacteria in the sewage treatment. Tests have shown that 94 per cent of the latter "soft" compound and only 68 per cent of the branched "hard" isomer were decomposed by standard aeration. The alkyl sulfates such as sodium lauryl sulfate ($C_{12}H_{25}SO_4Na$), sulfonated paraffins ($R—SO_3Na$) where R contains from ten to fourteen carbon atoms, and various sugar esters, are amenable to treatment. It is expected that of these, sodium alkane sulfonate and "soft" sodium benzenesulfonate will largely displace the "hard" type of detergents.

With the continuous growth of cities and industries, more reuse of water must be practiced. The effluent from domestic sewage or from one industry may be useable by other industries without further treatment. Such "tandem" use, now being carried on in certain areas, should be increased. It saves water, lowers costs, and reduces thermal, chemical, and biological pollution of natural waters.

Further Readings

Bolton, R. L., and Klein, L., *Sewage Treatment—Basic Principles and Trends* (London: Butterworths, 1961).

Clark, F. E., "Industrial Re-use of Water," *Industrial and Engineering Chemistry*, **54**, 2 (1962) 18.

Imhoff, K., and Fair, G. M., *Sewage Treatment* (New York: John Wiley, 1956).

Sewage Treatment Plant Design. Water Pollution Control Federation, 1959.

Third Report of the Standing Technical Committee on Synthetic Detergents (London: Her Majesty's Stationery Office, 1960).

Review Questions

1. Define BOD.

2. What is meant by "oxygen absorbed"?

3. How is the latter determined?

4. What is meant by strength of sewage?

5. Name five tests done on sewage or trade effluents.

6. Write an equation showing the oxidation of urea.

7. What is accomplished by anaerobic digestion?

8. What is meant by activated sludge digestion?

9. What is accomplished by trickling filters?

10. Give a formula for estimating the amount of sewage that a given stream can absorb without putrefaction.

11. What is the composition of digester gas?

12. What is the approximate relation between population and hp derived from sewage?

13. Describe Imhoff tanks and travis tanks.

14. What factors must be controlled in the anaerobic digestion of sewage sludge?

15. Draw a diagram of a two-stage purification plant.

16. Discuss the lagoon method of waste disposal.

23

Explosives

Nuclear explosives may eventually be used for removing mountains, excavating harbors, or liberating petroleum products from intractable tar sands, but for most engineering projects, chemical explosives will be employed.

Explosives are chemical compounds or mixtures designed and manufactured for the sudden release of chemical energy to do work. They furnish one of the most obvious applications of chemistry to engineering in the construction of tunnels, roads, rock cuts, in quarrying, mining, ditching, in removing log jams or ice jams, submerged reefs, rocks, or wrecks, demolition of old buildings or machinery, bringing in oil or gas wells, seismic prospecting, and even in riveting. These and other engineering uses consume something over a billion pounds of explosives per year in the United States.

23-1 The History of Explosives

Gun powder, the earliest explosive, is thought to have been invented by the Chinese. It was known to the Arabs and Hindus around 1250 A.D. and was described by Roger Bacon in 1270. It consists of a mixture of powdered charcoal, sulfur, and potassium nitrate or sodium nitrate. Such a mixture, when ignited, produces relatively large volumes of hot gases. The reaction may be represented by the equation

$$2\,NaNO_3 + S + 3\,C \longrightarrow Na_2S + N_2 + 3\,CO_2$$

although SO_2 and other gases are also produced. Here, as in many other explosives, oxygen is present in a readily available form, so that the combustion proceeds even when the powder is confined. The rapid phase change from solid to gas at high temperature, causes the propellant or bursting effect of the explosion.

Table 23-1. SOME HIGHLIGHTS IN THE HISTORY OF EXPLOSIVES

1230–50 A.D.	Gunpowder known and used by Chinese, Arabs, and Hindus
1267	Black powder described by Roger Bacon
1328	Its propulsive power investigated by Schwarz
1346	Used by the English in the battle of Crecy (Wooden Cannon)
1425	Granulated gunpowder
1604	Development of ordnance and fire arms, "fulminate of gold"
1605	The Gunpowder Plot
1771	Picric Acid used as a dye, but its explosive properties not discovered until 1805 and not used until 1885
1788	Discovery of the fulminates of silver by Berthollet
1800	Preparation of mercury fulminate by Howard, who described its detonation by an electric spark, by impact, and by concentrated sulfuric acid
1831	"Safety" fuse with waterproof cover introduced
1836	Percussion cap and firing pin gun invented
1845	Discovery of nitrocellulose by Schoenbein
1846	Preparation of nitroglycerine by Sobrero
1865	Nobel's dynamite, nitroglycerine in diatomaceous earth
1865	Smokeless powder from nitrated wood, $Ba(NO_3)$, and KNO_3
1869	Improved dynamite, nitroglycerine with wood flour, nitrate, and wax
1879	Nobel patented special dynamite containing nitrocellulose and ammonium nitrate. Preparation of tetryl
1920	RDX or Cyclonite, first prepared as a medicine in 1899, was patented as an explosive
1925	Pentryl, a high explosive
1935	Biazzi continuous process for the manufacture of nitroglycerine
1940	Canadian and American chemical team perfect new and continuous process for RDX

As indicated in Table 23-1, gunpowder or black powder held its place as the prime explosive for several hundred years. Military uses seem to have been most important until the nineteenth century, although the smoke produced on discharge of the firearms, illustrated by TV Westerns, was a fault which persisted until "smokeless" powder was invented in 1864. During the last half-century the chief use of black powder has been in coal mining, but the rapid fall in coal production during the last decade has reduced the consumption of blasting powder by 90 per cent. It is still employed for open strip mining, clay and shale displacement, construction work, and excavations where a slow heaving action is required. The speed of the combustion depends on the size and shape of the constituent grains. One company produces blasting powder of standard strength in seven different speeds by varying the grain size of the pellets from 0.03 in. to 0.5 in. in diameter. Since one of the components of the blasting powder is soluble in water, it must be protected from moisture.

23-2 Chemical Nature of Explosives

Explosives are groups of molecules containing atoms which will change their position in the molecular structure under the influence of shock, heat, electric spark, or friction. Chemical groups found in many explosives are nitrate ($-ONO_2$), —nitro ($-NO_2$), fulminate ($-ONC$), and azide ($-N= N\equiv N$). Specific examples will be discussed after noting the important properties used to compare explosives.

23-3 Classification of Explosives

Commercial explosives may be classified in a number of ways, for example, according to chemical type, strength, or velocity of detonation. They are commonly divided into propellants, high explosives, and detonators or initiating explosives. Propellants are relatively slow burning with flame speeds less than 100 m/sec. The decomposition and internal reaction of a high explosive such as blasting gelatin takes place in less than 0.00005 sec. The rapid energy release produces a shock wave, which travels at velocities of several miles per second. This shock wave can detonate other explosives and shatter solid materials. The shattering power or "brisance" of an explosive, depends on its velocity of detonation (V.O.D.) and its "strength" or energy liberated per gram. Small amounts of priming or initiating explosives may be required to detonate the main charge of high explosive. Their selection depends on another property of explosives—relative sensitivity.

23-4 The Measurement of Explosive Properties

Velocity of Detonation

The velocity of detonation can be measured by several methods. One optical method employs a prism which directs the light from a vertical sample

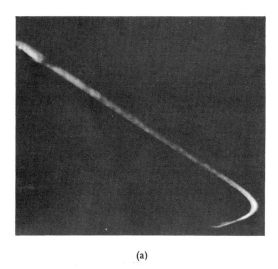

(a)

(b)   (c)

Figure 23-1 Detonations photographed by a rotating-drum camera. The hook at the bottom of each photograph is caused by the blasting cap initiator: (a) A low rate dynamite (1500 m/sec); (b) Medium rate dynamite (3500 m/sec), showing hot, luminous expanding gases; (c) A detonating fuse (7000 m/sec). Note the steep slope of the curve. The wrapper of the fuse has cooled the gases so that they are not luminous as in (b). [From *Hercules Chemist.* **33**, (1958), 3. Courtesy Hercules Powder Co.]

of the explosive through a 0.1 mm slit in a drum, to a film mounted on the inside surface. The drum is rotated at high speed so that the film is exposed for a fraction of a millisecond to the light from the exploding sample during each revolution. Successive rotations produce a streak of light on the film, the slope of which depends on the V.O.D.

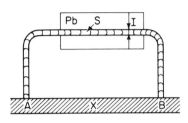

Figure 23-2 Comparative method for determining V.O.D. Standard explosive (*S*), explosive under test (*X*), lead sheet (Pb), impact point (*I*).

Figure 23-1 shows three pictures obtained by this method; (A) from the detonation of a low-velocity dynamite, (B) from a medium-rate dynamite and (C) from a detonating fuse with a V.O.D. of 7000 m/sec. The direction of propagation of the detonations was from the bottom to the top. The curved hook at the bottom of the photographs was caused by the blasting cap. The film travelled from left to right. The feathery appearance of the streak in (B) was caused by very hot luminous gases. This is not found in (A), indicating that the gases in the slower explosion were not heated to as high a temperature. The absence of the plume in (C) is attributed to the quenching effect of the fuse wrapper.

Another method for determining the V.O.D. is to measure the time it takes for the detonation to travel between two pairs of wires inserted into the explosive a known distance apart. The time may be measured in microseconds by a counter chronograph which registers the pulses generated by a megacycle oscillator checked against the United States Bureau of Standards 300 M transmitter. By using a series of spaced probes attached to an oscilloscope, changes in rate of detonation can be recorded.

If a sample with a known V.O.D. is available, the rate of detonation of another explosive can be determined by the simple method illustrated in Fig. 23-2. This method avoids direct time measurements.

A long loop of the standard explosives whose V.O.D. is known (V_s) is attached to a strip of the explosive X at points A and B. The loop of the standard S rests on a strip of lead. When X is detonated and the detonation wave reaches A, S is detonated. When the initial wave reaches B, the explosive S detonates at this point also. The two detonation waves in S travelling in opposite directions in the loop, meet at some point I. The impact will cut a sharp line in the soft metal.

The time for the detonation in S to travel the distance AI is equal to the time for the detonation in X to reach point B, plus the time for the wave in S to go from B to I. Thus

$$\frac{AI}{V_s} = \frac{AB}{V_x} + \frac{BI}{V_s} \quad \text{or} \quad V_x = \frac{AB \cdot V_s}{AI - BI}$$

The V.O.D. for X can be obtained by simple linear measurements. The

V.O.D. increases with the density, that is, the compression of the powdered explosive. The rate for TNT with a density of 1.0 is 4600 m/sec; if the density is 1.5, the rate is 6550 m/sec; and if it is 1.7, the rate is 7500 m/sec. The velocity ratings for several explosives are given below.

Explosive Strength

The strength of an explosive is expressed either as the energy liberated per unit weight (cal/g) or by direct comparison with a standard *blasting gelatin*, the strongest commercial dynamite. Blasting gelatin is given a rating of 100 per cent. A "straight" dynamite containing 40 per cent nitroglycerine, has a weight strength of 40. A special (ammonia) dynamite containing only 22 per cent nitroglycerine with 20 per cent ammonium nitrate has also a

Figure 23-3 The strength of an explosive can be measured with this ballistic mortar which fires a 36 lb shot 20 ft into a backstop. The recoil of the pendulum, on which the mortar is mounted, gives a measure of the energy released. Research engineer inserts the shot after loading a sample charge. [Courtesy Canadian Industries Ltd.]

weight strength of 40. The *bulk strength* is equal to the weight strength times the density divided by 1.5.

Explosive strength may be tested by several methods. The pressure developed by a standard sample may be measured by a Biechel gauge. The recoil of a heavy ballistic pendulum is measured when an attached mortar loaded with a standard charge is fired (Fig. 23-3). In the Trauzel test a charge is exploded in a small cylindrical cavity in a lead block and the increase in the volume of the cavity is compared with the increase produced by the same amount of a standard explosive. Explosive strength can also be estimated from the depression made in a $\frac{1}{4}$ in. steel plate by the detonation of the sample in contact with the plate.

Brisance

Brisance or shattering power is usually measured by the sand bomb test. In this test the sample is placed in the center of a steel cylinder containing sand of uniform particle size. The degree to which the sand is pulverized is a measure of this property, which is related to both strength and velocity of detonation.

Chemical Stability

This should not be confused with *sensitivity*. It is the ability of the explosive to maintain its original composition during storage or ageing. Traces of impurities affect the stability. Stabilization of nitrocellulose consists of removing residual sulfate which would catalyze the degradation of the nitrate. Substances which act as negative catalysts or stabilizers are then added. These are analogous to antioxidants and corrosion inhibitors. A stabilizer commonly used in propellants contains two substituted amine groups, namely, diethyldiphenyl urea,

$$
\begin{array}{ccc}
C_2H_5 & & C_6H_5 \\
\diagdown & & \diagup \\
& N-C-N & \\
\diagup & \| & \diagdown \\
C_6H_5 & O & C_2H_5
\end{array}
$$

Chemical changes during ageing are undesirable because the explosive may become sensitive to handling or may give rise to less-useful compounds.

23-5 Sensitivity

Explosives differ greatly in the ease with which ignition may be brought about by changes in conditions. Some compounds may be detonated by brushing them with a feather, while other explosives may not detonate when hit by a hammer. Some explosives may be burned without detonation, others explode on ignition. The use of an explosive depends on its type and degree of sensitivity as well as on the other properties discussed above.

Sensitivity to Impact

Various impact tests give a measure of the relative sensitivity of different explosives to percussion. In general, these measure the kinetic energy of the blow to give a 50 per cent probability of firing. The explosive is placed on a steel plate and a weight is dropped on it from increasing heights until ignition occurs. Data in the literature are expressed as heights of fall of the chosen weight (5 lb, 2 kg, or 5 kg). Such tests are influenced by a number of factors. It is, however, established that the explosives, mercury fulminate $Hg(ONC)_2$, lead azide $Pb(N{=}N{\equiv}N)_2$, nitroglycerine $(C_3H_5)(NO_3)_3$, and pentaerythritol tetranitrate PETN, are very sensitive to impact. Other modern explosives, Tetryl and RDX, are moderately sensitive, more so than picric acid, while TNT is one of the least sensitive of the high explosives. Gunpowder is relatively insensitive.

The drop height data give an indication of the relative hazards involved in handling different explosives. Mercury fulminate and lead azide with very low drop heights are used as initiators in percussion caps, being ignited by the blow from the firing pin. Other fulminates and azides are also very sensitive to impact and friction.

Sensitivity to Friction

The sensitivity of explosives to friction can be compared by means of the frictional impact pendulum or by the steel *torpedo* test. In the former, the explosive is spread in a thin layer on a curved surface matching the arc of a heavy pendulum. The pendulum is released from increasing heights until the frictional or shearing forces cause ignition. In the torpedo test, a steel cylinder with rounded ends slides down a groove onto a steel platform bearing a layer of the explosive. In both tests, thin films of liquid or compressed explosive show higher sensitivity than thick films.

Sensitivity to Heat

A small sample, for example 5 mg, is placed in a thin metal container and immersed in a bath or bomb at a constant temperature or at a constant rate of heat input. The sensitivity is indicated by the lowest temperature at which ignition or detonation occurs, or the temperature at which explosion occurs in a specified time, such as one or five seconds. Preignition decomposition can be detected by pressure measurements as the sample is subjected to increasing temperature in an enclosed bomb.

Most of the commercial explosives have ignition temperatures between 175° and 350° C. Silver and mercury fulminates, copper azide, and nitrocellulose are sensitive to heat. The high explosives RDX and TNT have detonating temperatures comparable to that required to ignite gunpowder, over 320° C. The explosion of these substances produces temperatures of several thousand degrees Centigrade.

Sensitivity to an Electric Spark

Some explosives are so sensitive to an electrical discharge that they can be detonated by the static generated when a person walks across a carpet, or when fabrics are rubbed together. Care must therefore be taken to eliminate or prevent the formation of electrostatic charges when handling sensitive explosives. Sensitivity to electrical discharge can be tested by using a variable condenser and increasing the energy of the spark until the sample detonates.

Sensitivity to a Detonator Wave

An explosive may be fired or detonated by a shock wave produced by a priming or initiating explosive, while another explosive would be unaffected. Differences in sensitivity to detonators may be measured by the *gap* or *card* test. In this test the detonator or donor explosive is separated from the test sample by a gap which is increased until the receptor explosive is no longer detonated by the primer. The gap may be made by inserting thin cellulose acetate discs or "cards" between the two explosives. The gap or total thickness of the 10 mil discs with which the detonator gives only a 50 per cent score, is taken as the card value. Obviously the higher the gap value the greater the sensitivity of the acceptor. The differences in the ease with which explosives are detonated is of very great importance in the design and use of blasting caps (page 426).

23-6 Oxygen Balance

Most common explosives have oxygen built into the molecule. This oxygen takes part in explosive oxidation of other components, notably carbon and hydrogen. Ammonium nitrate may disintegrate to give water, nitrogen, and excess oxygen, as is represented by the equation

$$2\,NH_4NO_3 \longrightarrow 4\,H_2O + 2\,N_2 + O_2$$

Such a compound is said to be in positive oxygen balance. A more powerful explosive is obtained if oxidizable material is added to the ammonium nitrate. Such substances as coal dust or fuel oil make use of the available oxygen giving a higher V.O.D. and energy output.

Glycol nitrate, $(NO_3)CH_2CH_2(NO_3)$, has sufficient oxygen present to convert the carbon to carbon dioxide and the hydrogen to water

$$2\,C + 4\,H \xrightarrow{6\,O} 2\,CO_2 + 2\,H_2O$$

or

$$(NO_3)CH_2CH_2(NO_3) \longrightarrow 2\,CO_2 + 2\,H_2O + N_2$$

This would be in exact oxygen balance if the reaction proceeded in this way. However if the carbon is only oxidized to carbon monoxide, all of the oxygen will not be used and the explosive would be said to have a positive oxygen balance. Since CO is undoubtedly formed in the detonation of many explosives, oxygen balance is usually calculated on the basis of $C \rightarrow CO$ instead of CO_2. It is expressed numerically as a percentage surplus or deficiency of oxygen by weight. Thus for a compound $C_aH_bN_cO_d$ the oxygen balance will be

$$d - \left(a + \frac{1}{2}b\right) \times \frac{16}{\text{mol. wt.}} \times 100$$

For trinitrobenzene

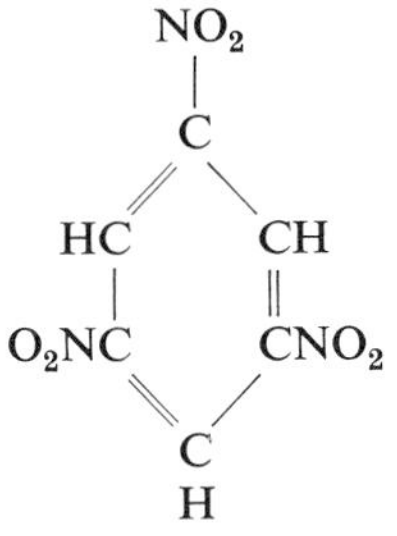

The molecular weight is 213, and the oxygen balance is

$$6 - \left(6 + \frac{3}{2}\right) \times \frac{1600}{213} = -11.3$$

For nitroglycerine, $C_3H_5(NO_3)_3$, the molecular weight is 227 and the oxygen balance is

$$9 - \left(3 + \frac{5}{2}\right) \times \frac{1600}{227} = +25$$

Ammonium nitrate would have an oxygen balance of $+20$.

Power and brisance increase from negative to zero and positive oxygen balance. The admixture of substances having positive balance with compounds having negative balance has been used to produce high explosives of desirable qualities. Ammonium nitrate with TNT gives the explosive *Amatol*.

Blasting and military explosives called *ammonals* contain a mixture of TNT, aluminum dust, and ammonium nitrate. The addition of nitroglycerine to TNT gives an explosive of better oxygen balance. However, the oxygen balance as calculated can only predict the properties of an admixture in a *qualitative* fashion because (1) the nature of the oxygen linkages (for example, $-NO_3$, $-NO_2$, $-O-O-$, $-OR$, $-O-N=$, $-ClO_4$) and molecular structure determine the energy output; (2) the combustion reactions are much more complex than can be assumed for the calculation of the oxygen balance; and (3) the physical properties may be altered during mixing.

23-7 Representative Modern Explosives

The most important advance in the development of explosives for engineering uses was the discovery of nitroglycerine and its adaption by Nobel for the manufacture of dynamite with its subsequent modifications.

Nitroglycerine, or more properly glyceryl nitrate, is the ester formed by the reaction of the alcohol glycerol with nitric acid and sulfuric acid.

$$
\begin{array}{l}
H_2C-OH \quad HONO_2 \\
\quad | \\
H-C-OH + HONO_2 \xrightarrow{H_2SO_4} \\
\quad | \\
H_2C-OH \quad HONO_2
\end{array}
\qquad
\begin{array}{l}
H_2C-ONO_2 \\
\quad | \\
H-C-ONO_2 + 3\ HOH \\
\quad | \\
H_2C-ONO_2
\end{array}
$$

Until 1935 nitroglycerine was manufactured by a batch process in which glycerol was added slowly with stirring to a cooled mixture of one part of nitric and two parts of sulfuric acids. In the early days, several fatal accidents occurred due to runaway reactions caused by inadequate temperature control, improperly washed product, and mistakes or mischance in handling this sensitive explosive.

The Biazzi continuous nitration process invented in Switzerland is much safer and more efficient. Smaller charges of reactants are fed continuously into the reactor of stainless steel. The reactor is designed for high dispersion of the glycerol in the nitrating mixture and for precise temperature regulation. The dispersed nitroglycerine and waste acids flow from the nitrator to a shallow separator. Both nitrator and separator have a dumping device by which the whole contents can be "drowned" in a tank of water, stopping further reaction. These and other safety devices act automatically in case of power failure or other abnormal circumstances. They may also be operated manually from several points inside and outside the plant.

From the separator the product goes to a wash tank where it is agitated with water, and thence the heavier glyceryl nitrate suspension flows to a second separator, followed by a further washing in dilute sodium carbonate solution. Additional washings and separations may be carried out to assure a high degree of purity. The pure liquid resembles glycerol in appearance. It has a sp gr of 1.6. It freezes at 13.2° C (55° F). Very small quantities can be burned without detonation, but in bulk, ignition at 220° C causes it to explode. It is very sensitive to impact, and this sensitivity increases with increasing temperature. It has one of the highest V.O.D., and its weight strength is 50 per cent greater than TNT. Pure nitroglycerine is chemically stable.

Glycol may be nitrated along with glycerol. The glycol nitrate and glyceryl nitrate are miscible, the glycol compound acting as an antifreeze for the nitroglycerine. Vapors of glycol nitrate are more toxic than those of nitroglycerine. The latter causes a dilation of the capillaries which is made use of in medicine for certain heart ailments.

Cellulose Nitrate or Guncotton

Cellulose nitrate was first prepared in 1846, the same year as the discovery of nitroglycerine. Its preparation also involves the esterification of alcohol groups with nitric acid, in the presence of sulfuric acid. As indicated in the chapter on plastics (Chapter 17), partial nitration produces modified polymers useful for films, lacquers, and rocket fuel. Gun cotton contains 13.0 to 13.4 per cent nitrogen, but complete nitration of all the alcohol groups would give 14.1 per cent nitrogen. Guncotton is used as a propellant. It has a larger molecular weight or polymer length than nitrocellulose used in dynamite or smokeless powder. Dry nitrocellulose is sensitive to shock or ignition and it can be detonated by a spark. Sensitivity is decreased by the incorporation of some aqueous alcohol. Chemical stability is achieved by washing the compound repeatedly to remove traces of sulfate groups and by the addition of stabilizers. Dry, compressed nitrocellulose has a strength of approximately 70 per cent (compared to nitroglycerine).

Dynamite and Related Explosives

Alfred Nobel was one of the first professional engineers to make use of nitroglycerine as an engineering aid. The dangerous sensitivity of the material, which caused the accidental death of his younger brother, led him to make an intensive research for safer methods of handling this powerful explosive. He found that by absorbing the nitroglycerine liquid on kieselguhr, a porous material like diatomaceous earth, sensitivity to shock was greatly decreased. The mixture, "dynamite," could be exploded by fuse and a small tube or *cap* containing gunpowder, or better, by detonating a mercury fulminate. Nobel later incorporated combustible absorbent fillers such as wood flour or charcoal in place of the kieselguhr. *Straight nitroglycerine dynamite* contains only nitroglycerine as the explosive. A typical 40 per cent straight dynamite contains 40 per cent nitroglycerine, 15 per cent wood pulp, 44 per cent sodium nitrate, with 1 per cent $CaCO_3$ as an antiacid. It has a V.O.D. of 13,800 ft/sec. Straight dynamites range from 15 to 60 per cent nitroglycerine with velocities from 8200 to 18,200 ft/sec. They have satisfactory water resistance, particularly those with a high nitroglycerine content. Since objectionable fumes are produced, straight dynamites are not recommended for underground work. Their high V.O.D. makes them valuable for demolitions, submarine blasting, and as a primer for other less-sensitive explosives.

Special dynamites are also called ammonia dynamites because part of the nitroglycerine has been replaced by *ammonium nitrate*. Ammonium nitrate, a cheap inorganic salt used originally as fertilizer, is detonated by the explosion of the nitroglycerine. The ammonia dynamites have a lower V.O.D. than the straight type and are not as water resistant. They are, however, being used in increasing volume because of their lower cost and their satisfactory performance for quarry and highway use, for open mining operations, and for removing stumps and boulders.

Blasting Gelatins

Blasting gelatin is a rubbery mixture of nitroglycerine and 8 per cent nitrocotton. It is the strongest commercial dynamite in use. Its water resistance is superior to all others. It is recommended for sinking shafts in very hard rock, in shooting oil wells, and in submarine blasting. Its fumes are objectionable for underground work in mines.

Other Nitroglycerine Gelatines

Admixture of nitroglycerine and cellulose nitrates produces a plastic material, the consistency of which varies from that of a soft jelly to a crumbly powder depending on the proportion of the different constituents. Nitroglycerine gelatins are obtainable in a wide range of grades. With a content of 20 to 60 per nitroglycerine, the gelatin detonations produce practically no fumes and are therefore suitable for blasting in mines and tunnels. All have excellent water resistance. The velocities of detonation range from 10,500 ft/sec for 20 per cent nitroglycerine gelatin to 22,300 ft/sec for 90 per cent nitroglycerine gelatin. *Special gelatins* contain ammonium nitrate. These are also known as *semigelatins*.

Smokeless powder may be made largely of nitrocellulose. The propellant Cordite contains approximately 65 per cent guncotton, 30 per cent nitroglycerine, and 5 per cent vaseline or mineral jelly. The material gets its name from the shape of the plastic product. The mixture of nitroglycerine dissolved in acetone, nitrocellulose, and vaseline is extruded through a perforated die, forming strings or cords.

Ammonium Nitrate

Mention has been made of the addition of ammonium nitrate to other explosives. This addition raises the oxygen balance and usually decreases the sensitivity. The salt is, however, an explosive in its own right. Although very insensitive to shock, friction, and spark, in the presence of a reducing substance, it can be detonated by heat or a suitable blasting cap. Prilled nitrate coated with inert clay to prevent caking is mixed with 6 per cent fuel oil by weight to form a blasting agent suitable for many jobs requiring a high explosive. Since ammonium nitrate is soluble in water, the mixed salt and reducing agent are packaged in sealed cans.

LOX, Liquid Oxygen

Liquid oxygen, like ammonium nitrate, gives an explosive mixture with a reducing substance. Cartridges filled with materials such as pulverized charcoal, lampblack, wood flour, coal dust, or aluminum powder, are soaked in liquid oxygen for about 30 minutes before use. They are sensitive to heat and shock. The LOX may be detonated by fuse ignition. Since the liquid oxygen will evaporate rapidly, the explosive must be detonated shortly after removal from the soaking box and any LOX cartridge that fails to fire, becomes harmless in a few hours.

The chief use for liquid oxygen explosives is in strip mining. About 22.5 million pounds was used in the United States in 1953, but the decrease in coal production and replacement by ammonium nitrate have cut this figure to less than half this amount.

PETN, Pentaerythritol-tetranitrate

Pentaerythritol,

$$
\begin{array}{c}
CH_2OH \\
| \\
HOH_2C-C-CH_2OH \\
| \\
CH_2OH
\end{array}
$$

like glycerol and cellulose is a polyalcohol. It is an important raw material for the manufacture of synthetic resins by esterification. When the reacting acid is nitric acid, a high explosive is obtained. This compound is a colorless crystalline solid, stable in storage and in ageing. Its explosion temperature is similar to that of nitroglycerine. It has a strength 95 per cent that of blasting gelatin and a V.O.D. of 8.3 km/sec (27,500 ft/sec). It is also used as a booster charge for detonators.

Other nitrates used as explosives are nitrostarch and nitrated sugars.

Trinitrotoluene, TNT

Trinitrotoluene,

$$
\begin{array}{c}
CH_3 \\
| \\
C \\
\diagup\!\!\diagup \quad \diagdown \\
O_2NC \qquad\ C\!\!-\!\!NO_2 \\
| \qquad\qquad \| \\
HC \qquad CH \\
\diagdown \quad \diagup \\
C \\
| \\
NO_2
\end{array}
$$

represents a class of explosives in which the NO_2 group is attached to a
carbon atom. These are true nitro compounds. TNT is a powerful explosive,
with an ignition temperature of 250° C. It is not sensitive to shock (impact)
or friction. A high explosive used during the last war contained TNT and
ammonium nitrate. It is called *Amatol*. A very similar explosive called
Ammonal contains powdered aluminum in addition to the ammonium nitrate
and TNT. A typical *Ammonal* contains 16 per cent Al, 12 per cent TNT, and
72 per cent NH_4NO_3. The tiny flakes of aluminum coat the grains of the salt
and help to prevent absorption of water vapor. The oxidation of the metal
produces very high temperatures, and therefore the gaseous products of the
explosive reach very high pressures.

A recent development in mixed explosives has been the addition of water
and a combustible thickening agent to TNT-ammonium nitrate, giving a
semi-fluid mush or soft plastic that can be packed into irregular shaped
blast holes. In the explosion the water takes part in the chemical reaction,
increasing the gas volume and pressure.

RDX or Cyclonite

This is the active material in the "plastic explosives" widely used by
Commandos and Resistance groups for demolitions. A strip of the putty-
like plastic wrapped around a girder or rail, upon detonation, would cut the
steel as with a torch, its velocity of detonation is so great. The same structures
would only be bent or buckled by a similar charge of TNT.

RDX, which has the structure

$$
\begin{array}{c}
CH_2 \\
\diagup \quad \diagdown \\
O_2N\!\!-\!\!N \qquad N\!\!-\!\!NO_2 \\
| \qquad\qquad | \\
H_2C \qquad\ CH_2 \\
\diagdown \quad \diagup \\
N \\
| \\
NO_2
\end{array}
$$

was discovered in 1899 and suggested for use as a drug. Its explosive properties were recognized and patented in 1920. At that time the raw materials
required for its manufacture were too expensive for it to compete with older,
established explosives for civilian use. Furthermore the explosive was very
sensitive. It was suspected that the accidental explosions in its manufacture
were caused by unstable by-products. This was investigated by the Research

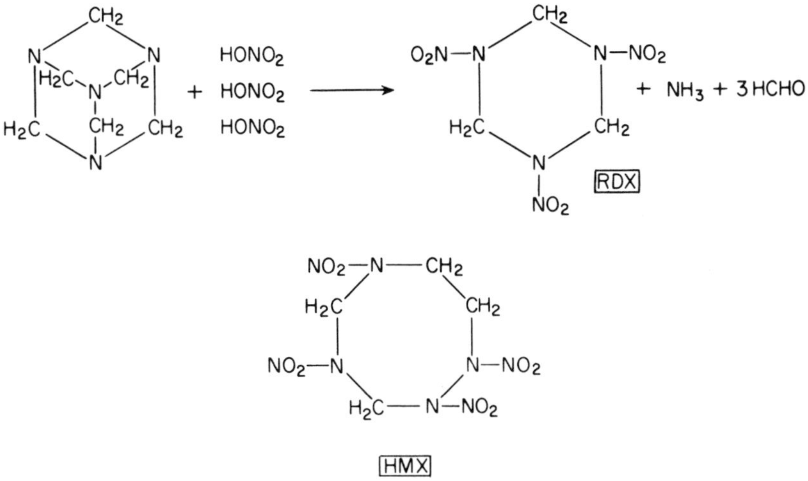

Figure 23-4 The nitration of hexamethylene tetramine to give
RDX and the structure of HMX.

Department of the Woolwich Arsenal in Great Britain. The project was called
RDX (Research Department Explosive), and just before World War II, pilot
plants were making the purified material. RDX was prepared from hexamethylene tetramine, $(CH_2)_6N_4$, and nitric acid. Hexamethylene tetramine is
a complex cyclic compound formed from formaldehyde and ammonia, also
used in the manufacture of bakelite resins. Nitration of the compound gives
the explosive RDX and the regeneration of some formaldehyde, as shown in
Fig. 23-4.

In 1940 a team of chemists headed by Dr. J. H. Ross of McGill University
developed a much more economical and simpler method of manufacture.
Dr. Bachman of the University of Michigan and Dr. G. F. Wright, University
of Toronto, improved the new method further to make the process continuous.
In the combination process, the ingredients, dissolved in glacial acetic acid or
anhydride, react in a large glass coil giving continuous production of the
RDX in crystalline form. A by-product of the reaction is a new explosive
derivative of hexamethylene. It has been labelled HMX. Its structure is
shown in Fig. 23-4.

RDX, or Cyclonite, is 35 per cent more powerful than TNT. It has a

V.O.D. of 8500 m/sec, being somewhat superior to PETN in brisance and strength. Its sensitivity to impact lies between PETN and Tetryl. RDX is crystalline with a melting point of 204° C with decomposition. It detonates above 360° C. When mixed with TNT, the melting point is lowered. The plastic explosive is made by adding oil until the desired consistency is attained. A mixture of RDX, TNT, and aluminum powder was used for torpedo war heads.

Other Engineering and Military Explosives

Trinitrobenzene,

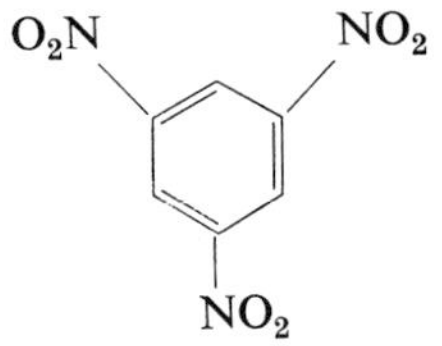

is a yellow crystalline compound which is one of the most stable explosives to heat, its ignition temperature being 550° C. It is more powerful then TNT.

Picric acid, or trinitrophenol,

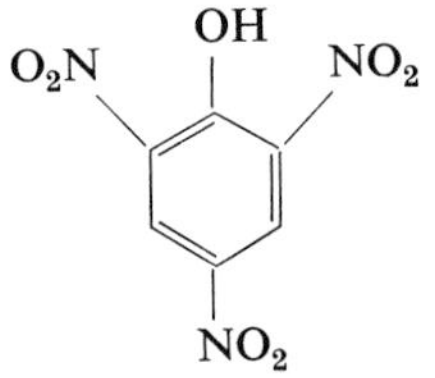

is an old military explosive intermediate in properties between TNB and TNT. The ammonium salt is very insensitive to impact and was therefore used in armor piercing shells.

Tetryl,

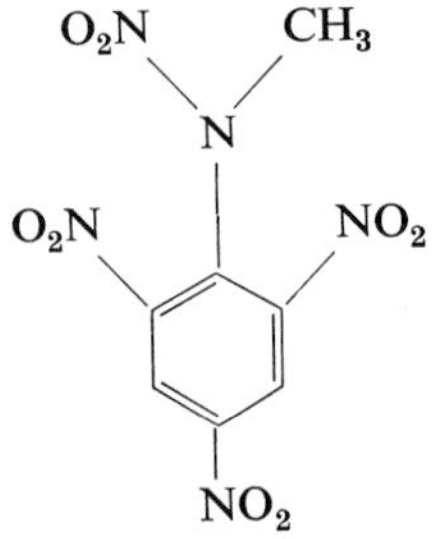

is made by nitrating dimethyl aniline,

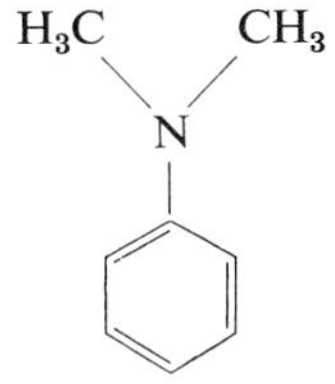

$$\begin{array}{c} H_3C \qquad CH_3 \\ \diagdown \qquad \diagup \\ N \end{array}$$

It is a sensitive explosive with a strength of 84 per cent and a V.O.D. of 7500 m/sec.

Detonators, Primers, Initiators

A number of explosive substances are very sensitive to impact, heat, and friction. Among the most sensitive are compounds known as the fulminates and the azides. While several metallic derivatives of each group have been prepared, the two which find extensive use are mercury fulminate, $Hg(ONC)_2$, and lead azide, $Pb(-N=N\equiv N)_2$.

The discovery of lead fulminate in 1800 led to the development of the percussion cap and firing pin, replacing the flintlock and flashpan of the musket. Nobel made use of this compound in a blasting cap which he patented in 1867. The cap consists of a thin metal tube containing the priming explosive and a fuse, or electrical connections, to an igniter. The ignited fulminate produces a sharp detonation wave, which explodes the charge of dynamite.

Lead azide is a more efficient priming agent in that much smaller amounts will initiate the detonation of other explosives (Table 23-2). It is, however,

Table 23-2.

Detonator	Minimum Amount Required to Detonate		
	Tetryl	Picric acid	TNT
$Hg(ONC)_2$	290 mg	300 mg	360 mg
$Pb(-N=N\equiv N)_2$	25 mg	25 mg	90 mg

less sensitive to heat; its ignition temperature is $327°$ C, as compared to $218°$ C for mercury fulminate. Lead azide is also less sensitive to electric spark, requiring a sensitizer. A sensitizer is usually a small amount of a second, more sensitive but less powerful, explosive. The lead salt of trinitro-resorcinol sensitizes lead azide; ammonium nitrate is sensitized by nitro-cellulose and several other substances.

Short-Delay Blasting

It has been found that more economical use of explosives and less possibility of damage to nearby structures can be obtained by short-delay firing. In multiple blasting, the shot holes are drilled in more or less concentric circles or in rows in the rock face. If the explosives in the center circle or section are fired a few milliseconds ahead of the shots in the second circle, the first explosion starts some of the rock moving out of the way in about 5×10^{-3} sec and the compression and following tension or expansion in the rock produces cracks which facilitate the disruption of the next

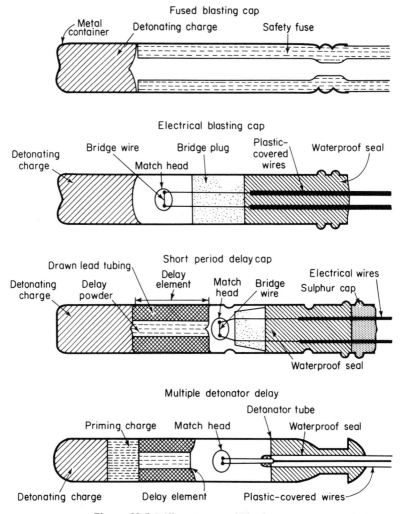

Figure 23-5 Different types of blasting caps.

section a few milliseconds later. Successive shots at 25 to 75 millisec intervals produce better fragmentation, debris is projected shorter distances and earth vibrations are less than with instantaneous detonation.

Short-delay blasting makes use of the type of blasting caps illustrated in Fig. 23-5. The short-delay component consists of a length of lead tubing packed with a standardized fast-burning composition, such as powdered antimony or aluminum, or silicon with solid oxidizing agents, for example, $KMnO_4$ and PbO_2. The length of the insert determines the delay in microseconds.

Short-delay blasting was used in the construction of the St. Lawrence Seaway to prevent damage to nearby installations.

Permissible Explosives

Permissible or permitted explosives are explosives which comply with specifications for blasting agents for use in coal mines, where the presence of methane gas and coal dust constitutes an explosion hazard. Suitable explosives are formulated which produce low flame temperatures. This is effected by incorporating finely divided salt (NaCl) or a mixture of ammonium chloride and sodium nitrate, or sodium chloride with ammonium nitrate. For added safety the explosive may be encased in salt or chalk and placed in the bottom of the drill hole with a long plug of clay. The use of short-delay blasting caps reduces the chance of ignition of the methane or aerosol. The loss of thermal energy is so rapid that the ignition temperature of the dust suspension is not reached. Permitted explosives represent about 10 per cent of industrial explosives.

Further Readings

Cook, M. A., *Science of High Explosives* (New York: Reinhold, 1958).

Olin Industries, Inc., *Explosive Products* (2d ed., East Alton, Ill., 1961).

Pennie, A. M., "ROX, Its History and Development," *Chemistry in Canada*, **10**, 11 (1958), 37.

Prince, D., "Explosives," *Chemical Reviews*, **59** (1959), 801.

Taylor, W., *Modern Explosives: Lectures, Monographs and Reports* (London: Royal Institute of Chemistry, 1959), No. 5.

Review Questions

1. Define an explosive.

2. What chemical groups impart explosive properties to a compound?

3. Distinguish between a propellant, high explosive, and a detonating explosive.

4. Name two examples of each of the compounds listed in Question 3.

5. What is meant by the sensitivity of an explosive?

6. How is sensitivity to impact determined?

7. Define brisance, permissible explosive, and VOD.

8. How may the strength of an explosive be determined?

9. Show by formulas the structure of nitroglycerine, TNT, PETN, RDX, and lead azide.

10. Show by a diagram the difference between an instantaneous and a delay blasting cap.

11. What is the difference between dynamite and blasting gelatin?

12. What is the advantage in replacing some nitroglycerine by NH_4NO_3 in dynamite?

13. Black blasting powder of constant composition is available in different grades according to speed. How is this?

14. According to report,

> "There was a young chemist who tried
> To make an explosive—(He died);
> It was o-hydroxy, p-methoxy
> Trinitrobenzaldehyde"

If a methoxy group is —OCH_3 write the formula for the compound.

15. A semigelatin, VOD 12,000 ft/sec, was used to estimate the detonation rate of an ammonia gelatin by the method illustrated in Fig. 23-2. If the length of the loop of standard explosive was 24.0 ft, the length of the test strip (AB) 20.0 ft, and the point of impact 4.5 ft from the point B, what was the VOD of the ammonia gelatin?

Appendix

A-I Surface Tension

The molecules of liquid in the surface layer are subjected to a differential force toward the bulk of the liquid due to the attraction of the neighboring molecules. It therefore requires the expenditure of energy to create a surface since molecules have to be pulled to the surface against the attraction of the adjacent molecules. Surface tension force prevents the escape of all but the fastest molecules.

Surface tension is a force in dynes per unit length measured in a direction tangential to the surface. This will be seen from a simple arrangement consisting of a wire loop with a movable bar attached to a weight. Suppose a soap film covers the enclosed surface. Let the wire be moved a distance x cm. Work done equals $FX =$ the work done against the surface tension:

$$\text{S.T.} \times \text{area} = \text{S.T.} \times 2lx$$

(since there is film on two sides). That is,

$$FX = (\text{S.T.}) \times 2lX, \qquad \text{S.T.} = y = \frac{F}{2l}$$

or, force/length.

If the film is drawn out it might be expected that the surface tension would decrease. This is true only when the thickness decreases to molecular dimensions. Films thicker than 10^{-6} cm show no difference in surface tension; that is, the surface tension of a drop of seawater is the same as the surface tension of the ocean, at the same temperature.

If an immiscible liquid C is placed on the liquid A, the surface tension at the surface will be changed, usually reduced because of the immediate

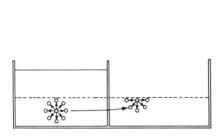

Figure A-1 A molecule in the body of the liquid is attracted by molecules on all sides. If the surface is extended, many molecules will have to be forced to the surface against the differential downward pull.

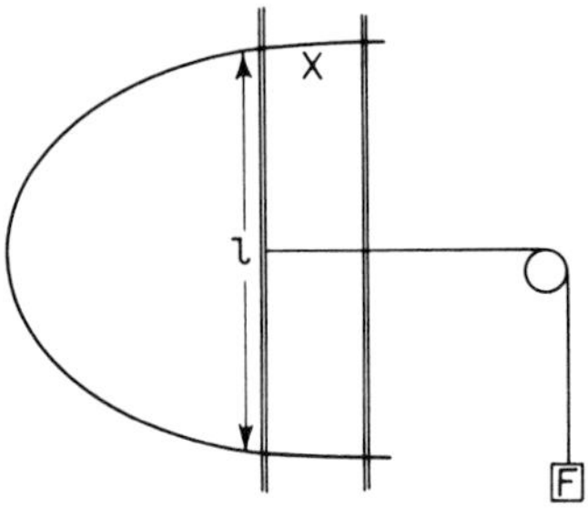

Figure A-2 Increase in area of a soap film requires work.

presence of C molecules above liquid A. The tension at an interface is called *interfacial tension*.

Surface energy is the energy bound in a surface, being the product of the surface tension and the area. Materials possessing high specific surface have large quantities of energy as surface energy. Many of the properties of

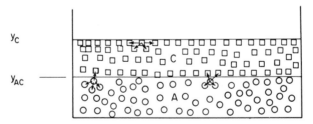

Figure A-3 Interfacial tension. This is usually lower than the surface tension of either of the substances in contact.

such materials depend more on the surface energy than on their chemical composition.

The spreading of a liquid over a surface, wetting, water proofing, the action of detergents, the properties of penetrating oil, the formation of emulsions, flotation, frothing, and lubrication are all determined by surface tension and interfacial tension relationships.

If a drop of liquid is placed on liquid B the spreading of A will be determined by the three surface tensions involved. Spreading will only take place if by such reaction the total surface energy of the system is lowered.

A-2 Surface Tensions and Interfacial Tension

If y_1 is the surface tension of the top liquid A, y_2 that of the lower liquid B, y_3 will be the interfacial tension between A and B. Suppose the drop spreads

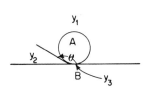

Figure A-4 Droplet of liquid A with angle of contact greater than 90°.

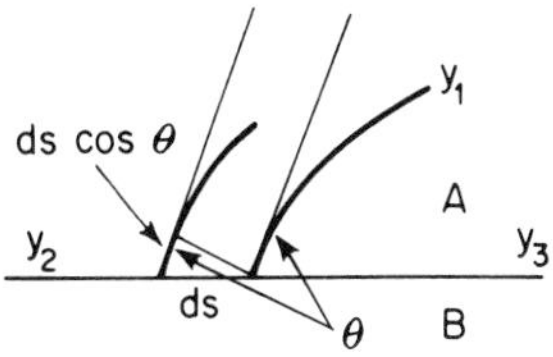

Figure A-5 The spreading of a liquid making a positive contact angle less than 90°.

over a small increment of surface ds until equilibrium is reached. This will produce a change in free surface energy

$$dF = y_1 ds + y_3 ds - y_2 ds$$

because the surface tension y_1 is now operating over greater area and so is the interfacial tension, that is, the change due to these is positive. The surface tension of the lower liquid B is operating on a smaller area so its change in surface energy is negative.

There is a law of thermodynamics which states that when a system is in equilibrium, its total free energy is a minimum. Thus, if F is a minimum, the change in free energy with surface, $dF/ds = 0$, and

$$y_1 ds + y_3 ds - y_2 ds = \text{minimum}$$

That is,

$$\frac{dF}{ds} = y_1 + y_3 - y_2 = 0 \quad \text{or} \quad y_1 = y_2 - y_3$$

This assumes that the spreading liquid makes a contact angle of zero degrees. However, there is usually a definite angle of wetting.

Suppose that the drop makes an angle with B of $\theta°$. Let the drop now spread over a surface ds to its equilibrium position. This time the extension of air-liquid A surface is not ds but $ds \cos \theta$. The surface air-liquid B has been decreased by *ds* and the interface increased by the same amount. That is,

$$y_1 ds \cos \theta + y_3 ds - y_2 ds = dF = \text{minimum}$$

$$\frac{dF}{ds} = 0$$

so
$$y_1 = \frac{y_2 - y_3}{\cos \theta} \tag{1}$$

Measuring Surface Tension

One method used for the evaluation of the surface tension is to measure the rise of the liquid in a capillary tube of known radius. This is really an example of wetting or spreading. If the liquid does not wet the tube, the meniscus is depressed.

Suppose the liquid rises to a height *h* and we assume it climbs an infinitely small distance further. If we represent the surface tension forces which are pulling the liquid upward as positive, then gravitational forces acting downward are negative in sign. Consider the work done by the surface tension first.

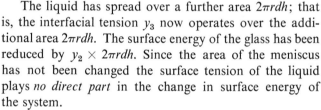

The liquid has spread over a further area $2\pi r dh$; that is, the interfacial tension y_3 now operates over the additional area $2\pi r dh$. The surface energy of the glass has been reduced by $y_2 \times 2\pi r dh$. Since the area of the meniscus has not been changed the surface tension of the liquid plays *no direct part* in the change in surface energy of the system.

The work done against gravity is $-\rho g dh(\pi r^2 h + V)$, where ρ = density, g = gravitational constant, and V = the volume of the meniscus. Equating

Figure A-6 Rise of liquid in capillary tube. Vol. of meniscus = vol. of a cylinder of radius *r* and height *r*, less the vol. of a hemisphere of radius *r*.

$$-\rho g dh(\pi r^2 h + V) = y_3 2\pi r dh - y_2 2\pi r dh = 2\pi r dh(y_3 - y_2) \tag{2}$$

The approximate volume of the meniscus equals the volume of a cylinder of radius *r* and height *r* minus one-half the volume of a sphere of radius *r*, or

$$\pi r^2 \cdot r - \tfrac{1}{2} \times \tfrac{4}{3}\pi r^3 = \tfrac{1}{3}\pi r^3$$

That is,

$$-\rho g(\pi r^2 h + \tfrac{1}{3}\pi r^3) = 2\pi r(y_3 - y_2)$$

Changing the sign and simplifying we obtain

$$\rho g \pi r^2 \left(h + \frac{r}{3}\right) = 2\pi r(y_2 - y_3)$$

But $y_2 - y_3 = y_1 \cos \theta$ from (1) so

$$y_1 = \frac{\rho g r(h + r/3)}{2 \cos \theta} \tag{3}$$

For a tube of small radius and liquids with zero contact angle the expression becomes

$$y_1 = \frac{r\rho g h}{2} \tag{4}$$

Other methods of determining surface tension are the bubble pressure method, the drop number or weight method, and the tensiometer method.

The bubble pressure method consists of measuring the pressure necessary to force the liquid downward in the tube until the meniscus coincides with the liquid level outside the capillary.

When a liquid emerges from a fine orifice the surface tension resists the extension of the surface of the liquid and tends to form droplets. If the surface tension is great, the drop will be large before it is torn from the tube by gravity. If the surface tension is very low, the critical size of the droplets will be very small. That is, the number of drops delivered per cubic centimeter of liquid will vary directly as the density and inversely as the surface tension.

$$\frac{N_1}{N_x} = \frac{d_1 y_x}{d_x y_1}$$

If N_1 is the number of drops for a standard liquid of known density and surface tension, and N_x is determined for the liquid of density d_x, then y_x can be calculated.

The tensiometer measures directly the force in dynes required to pull a wire loop out of the surface of the liquid, thus creating a new surface of unit area.

The last two methods are readily used to determine interfacial tensions.

A-3 The Spreading Coefficient

Harkins derived a "spreading coefficient," which serves to predict quantitatively the tendency one liquid will have to spread over another. He defines the spreading coefficient S as the difference between the work of adhesion and the work of cohesion. Substance A will spread over substance B if the force of attraction of A for B, that is, adhesion, is greater than the attraction of molecules of A for each other. See Figs. A-7 and A-8.

$$S = W_a - W_c$$

Suppose two liquids are in contact and are pulled apart. The work equals

$$\text{work of adhesion} = \pi r^2 y_a + \pi r^2 y_b - \pi r^2 y_{ab}$$
$$\text{the work of cohesion} = 2\pi r^2 y_a - 0$$

Subtracting,

$$S = \pi r^2(y_a + y_b - y_{ab} - 2y_a)$$
$$= \pi r^2[y_b - (y_a + y_{ab})]$$

or, for unit area,

$$S = y_b - (y_a + y_{ab})$$

Liquid A will spread over B only if the surface tension of B is greater than the sum of the other two tensions.

Figure A-7 Work done against adhesion.   **Figure A-8** Work done against cohesion.

Thus for gasoline and water, $S = -0.22$, so the gasoline has very little tendency to spread. Nitrobenzene definitely forms lenses, or drops, on the water, $S = -3.76$. Benzene has a much greater tendency to spread over water than does gasoline, $S = +9.4$.

Oleic acid not only spreads very rapidly over water but forms an orientated film. The surface tension values give $S = +24.6$.

Studies by Adams, Langmuir, and others on the spreading of films have shown that the surface tension and spreading depend on the chemical structure of the molecules. Halogen and hydrocarbon endings give poor spreading. Terminal groups that promote spreading are

$$-CH_2OH, \quad -COOH, \quad -COONa, \quad -CN, \quad -CONH_2$$

Very strong spreading and wetting are shown by sulfonate

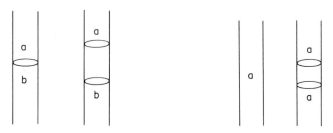

sulfate, $-OSO_3H$, and phosphate groups attached to long carbon atom chains or radicals. The latter discovery is the basis for the new detergents used as substitutes for soap in heavy duty oils, penetrating oils, and wetting agents. One of the most active wetting agents known is a sulfonated dibasic acid ester of succinic acid

$$\begin{array}{l} CH_2-COOH \\ | \\ CH_2-COOH \end{array}$$

This superlative wetting agent has the formula

$$CH_2COO—(R_1), \qquad R_1 = \text{2-ethylhexyl}$$
$$Na—O_3S—CH—COO—(R_2), \qquad R_2 = \text{1-methylheptyl}$$

A-4 Preferential Wetting

If an insoluble powder is shaken with two immiscible liquids, for example, oil and water, the powder may go into suspension in the oil or the water or into the interface. This is determined by interfacial tensions. If

$$y_{o.s.} > y_{w.s.} + y_{o.w.} \quad \text{the powder goes into the water}$$
$$y_{w.s.} > y_{o.s.} + y_{o.w.} \quad \text{the powder goes into the oil}$$
$$y_{o.w.} > y_{w.s.} + y_{o.s.} \quad \text{the powder goes into the interface}$$

or if no one is less than the sum of the others, the powder goes into the interface.

This is important in flotation and any system where dirt or powder is in contact with two liquids.

A-5 Surface Tension and Emulsions

An emulsion is a suspension of one liquid in another. Any substance which lowers the surface tension of a liquid will make it easier to break up the fluid into droplets, and if such a surface-active substance spreads over the surface of the droplet to give an oriented layer or a layer of high viscosity, emulsification will occur readily. Many of the new wetting agents are excellent emulsifying agents. Emulsions are stabilized by protective colloids, by finely divided solids which concentrate in the interface, and also by synthetic resin materials, which form a stable rigid skin around the emulsion droplet. "Solid gasoline," developed by British chemists during World War II, is a rigid emulsion containing more than 96 per cent gasoline, which can be cut into slabs, stored in the harbor, or stacked like wood. The gasoline is recovered, when needed, by putting a five-gallon slab in a hand-operated hydraulic press.

N	0	1	2	3	4	5	6	7	8	9	P.P. 1	2	3	4	5
10	0000	0043	0086	0128	0170	0212	0253	0294	0334	0374	4	8	12	17	21
11	0414	0453	0492	0531	0569	0607	0645	0682	0719	0755	4	8	11	15	19
12	0792	0828	0864	0899	0934	0969	1004	1038	1072	1106	3	7	10	14	17
13	1139	1173	1206	1239	1271	1303	1335	1367	1399	1430	3	6	10	13	16
14	1461	1492	1523	1553	1584	1614	1644	1673	1703	1732	3	6	9	12	15
15	1761	1790	1818	1847	1875	1903	1931	1959	1987	2014	3	6	8	11	14
16	2041	2068	2095	2122	2148	2175	2201	2227	2253	2279	3	5	8	11	13
17	2304	2330	2355	2380	2405	2430	2455	2480	2504	2529	2	5	7	10	12
18	2553	2577	2601	2625	2648	2672	2695	2718	2742	2765	2	5	7	9	12
19	2788	2810	2833	2856	2878	2900	2923	2945	2967	2989	2	4	7	9	11
20	3010	3032	3054	3075	3096	3118	3139	3160	3181	3201	2	4	6	8	11
21	3222	3243	3263	3284	3304	3324	3345	3365	3385	3404	2	4	6	8	10
22	3424	3444	3464	3483	3502	3522	3541	3560	3579	3598	2	4	6	8	10
23	3617	3636	3655	3674	3692	3711	3729	3747	3766	3784	2	4	5	7	9
24	3802	3820	3838	3856	3874	3892	3909	3927	3945	3962	2	4	5	7	9
25	3979	3997	4014	4031	4048	4065	4082	4099	4116	4133	2	3	5	7	9
26	4150	4166	4183	4200	4216	4232	4249	4265	4281	4298	2	3	5	7	8
27	4314	4330	4346	4362	4378	4393	4409	4425	4440	4456	2	3	5	6	8
28	4472	4487	4502	4518	4533	4548	4564	4579	4594	4609	2	3	5	6	8
29	4624	4639	4654	4669	4683	4698	4713	4728	4742	4757	1	3	4	6	7
30	4771	4786	4800	4814	4829	4843	4857	4871	4886	4900	1	3	4	6	7
31	4914	4928	4942	4955	4969	4983	4997	5011	5024	5038	1	3	4	6	7
32	5051	5065	5079	5092	5105	5119	5132	5145	5159	5172	1	3	4	5	7
33	5185	5198	5211	5224	5237	5250	5263	5276	5289	5302	1	3	4	5	6
34	5315	5328	5340	5353	5366	5378	5391	5403	5416	5428	1	3	4	5	6
35	5441	5453	5465	5478	5490	5502	5514	5527	5539	5551	1	2	4	5	6
36	5563	5575	5587	5599	5611	5623	5635	5647	5658	5670	1	2	4	5	6
37	5682	5694	5705	5717	5729	5740	5752	5763	5775	5786	1	2	3	5	6
38	5798	5809	5821	5832	5843	5855	5866	5877	5888	5899	1	2	3	5	6
39	5911	5922	5933	5944	5955	5966	5977	5988	5999	6010	1	2	3	4	6
40	6021	6031	6042	6053	6064	6075	6085	6096	6107	6117	1	2	3	4	5
41	6128	6138	6149	6160	6170	6180	6191	6201	6212	6222	1	2	3	4	5
42	6232	6243	6253	6263	6274	6284	6294	6304	6314	6325	1	2	3	4	5
43	6335	6345	6355	6365	6375	6385	6395	6405	6415	6425	1	2	3	4	5
44	6435	6444	6454	6464	6474	6484	6493	6503	6513	6522	1	2	3	4	5
45	6532	6542	6551	6561	6571	6580	6590	6599	6609	6618	1	2	3	4	5
46	6628	6637	6646	6656	6665	6675	6684	6693	6702	6712	1	2	3	4	5
47	6721	6730	6739	6749	6758	6767	6776	6785	6794	6803	1	2	3	4	5
48	6812	6821	6830	6839	6848	6857	6866	6875	6884	6893	1	2	3	4	4
49	6902	6911	6920	6928	6937	6946	6955	6964	6972	6981	1	2	3	4	4
50	6990	6998	7007	7016	7024	7033	7042	7050	7059	7067	1	2	3	3	4
51	7076	7084	7093	7101	7110	7118	7126	7135	7143	7152	1	2	3	3	4
52	7160	7168	7177	7185	7193	7202	7210	7218	7226	7235	1	2	2	3	4
53	7243	7251	7259	7267	7275	7284	7292	7300	7308	7316	1	2	2	3	4
54	7324	7332	7340	7348	7356	7364	7372	7380	7388	7396	1	2	2	3	4

NOTE:

N	0	1	2	3	4	5	6	7	8	9	P.P. 1	2	3	4	5
55	7404	7412	7419	7427	7435	7443	7451	7459	7466	7474	1	2	2	3	4
56	7482	7490	7497	7505	7513	7520	7528	7536	7543	7551	1	2	2	3	4
57	7559	7566	7574	7582	7589	7597	7604	7612	7619	7627	1	2	2	3	4
58	7634	7642	7649	7657	7664	7672	7679	7686	7694	7701	1	1	2	3	4
59	7709	7716	7723	7731	7738	7745	7752	7760	7767	7774	1	1	2	3	4
60	7782	7789	7796	7803	7810	7818	7825	7832	7839	7846	1	1	2	3	4
61	7853	7860	7868	7875	7882	7889	7896	7903	7910	7917	1	1	2	3	4
62	7924	7931	7938	7945	7952	7959	7966	7973	7980	7987	1	1	2	3	3
63	7993	8000	8007	8014	8021	8028	8035	8041	8048	8055	1	1	2	3	3
64	8062	8069	8075	8082	8089	8096	8102	8109	8116	8122	1	1	2	3	3
65	8129	8136	8142	8149	8156	8162	8169	8176	8182	8189	1	1	2	3	3
66	8195	8202	8209	8215	8222	8228	8235	8241	8248	8254	1	1	2	3	3
67	8261	8267	8274	8280	8287	8293	8299	8306	8312	8319	1	1	2	3	3
68	8325	8331	8338	8344	8351	8357	8363	8370	8376	8382	1	1	2	3	3
69	8388	8395	8401	8407	8414	8420	8426	8432	8439	8445	1	1	2	3	3
70	8451	8457	8463	8470	8476	8482	8488	8494	8500	8506	1	1	2	2	3
71	8513	8519	8525	8531	8537	8543	8549	8555	8561	8567	1	1	2	2	3
72	8573	8579	8585	8591	8597	8603	8609	8615	8621	8627	1	1	2	2	3
73	8633	8639	8645	8651	8657	8663	8669	8675	8681	8686	1	1	2	2	3
74	8692	8698	8704	8710	8716	8722	8727	8733	8739	8745	1	1	2	2	3
75	8751	8756	8762	8768	8774	8779	8785	8791	8797	8802	1	1	2	2	3
76	8808	8814	8820	8825	8831	8837	8842	8848	8854	8859	1	1	2	2	3
77	8865	8871	8876	8882	8887	8893	8899	8904	8910	8915	1	1	2	2	3
78	8921	8927	8932	8938	8943	8949	8954	8960	8965	8971	1	1	2	2	3
79	8976	8982	8987	8993	8998	9004	9009	9015	9020	9025	1	1	2	2	3
80	9031	9036	9042	9047	9053	9058	9063	9069	9074	9079	1	1	2	2	3
81	9085	9090	9096	9101	9106	9112	9117	9122	9128	9133	1	1	2	2	3
82	9138	9143	9149	9154	9159	9165	9170	9175	9180	9186	1	1	2	2	3
83	9191	9196	9201	9206	9212	9217	9222	9227	9232	9238	1	1	2	2	3
84	9243	9248	9253	9258	9263	9269	9274	9279	9284	9289	1	1	2	2	3
85	9294	9299	9304	9309	9315	9320	9325	9330	9335	9340	1	1	2	2	3
86	9345	9350	9355	9360	9365	9370	9375	9380	9385	9390	1	1	2	2	3
87	9395	9400	9405	9410	9415	9420	9425	9430	9435	9440	0	1	1	2	2
88	9445	9450	9455	9460	9465	9469	9474	9479	9484	9489	0	1	1	2	2
89	9494	9499	9504	9509	9513	9518	9523	9528	9533	9538	0	1	1	2	2
90	9542	9547	9552	9557	9562	9566	9571	9576	9581	9586	0	1	1	2	2
91	9590	9595	9600	9605	9609	9614	9619	9624	9628	9633	0	1	1	2	2
92	9638	9643	9647	9652	9657	9661	9666	9671	9675	9680	0	1	1	2	2
93	9685	9689	9694	9699	9703	9708	9713	9717	9722	9727	0	1	1	2	2
94	9731	9736	9741	9745	9750	9754	9759	9763	9768	9773	0	1	1	2	2
95	9777	9782	9786	9791	9795	9800	9805	9809	9814	9818	0	1	1	2	2
96	9823	9827	9832	9836	9841	9845	9850	9854	9859	9863	0	1	1	2	2
97	9868	9872	9877	9881	9886	9890	9894	9899	9903	9908	0	1	1	2	2
98	9912	9917	9921	9926	9930	9934	9939	9943	9948	9952	0	1	1	2	2
99	9956	9961	9965	9969	9974	9978	9983	9987	9991	9996	0	1	1	2	2

Element	Symbol	Atomic number	Average atomic mass	Element	Symbol	Atomic number	Average atomic mass
Actinium......	Ac	89	227	Mercury.......	Hg	80	200.66
Aluminum......	Al	13	26.99	Molybdenum...	Mo	42	95.98
Americium.....	Am	95	[243]	Neodymium....	Nd	60	144.31
Antimony......	Sb	51	121.79	Neon.........	Ne	10	20.188
Argon.........	A	18	39.955	Neptunium.....	Np	93	[237]
Arsenic........	As	33	74.93	Nickel........	Ni	28	58.73
Astatine.......	At	85	210	Niobium.......	Nb	41	92.94
Barium........	Ba	56	137.40	Nitrogen.......	N	7	14.012
Berkelium......	Bk	97	[249]	Nobelium......	Nl	102	[253]
Beryllium......	Be	4	9.015	Osmium........	Os	76	190.3
Bismuth........	Bi	83	209.06	Oxygen........	O	8	16.0044
Boron.........	B	5	10.82	Palladium......	Pd	46	106.4
Bromine........	Br	35	79.938	Phosphorus.....	P	15	30.983
Cadmium......	Cd	48	112.44	Platinum.......	Pt	78	195.14
Calcium........	Ca	20	40.09	Plutonium......	Pu	94	[242]
Californium....	Cf	98	[249]	Polonium......	Po	84	210
Carbon........	C	6	12.014	Potassium......	K	19	39.111
Cerium........	Ce	58	140.17	Praseodymium .	Pr	59	140.96
Cesium........	Cs	55	132.95	Promethium....	Pm	61	[145]
Chlorine.......	Cl	17	35.467	Protactinium...	Pa	91	231
Chromium.....	Cr	24	52.02	Radium........	Ra	88	226.11
Cobalt.........	Co	27	58.96	Radon.........	Rn	86	222
Copper........	Cu	29	63.56	Rhenium.......	Re	75	186.27
Curium........	Cm	96	[245]	Rhodium......	Rh	45	102.94
Dysprosium....	Dy	66	162.55	Rubidium......	Rb	37	85.50
Einsteinium....	E	99	[255]	Ruthenium.....	Ru	44	101.7
Erbium........	Er	68	167.32	Samarium......	Sm	62	150.39
Europium......	Eu	63	152.0	Scandium......	Sc	21	44.97
Fermium.......	Fm	100	[255]	Selenium.......	Se	34	78.98
Fluorine.......	F	9	19.01	Silicon........	Si	14	28.10
Francium......	Fr	87	223	Silver.........	Ag	47	107.909
Gadolinium....	Gd	64	157.30	Sodium........	Na	11	22.997
Gallium........	Ga	31	69.74	Strontium......	Sr	38	87.65
Germanium....	Ge	32	72.62	Sulfur.........	S	16	32.075
Gold..........	Au	79	197.1	Tantalum......	Ta	73	181.00
Hafnium.......	Hf	72	178.55	Technetium....	Tc	43	[99]
Helium........	He	2	4.004	Tellurium......	Te	52	127.64
Holmium......	Ho	67	164.98	Terbium.......	Tb	65	158.97
Hydrogen......	H	1	1.0083	Thallium.......	Tl	81	204.45
Indium........	In	49	114.85	Thorium.......	Th	90	232.11
Iodine.........	I	53	126.94	Thulium.......	Tm	69	168.99
Iridium........	Ir	77	192.2	Tin...........	Sn	50	118.73
Iron..........	Fe	26	55.87	Titanium.......	Ti	22	47.91
Krypton.......	Kr	36	83.82	Tungsten......	W	74	183.91
Lanthanum.....	La	57	138.96	Uranium.......	U	92	238.13
Lead..........	Pb	82	207.27	Vanadium......	V	23	50.96
Lithium........	Li	3	6.942	Xenon.........	Xe	54	131.34
Lutetium.......	Lu	71	175.04	Ytterbium......	Yb	70	173.09
Magnesium.....	Mg	12	24.33	Yttrium.......	Y	39	88.94
Manganese.....	Mn	25	54.95	Zinc..........	Zn	30	65.40
Mendeleevium..	Mv	101	[256]	Zirconium......	Zr	40	91.24

Index